WOODLANDS T

ENGLAND AND WALES 1995

A guide to over 700 woodlands and forests where visitors are welcome for enjoyment and education

The Forestry Trust for Conservation and Education

The Old Estate Office, Englefield Road, Theale, READING, Berks RG7 5DZ

Telephone 01734-323523

Registered Charity 327856

CONTENTS

Cover photographs
Front - Forest Life Picture Library - Queen's Inclosure, New Forest (see page 106)
Back - Roy J Westlake ARPS - Dart Valley Woods, Devon (see page 64)
Text printed and bound by   Severn Print, Gloucester

ISBN 0-9521001-2-6
ISSN 1352-6324

WELCOME ...

When I was a small child in Yorkshire I was often taken to woods to see the bluebells and primroses in the spring. Many of those woods have gone now. Twenty-five years ago I set a novel partly in a real, small and very old wood in the West Country, in the lee of which I rented a cottage. To my distress, returning to the place ten years ago, I saw only a bare, treeless, hedgeless, open corn prairie where my beautiful wood had once been. That really brought home to me how much woods mattered and were being destroyed, how very much I wanted to find others to visit in place of that one. Now thanks to this goldmine of a handbook, I will be led to over seven hundred of them. So can you. It's an invaluable book to keep in the car, to refer to when planning a journey or holiday or day out and an inspiration too. What refreshment, solace, calm and delight so many people will be able to find from visiting some of these woods; in spring, to see wild wood anemones and bluebells en masse: in high hot summer, when they are so shady, dense, cool and green: in autumn, to scuff through piles of gold - if an adult feels embarrassed about doing so, they can always take a small child with them! - and have bright bits of fiery orange and yellow fall gently onto your head and look up to see the patches of blue sky through the new gaps in the branches: but perhaps woods are best in winter, when the trunks and branches are seen bare against the sky and the countryside is glimpsed here and there through the open arches. We all have our favourite time and our favourite wood and every wood, every visit to a wood is different, in each on one you will find some small new pleasure. Take your children, teacher, parent, grandparent, friend for a walk in the woods - find where they are with the help of this splendid guide and after you've been, tell someone else about it, spread the word.

Susan Hill

Susan Hill

THE FORESTS AWAIT YOU

Welcome to the forests and woodlands of England and Wales. Who has not heard of Sherwood, Rockingham, Epping, Wyre or Windsor? Famous forests as closely woven into our history as the great castles and cathedrals of our land. There is a magic about these ancient forests with giant trees whose life-span dwarfs our own. The New Forest, however, reminds us what is now old was once new. Many of you will have seen that in our own generation "new" forests are being created that will in the course of time become as much appreciated by our grandchildren as the ancient woodland heritage that we enjoy. Kielder, Thetford, Hamsterley, Dalby and the great new forests of Wales may be as cherished as the Forest of Dean or the New Forest itself.

The major forests, though, are just pearls in a much wider chain of woodlands young and old, large and small, steep and flat, wet and dry, deciduous and evergreen, which clothe about one tenth of our land. Small woods and copses are often prominent and attractive features of an otherwise farmed landscape. Variety is certainly the spice of life! Not only do the woods themselves vary greatly but so do the purposes for which they were - and still are - used. Timber production, produce from coppicing like hurdles and pea sticks, bark, firewood and grazing all give value to a wood which can equally be appreciated for its beauty and its wildlife. There is also variety in the owners and carers for woodland - private estates, Forest Enterprise, local councils and conservation bodies like the National Trust, Woodland Trust and County Wildlife Trusts.

Over the last century since the industrial revolution and the movement of people to the towns, many folk have lost the traditional association with the woods that provided so many essentials for our ancestors. There is a keen desire to restore this particular missing link. Happily the opportunities are growing all the time as you will discover in these pages. The key lies in a wider concept of woodland management where a variety of purposes may be served. Older plantations are being adapted - and new forests designed - to combine timber production with landscape appeal and wildlife conservation. But above all more forests are being managed to cater for the visitor who is looking for a place to be where motor traffic and city stress can be forgotten among the stately oaks or towering firs of the forest.

We are fortunate too that so many of the traditional woodlands of the countryside have been bought and protected by conservation bodies. Many of these are being managed by them to recreate the wildlife-rich conditions of their historic past. Some harvest woodland produce and so any barriers which may in the past have set apart the forester and the conservator are now breaking down. They have more and more in common and happily we are seeing the reunion of all who love trees, especially you the visitors. Conserving ancient woodlands, revitalising derelict ones, creating new, all these express belief in a shared and sustainable land use which respects the environment and offers something for everyone.

IN SUPPORT OF WOODLANDS TO VISIT IN ENGLAND AND WALES

Together with the Forestry Trust - the Countryside Commission, the Countryside Council for Wales and the Forestry Authority are cooperating in this venture to publish a guide to woodlands and forests where visitors will be assured a welcome. Over three years the funding partners have supported the venture with the expectation that it becomes self financing. We wish the Forestry Trust every success in this project which should encourage and increase the enjoyment for woodland visitors and also recruit more woodland owners and managers to extend a welcome.

This guide focuses on private woodlands but also lists some Forestry Commission and other woods where visitors are welcome. There are of course many other woods owned by public and other bodies in which you will be welcome, only some of which are listed here. These include:

● national woodlands managed by Forest Enterprise where visitors on foot generally have the freedom to roam throughout the forest.

● local authority owned woods whether in urban or country parks.

●woods owned by National Parks and in some National Nature Reserves; and

● woods managed by the National Trust, Woodland Trust and other voluntary bodies.

For further details of such woods in your area contact the relevant local office. Meanwhile we hope that visiting the woods in this guide will add to your enjoyment.

The Countryside Commission

The Countryside Commission works to conserve and enhance the beauty of the English countryside and to help people enjoy it.

The Countryside Council for Wales

The Countryside Council for Wales is the statutory adviser to government on sustaining natural beauty, wildlife and the opportunity for outdoor enjoyment in rural Wales and its inshore waters and is the national wildlife conservation authority.

The Forestry Authority

The Forestry Authority, part of the Forestry Commission, promotes good forestry and the expansion of woodland and forest, so increasing the social and environmental benefits of forestry in Great Britain. The Forestry Authority does this through research, setting standards, providing advice, grant-aid and training.

MAIN SPONSOR OF 1995 BOOK

Esso

The Forestry Trust is delighted to be receiving the support of Esso UK plc for the 1995 volume. Esso has a long history of support for environmental initiatives, especially ones relating to trees.

HOW TO USE THIS BOOK

The key to using this book is first to establish:

1. How far are you prepared to travel? Start by looking at the map of England and Wales and then focus on the relevant county map.

2. Are you looking for informal recreation on the spur of the moment or a visit from which you may learn something about the working countryside? Do you mind if there are likely to be lots of other people there or do you wish to visit somewhere not usually open to the public? The guide divides access into four categories which are described in more detail below but for quick reference on the map these are divided into two broad categories of readily available (categories F and R combined) and more limited access (categories P and A combined). Where access is readily available it is denoted by a square outline - ☐ - round the size symbol.

3. Are you looking for a quick or detailed visit to a small wood or a long walk in a large forest? It is important to check the size carefully first to avoid disappointment. On the map the woods and forests are shown by size symbols which are approximately reproduced here - ■ for less than 10 hectares, ■ between 10 and 100 hectares, ■ between 100 and 1000 hectares and ■ for forests over 1000 hectares. A hectare is 100 metres square. Even copses smaller than this can be a source of considerable enjoyment and learning but are unlikely to provide a bracing country walk. At the other extreme it is not possible to gain more than a superficial insight to forests such as Kielder, at 60000 hectares, on a day visit.

4. Is the purpose of your visit educational? Those woods that provide opportunities to study both timber production and wildlife conservation (Study Woods) are shown in the key below each map with an *.

Once you have decided the area, size and level of access you are looking for you can find out further details from the individual woodland entry by looking under the relevant county in the gazetteer. Entries are listed firstly under England or Wales, alphabetically by county and finally alphabetically by the name of the wood. The key to individual entries is described below:

The name of the wood is shown in **large bold print**. Woods that provide educational opportunities to study both timber production and wildlife conservation are preceded with an *. The name of the owner, and/or where the responsibility for management has been given to another organisation, the manager, is shown in (brackets) . The size of the wood is shown in hectares - ha. *Please note this carefully before you commit yourself to a long journey.* The name is followed by a letter in **bold** print denoting the level of access:

F denotes full and free access for walkers and dogs though some areas or even whole woods may have to be temporarily closed off for safety or conservation reasons. Access off paths and rides should not be assumed unless stated. Organized group visits of more than 10 people to privately owned woodland should, out of courtesy, be cleared with the owner whether or not this is stated as a specific requirement. Access for horses should not be assumed unless bridleways or horses are specifically mentioned.

R denotes regular or routine access but with some restrictions. These may be of time (seasons, days of the week or times of day), of space (rights of way, permissive paths, self guided trails or zoned areas), of payment (for car parking or an admission charge) or a combination of these or other specific conditions.

P denotes periodic access - where a wood is open only for a very short season or where only set days are specified. Periodic access does not in itself preclude visits at other times by appointment. See individual woods for details.

A denotes by appointment only. Access to some woods may need to be carefully controlled. Almost without exception those who have restricted access to their woods to visits by appointment have expressed a willingness to conduct visits for schools and special interest groups.

A further letter or letters in **bold** print - **C, D , E** or **M** - denotes the award in the last ten years of one or more of the three main woodland management prizes. Upper-case denotes overall winners and lowercase denotes placed or commended woods. Woods which have won these awards are strongly recommended for visits . These major awards are:

The Duke of Cornwall's Award for Forestry and Conservation (**C**) - the premier award of the Royal Forestry Society of England, Wales and Northern Ireland presented annually to encourage the owners of commercial woodlands to manage them in a way which is sympathetic to the landscape and likely to conserve and enhance the wildlife interest in them, in both the short and long term, whilst still consistent with the primary purpose of timber production.

The Dulverton Flagon (**D**) - the principal award of the Timber Growers Association (TGA) presented annually for demonstrating the principles of the TGA's Forestry and Woodland Code by combining good environmental practice with timber production.

The Centres of Excellence Award (**E**) - the principal award of the Forestry Authority in England for trees, woods and forests that demonstrate the highest management standards in at least one of the following categories: improving the quality of the landscape, creating benefits for wildlife, providing access for people or growing timber in environmentally-sound ways.

The Merit Award (**M**) - is the comparable Forestry Authority award in Wales.

The Ordnance Survey Landranger 1:50000 Map Sheet Number and National Grid Map Reference are given in most instances to get you to the meeting point or close to the wood with the aid of a map. Please note that some woods cannot be reached by car and the meeting point may be some distance from the wood itself. Whilst every effort has been made to verify the Grid References given, they should be used in conjunction with any directions. The Forestry Trust regrets it cannot guarantee that the six figure reference will put you within 100 metres of the described point.

Telephone numbers or addresses are given for most woods. This is the contact for further information, of particular relevance for visits by appointment.

Symbols

The following symbols have been used to provide further information:

Basic admission charge (if any) in £ and p. Some of the commercial sites have complex admission charges and some are subject to change during the season. This figure should be used only as a rough guide. For full details contact the number or address given.

Car Parking - numbers (cost in £ and p in brackets). Some car parking charges are variable. We have only shown a basic rate. If no number is shown this implies that there is adequate parking for the anticipated level of visitors.

Coaches - numbers (cost in £ and p in brackets) Charges may vary - only a basic charge, where given, is shown . Whether or not the number of coach spaces is given, all coach party visits should be cleared with the owners in advance.

Dogs allowed

Dogs allowed on leads

Dogs not allowed

If we have been unable to verify whether dogs are allowed it should be assumed that they are not allowed in private woods or those managed by wildlife trusts. As a general rule Forest Enterprise and local authority woods do allow dogs but if in doubt check with the owner, forester or agent. Dogs may not appear to cause much disturbance but in some woods and in specific seasons their presence may be harmful to wildlife.

Riding / Bridleways - advice available on request from contact number or address shown.
Where this symbol is shown please contact the number or address given first unless you already have clearance to ride there. Riders should keep to bridleways unless specifically permitted to use other tracks. To do otherwise is an abuse of the owner's hospitality and a disservice to visitors on foot. It should be assumed that horses are not allowed in the woods without this symbol.

Broadleaved wood (at least 75% broadleaves)

Coniferous wood (at least 75% conifers)

Mixed woodland (at least 25% of both broadleaves and conifers)

☀ Viewpoint(s)

Deer sighting possible

WC WCs - the number and type unspecified

♿ WCs for disabled

[i] Information literature available

Education materials available

Self guided trail(s)

Trail(s) for disabled

Guided walks

FP Forest produce for sale

Picnic site(s)

Refreshments available

Food available

Pub within close walking distance (1 mile)

Camp site(s)

Caravan site(s)

Forest accomodation

Children's play area(s)

Shop

Directions and Visitor Guidance

For 1995 most entries have directions and further guidance notes. We have tried to reduce the description of facilities through the use of symbols but where further amplification is required this is shown in the italicized paragraph. Please take note of special instructions or guidance that owners have given. We have used the following abbreviations:
E,S,N,W - for the points of the compass.
m - for metres (but miles in full)
L and R - for left and right
R - for River ... (where followed by the name)

Description

Most, but still not all, of the 1995 entries have a description of the wood. We have checked the entries for general accuracy and have in some instances reduced the length of entries to conform to the overall layout. However, we do not have the resources to verify aspects referring to specific woods. The entries are in the words of the individual owners. The Forestry Trust is extremely grateful to all the entrants for contributing to this book **We cannot vouch for the specific accuracy of individual entries** nor is it our intention to alter significantly what owners have provided without clearing it with them first. Part of the attraction of the woods of Britain is their individuality. We believe this is best portrayed in the words of the owners though **we welcome any constructive comments and suggestions that can be passed on directly to owners to help them in making better visitor provision for their 1996 entry.**

Abbreviations. We have tried to restrict the overuse of abbreviations but the following land use designations in particular, have been abbreviated - Area of Outstanding Natural Beauty (AONB), Environmentally Sensitive Area (ESA), Site of Special Scientific Interest (SSSI).

Extending Your Enjoyment

A short section of the book following the gazetteer section covers visitor centres, pubs and woodland walks, staying in the forest, getting there by public transport and short notes on different types of forest management. Also included is a list of those woods and forests offering some form of riding facilities, and those with facilities for disabled (both WCs and trails).

Forests for Learning

The short educational section includes a summary of Forestry Trust educational resources, a brief statement about the Forest Education Initiative, details of other forestry, woodland and tree organisations and a short bibliography. Also listed are woods and forests providing information literature, educational material, self guided trails, guided walks and forest produce, together with a list of **Study Woods**.

Advertisements

National advertisements are mainly at the back of the book except for those specific to particular woods which are shown under the county concerned. County specific advertisements are either shown under the relevant county or under a county heading in the back.

The Forestry Trust

The final section, on coloured paper, gives a short summary about the Forestry Trust and includes details of staff and supporters together with three question-naires:

1. Readers' and Visitors' Comments. The purpose of this questionnaire is twofold. Firstly, to help us to enhance the book and to make it more useful to readers. Secondly, as an aide memoire for comments to owners both to improve the provision made for visitors at woods and to pass on constructive suggestions and record your appreciation of particular woods. Details will be forwarded to owners at the same time as their entry forms for the 1996 book, or on a subsequent mailing to them . We would welcome comments on both aspects, as it is only with customer input that we can make the necessary improvements.

2. New Entry Form for 1996. We seek to increase the number of woods significantly in 1996 and ask readers who do not own woods themselves to bring the book in general, and this form in particular, to the attention of any friends of theirs who do. Similarly if you know of any woods (other than Forest Enterprise, National Trust and Woodland Trust properties) that already encourage access but are not included in this book we would be grateful if you would suggest to them that they join the scheme. There is no charge made for woodland entries in the book.

3. Membership Form. The Forestry Trust is initiating its membership scheme in 1995. Membership helps the Forestry Trust to carry out its educational role. Basic membership is £10 per annum and membership benefits include a copy of the annually updated *Woodlands to Visit*, two newsletters, information sheets on forestry conservation topics and a calendar of events members can attend. The membership subscription for 1996 is not due until March 1996 but completion of the form now by standing order will ensure that no payment is necessary in advance and renewal does not lapse.

Forest Enterprise Woods

There is a large number of Forest Enterprise woods listed in this book which are generally open to all. Forest Enterprise manages almost half of the nation's woods, where visitors have freedom to roam wherever there are no legal or other restraints. Their facilities include camping and caravan sites, picnic places, self guided trails, cycle trails, horse trails, forest cabins and holiday houses and visitor centres. This book cannot cover them all comprehensively. Many Forest Enterprise entries do not yet have directions or descriptions but the main 'flagship' forests should have both. directions and descriptions All Forest Enterprise entries have grid references and telephone number and can therefore be reached without too much difficulty though in the case of the 60000 hectare Kielder Forest a grid reference is perhaps academic! To emphasize the distinction between state and private woods all entries owned by the Forestry Commission or managed by Forest Enterprise are shown in italics ie

Kielder Forest

Brief Entries

Entries that are lacking either directions or descriptions will hopefully be amplified in the 1996 edition.

PERFORMANCE BEYOND PRICE.

REGATTA
GREAT OUTDOORS

Enjoy the great outdoors with Regatta advantage!
Regatta's uniquely affordable quality means that every item in our comprehensive range of outdoor
clothing easily out performs its price tag! Giving you tried and tested designs, using
technically advanced materials, that keep you comfortably impervious to the elements.
For example, versatile, interactive jackets in waterproof, breathable Isotex start from around £75.

For further information on the extensive Regatta collection of outdoor clothing, just write to:
Dept WV, Regatta, Risol House, Mercury Way, Dumplington,
Urmston, Manchester. M41 7RR Direct Customer Line : 0161 747 2971

Mapping Index

This index shows the relationship between Landranger,[®]
Outdoor Leisure, Explorer and Pathfinder[®] Maps

Available **free of charge** from
Ordnance Survey - Customer Information

☏ 01703 792763 (24 Hour answerphone only)

 **Ordnance Survey**[®]

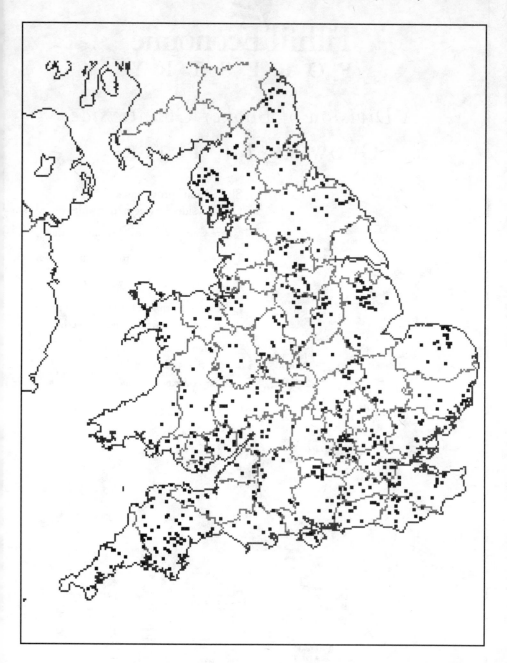

For details of woods in England turn to pages 15 - 217 and for those in Wales to pages 218 - 251

Tilhill Economic
F O R E S T R Y

A Division of Booker Countryside
GROWING THE FUTURE

Skilled staff providing a Countryside Service nationwide.

🌲 Are your woodlands growing in value?

🌲 Are you benefiting from the grants available?

🌲 Have you considered your options?

🌲 Use the depth and breadth of our practical experience to fit the pieces together.

A telephone call could be the key to cost effective and enjoyable forestry.

Your local manager is your helpline.

John McGlade
01463 234633

Stuart Wilkie
01651 842038

Miller Harris
01397 705101

Peter Matthews
01307 465175

Tom McLellan
01631 62906

Colin Blyth
01786 811721

Stephen Tong
01369 6641

Colin Calvert
01620 810371

Martin Craig
01683 20372

Bryson Middleton
01835 863244

Charlie Fulton
01556 670301

Roger Smith
01665 510273

Terry Proctor
015242 72249

Tim Liddon
01845 525460

David Owen
01678 530206

Richard Sochacki
01949 843600

Andrew Bronwin
01694 781511

Rupert Pearson
01284 728542

Graham Heath
01550 21442

Stephen Smith
01844 279911

Peter Middleton
01892 861305

Roger Lewis
01884 35135

Neil Austin
01252 794771

HEAD OFFICE
Tel: 01786 811721   Fax: 01786 816200

AVON

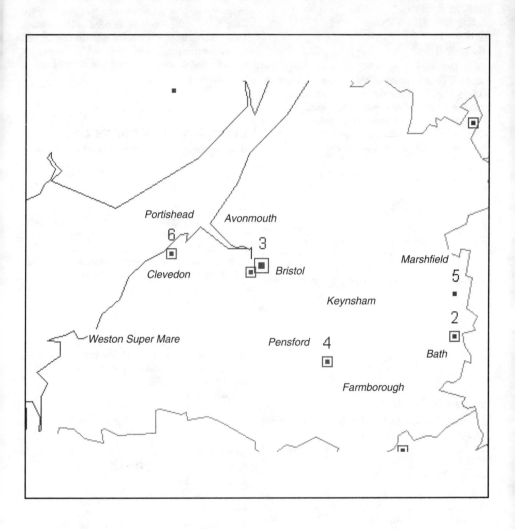

1. Avon Gorge
2. Brown's Folly
3. *Leigh Woods*
4. Lords Wood
5. *Rocks East
6. Weston Big Wood

Avon Gorge National Nature Reserve: Leigh Woods
(National Trust - Managed by English Nature) **F** 63ha
O.S.S. 172 - ST 555 730
0117 9731645

🚗🚶 ● *i*

From Bristol take the A369 towards Portishead. Just before the traffic lights at the junction with the B3129 turn R into North Road. The entrance to the reserve is over a stile after 150 yards on the L. Park at the side of road. Free leaflet available. Open at all times. Access is on foot only. Please keep to the paths and away from cliff edges.

The reserve is mixed broadleaf woodland on the edge of the famous Avon Gorge. Areas of ancient woodland with small-leaved lime coppice, wild service trees and rare whitebeams. The reserve is managed for nature conservation by coppicing, selective felling and the clearance of scrub from areas of grassland. The wide range of plants found on the reserve supports a variety of insects and other animals. Rarities found here include the white-letter hairstreak butterfly, the dormouse and the elusive hawfinch. The woods are particularly attractive in autumn and are well known for their fungi.

Brown's Folly
(Wildlife Trust, Bristol Bath & Avon) **R** 40ha
O.S.S. 172 - ST 794 660
Bristol Wildlife Centre, 32 Jacob's Wells Rd, BRISTOL BS8 1DR

🚗6🚶 ● ✳ *i*

2.5 miles NE of Bath. Take minor road from Bathford to Kingsdown, taking steep R turn to Monkton Farleigh. Car park is near brow of hill at Prospect Place. Take extreme caution when approaching rock faces. Mines should not be entered.

Standing high above the River Avon, with commanding views towards Bath, Brown's Folly boasts woodland, scrub and rich grassland which carpet the

remains of the old Bath limestone quarries. Pockets of ancient ash and oak woodland on the lower slopes are home to unusual plants like Bath asparagus. Secondary woodland dominated by ash and sycamore has grown up over the downland which once cloaked the hillside. The wood is an SSSI. The Wildlife Trust manage the nature reserve, planted conifers and non-native trees are being removed and areas are being thinned to improve both the quality of standing trees and the ground flora.

Leigh Woods: Abbotts Leigh
(Managed by Forest Enterprise) **F** 122ha
O.S.S. 172 - ST 559 738
01594 833057

🚗🐎 ♦ 🏕 ♦

Take the A369 Bristol to Portishead road. The entrance is 1 mile NE of Ashton Court, signposted by a big stone arch. There is a car park and picnic area, and forest walks. Open at all times. This is a forest nature reserve. Horse riders and mountain bikers are requested not to use this wood.

Leigh Woods is an ancient woodland containing some small-leaved lime. The wood is located by the side of the River Avon, immediately to the west of the City of Bristol. Management is balanced between maintaining the high conservation value of the wood and providing recreational opportunities for the people of Bristol. See also Avon Gorge: Leigh Woods - adjoining site.

Lords Wood
(Lords Wood Trust) **R** 61.5ha
O.S.S. 172 - ST 631 632
01749 812244 or 850378

🚗4🚶 ♦

The entrance to the wood at the junction of Birchwood Lane and A37 at Whitley Batts is exceedingly dangerous. The lane is narrow with no passing places. There are no facilities. There are footpaths through the wood, and you are free to wander off them unless there is shooting in progress. Dogs welcome under control. Please keep on leads near pheasant pens and on shoot days. *For further details ring James Lang Brown on the above number(s).*

Lords Wood is mixed woodland of ancient origin - i.e. as far as records show most of the site has been wooded since time immemorial. Largely felled in 1960, and replanted with softwoods. Seedling ash, wild cherry, oak and birch have thrived among the conifers. The vegetation and shrub layer are rich in species and the wide rides and pond support a great variety of butterflies, moths and damselflies. Note particularly white admirals and orange tips. Wild daffodils, bluebells and wild cherry blossom in spring.

*Rocks East Woodlands
(Mr & Mrs A G Phillips) **A** 38 ha
O.S.S. 172 - ST 775 706
01225 852518 (& fax)

🚗50🚌2✕ 🚶 WC 4 ☐ ☂ ⚓ ▲ ⛽ FP

From M4 Jn 18 - Marshfield A420, take unclassified Colerne road. Three miles on R at top of valley. There are two lecture rooms, showers kitchen facilities by arrangement. Lectures and training courses are also offered by prior arrangement. All visits are by appointment only, please contact Mrs M E Timms, Secretary, Rocks East Woodland, Ashwicke, Chippenham, Wilts, SN14 8AP. A minimum of 7 days notice is required for all group visits. Prices on application. Donations made to the Forestry Trust on Forestry Trust open days.

Situated in AONB in St Catherine's Valley. Mainly created by linking a collection of small woods and planting in the 1950s/1960s on steep slopes previously used for agriculture. Could be called farm woods 30 years on. Area of high landscape and scenic value. Victorian woodland garden, grotto and pond. Ideal site for ash, planted mainly with beech and larch in the 1960s. Good natural regeneration. The site has a range of plants including garlic and comfrey. Birds include buzzard. Roe and muntjac deer resident; fallow deer regular visitors. Badger setts in forest.

Weston Big Wood
(Managed by Wildlife Trust, Bristol, Bath & Avon **) R** 38ha
O.S.S. 172 - ST 456 750
 Bristol Wildlife Centre, 32 Jacob's Wells Road ,Bristol BL BS8 1DR

From B3124 Clevedon-Portishead road turn into Valley Rd. Park in lay-by approx 300m on R and walk up hill. Steps lead into wood from the road. Paths can be muddy and steep sided. Keep well away from dangerous quarry sides.

One of Avon's largest ancient woodlands, old stones, ditches and banks are thought to be mediaeval boundaries. The woodland slopes are covered with uncommon small-leaved lime trees, while oak and hazel are more abundant on top of the hill. Rare whitebeams are also dotted throughout the wood. In springtime there is a rich ground flora including herb paris. The main ride is excellent for butterflies. The wood is an SSSI. Areas of the nature reserve are thinned and coppiced by the Wildlife Trust.

BEDFORDSHIRE

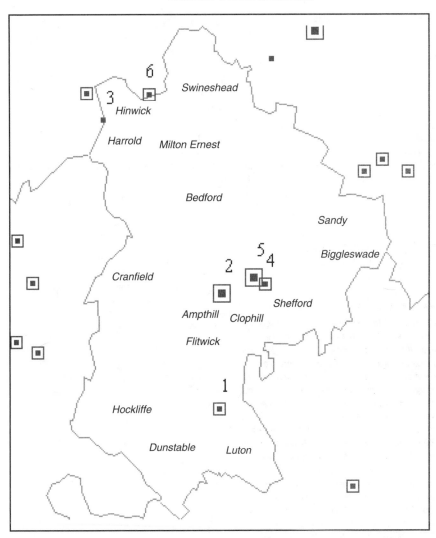

1. Bramingham Wood
2. *Maulden Wood*
3. *Park Wood
4. *Rowney Warren*
5. Rowney Warren (2)
6. *West Wood*

Bramingham Wood
(Woodland Trust) **F** 18.21ha
O.S.S. 166 - TL 068 259
01476 74297

From the centre of Luton take the A6 towards Bedford. Near the outskirts of the town turn L into Icknield Way. Take the R fork after about 1/2 mile, then the first R (Northwell Drive), then turn R at the roundabout into Lygetun Drive. There is space for a few cars at the end of this drive.

Bramingham Wood is one of the Trust's community woodlands. There is a rich variety of flora from spring right through summer with flowers such as snowdrop, bluebell, red campion and enchanter's nightshade. Most typical woodland birds can be seen during the year, including tawny owl, treecreeper and sparrowhawk. A wide variety of animals live in and around the wood but many, like the voles and shrews, are difficult to see. Several species of fungi are found in Bramingham Wood which are not found elsewhere in the country.

*Maulden Wood
(Managed by Forest Enterprise) **F** 183ha
O.S.S. 153 - TL 073 395
01296 625825

🚗30🐄◯▲❄🌾ⓘ⛺🏃⛺

Lay-by off A6, at the top of hill between Clophill and Haynes West End. There is car parking in the lay-by.

The wood is an SSSI and has forest trails.

*Park Wood
(Heygate & Sons) **A** 65ha
O.S.S. 153 - SP 933 595
01234 720932

🚶▲🏃

The wood is situated between Harrold and Hinwick, 10 miles NW of Bedford. Visits for at least 6 people can be arranged any time, by appointment with Peter Hall, Forester, on the above telephone number.

There is natural regeneration of ash at various stages up to 10 years old, plus general conservation work and rehabilitation of semi-derelict woodlands.

Rowney Warren
(Managed by Forest Enterprise) **F** 71ha
O.S.S 153 -TL 124 404
01296 625825

🚗20🐄◯▲🌾⛺🅿⛺

From A600 follow sign for RAF Chicksands, in approx 2 miles, NW of Shefford. Car Park. Forest walks.

Rowney Warren (2)
(SC Whitbread Southill Estate) **R** 112ha
O.S.S. 153 - TL 112 414
01462 813209

Situated on A600 approx 6 miles S of Bedford

Private woodlands in part leased to Forestry Commission.

West Wood
(Forest Enterprise) **F** 84ha
O.S.S. 153 - SP 986 623
01604 696239

🚗4🐄◯▲🌾

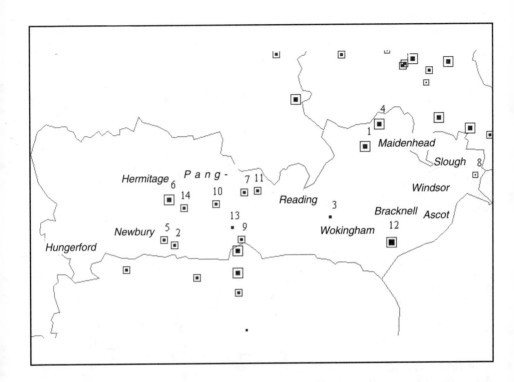

1. *Ashley Hill*
2. Baynes Reserve
3. *Bearwood
4. Bisham Woods
5. Bowdown Woods
6. *Fencewood
7. Moor Copse

8. Poyle Poplars Community Woodland
9. *Round Oak Piece
10. *Rushall Woods
11. *Sulham Wood*
12. *Swinley and Bagshot Forest
13. *Ufton Park
14. Westrop Wood

*Ashley Hill

(Forest Enterprise) **F** 117ha
O.S.S. 175 - SU 833 805
01296 625825

N of the A4 Knowl Hill roundabout. Access can be gained about 0.25 mile along the Burchetts Green road. There are rights of way through the wood. Guided visits can be arranged by appointment; cost can be negotiated (donations to the Forestry Trust). Please contact Mr Wallis on the above number, or Derek Paxton on 0753-861891.

The main tree species are oak, beech, Scots pine and European larch. The hill rises to 144m above sea level where the extensive rights of way converge. The woodland is extremely fragmented from the 1950s plantings and subsequent windblows. These areas are being left as open areas returning to natural regeneration in the future. There is an ex-Forestry Commission house at the centre of the wood: woodland users are asked to give the occupants privacy and consideration whilst in the vicinity. The wood is especially pleasant on a frosty morning or a summer's evening.

Baynes Reserve

(Berks, Bucks and Oxon Naturalists Trust) **F** 16ha
O.S.S. 174 - SU 511 649
01734 341721

Take unclassified road S past Thatcham station and as the road rises fork R (Burys Bank Road) which goes around Greenham Common. After half a mile turn R down a gravel track, pass Thatched Lodge to a small car park. A leaflet describing a widlife walk around this reserve is available from the above phone number. No charge is made for access and the wood is open all year. A BBONT nature reserve and SSSI.

This ancient woodland covers two stream valleys cutting through gravel and clays. On the higher slopes acid soils support birch and rowan with oak and hazel; here bluebells flower in spring and honeysuckle and foxglove in summer. The wetter and richer lower slopes have alder with hazel under which moschatel

and cuckoo pint flower with golden saxifrage marking the wetter flushes. The nightingale is present in this reserve as are dormice and many species of dragonflies.

*Bearwood

(Royal Merchant Navy School Foundation) **A** 25ha
O.S.S. 175 - SU 777 692
01734 787645

A329 Reading - Wokingham road, at Winnersh lights take B3030 for Arborfield Cross, L at mini roundabout, Bearwood College is first R. Parking, WC. By appointment only; a small charge may be required.

Until the early 1800s the estate was an outlier of Windsor Forest. During this time Bearwood House was built and the land turned into a gentleman's estate. Exotics were planted, the lake dammed and the area landscaped. Among the exotics were rhododendron ponticum which has in places taken over and swamped out the native species. In addition to the Wellingtonia Avenue, there are a number of unusual trees - Japanese cedar, swamp cypress, Himalayan spruce and others. Fauna includes usual animals - roe deer, muntjac, viper and grass snake. Bearwood lake has a wide range of birds, varying with the season.

Bisham Woods

(Woodland Trust) **F** 153ha
O.S.S. 175 - SU 856 850
01476 742297

From Maidenhead take the A308 towards Bisham. Follow this road to the roundabout where it joins the A404. Turn L at the roundabout then immediately L again and park in the council car park. Apart from the car park there are no facilities on the site. There is no charge made to walk in the wood and it is open at all times of the year.

Ancient maps at Bisham Abbey indicate that most of this large woodland is at least 500 years old. It is understood to be the inspiration for the Wild Wood in Kenneth Grahame's "Wind in the Willows". There are excellent examples of Chiltern beech; high forest on the chalk slopes and oak, birch and sweet chestnut elsewhere. Bisham Woods have some unusual plant species including bird's nest orchid, thin-spiked wood sedge and yellow archangel. Large areas of bluebell can be seen in the spring. The great spotted woodpecker, green woodpecker and nuthatch inhabit the wood, along with muntjac deer.

Bowdown Woods

(Berks, Bucks and Oxon Naturalists Trust)
F 38ha
O.S.S. 174 - SU 504 657
01734 341721

From the A34 S of Newbury, turn L at a roundabout towards Greenham village. After about 1.5 miles along Burys Bank Road turn L down the track signposted "Newbury Trout Lakes", the car park is on the R a little way down the track. A leaflet describing a wildlife walk around this reserve is available from the above phone number. No charge is made for access and the wood is open all year. A BBONT nature reserve and SSSI.

Bowdown has extremely varied topography and vegetation. Gullies filled with alder coppice blend into ash and maple on the clay while old oaks and rowans are scattered throughout relict ancient heathland reminiscent of wood pasture. White admiral, purple hairstreak and silver washed fritillary are amongst the butterflies present. Spring flowers include Solomons seal, moschatel, yellow archangel and wood anemone.

*Fencewood

(Gerald Palmer Trust) **R** 152ha
O.S.S. 174 - SU 513 723
01635 200878

From Newbury, take the B4009 to Hermitage. Turn R on Marlston Road, under the railway bridge. The wood will be found on the R. There is

parking for a limited number of cars. There is full access for walkers and dogs and between 1 May and 30 Sept there is also full access for horse and pony riders. Outside this period riders must stay on the bridleway. Group and guided visits must be arranged by contacting Mr L O Birch on the above number. Please give 3 weeks notice for all such visits. Donations to the Forestry Trust.

Fence Wood has been woodland for very many years. Over half the wood has been restocked since 1950 with a variety of species, retaining belts of old broadleaved trees. Grimsbury Castle is an iron age hill fort. The folly in the centre of the fort is a private house. The wood has been open to the public for many years but visitors are asked to obey the rules set out on the notice boards at the principal entry points.

Moor Copse

(Berks, Bucks and Oxon Naturalists Trust)
F 27ha
O.S.S. 175 - SU 635 742
01734 341721

Leave Pangbourne southwards on the A340. Just past Tidmarsh, as you rise to cross the M4, turn L into a lay-by with a car park. A leaflet describing a wildlife walk around this reserve is available and there is an Open Day on Sun, 26 Apr 1995: contact the woodlands officer on the above number for further details. No charge is made for access. A BBONT nature reserve and SSSI.

An ancient woodland lying in the flood plain of the river Pang, Moor Copse is a diverse mixture of wet ash and alder standing on peat and gravel. Coppicing has taken place over the last seven years and the regrowth has provided habitats for various plants, insects and breeding birds. Primroses, bluebells and early purple orchids can be seen in the spring. White admiral butterflies (on the wing in July and Aug) lay their eggs on honeysuckle which can been seen hanging from many trees.

Poyle Poplars Community Woodland

(Thames Water Utilities Ltd) **F** 6ha
O.S.S. 176 - TQ 023 757

🚗16🚻 ♥ ♬

1 mile W of M25, junction 14, on Horton Road. Pub at eastern end on Colne Valley Way.

This is a 20 year old hybrid poplar plantation being converted by phased felling to native species deciduous woodland. Nearly 10,000 trees have been planted by local schools, volunteers and contractors from 1990 to 1993. 26 species of native trees and shrubs have been planted to create different woodland characters. The path through the wood is part of the Colne Valley Way.

*Round Oak Piece

(R H R Benyon) **F** 61ha
O.S.S. 175 - SU 627 651
01734 302504

🚗🚻U ♠ Y i ☂ 🍴 ♬

W of Reading and S of the A4(T). From junction 12 of the M4 take the A4, Theale bypass, for about two miles, then take first road L through Ufton Nervet towards Mortimer, then R at T junction towards Tadley and Heath End. Parking is being provided at the Round Oak pub, about 800m on L. There will be four Forestry Trust Open Days starting at 2 o'clock on the first Sunday in May, July, Oct, and Dec. These will cover the changing habitats and seasons, the different stages of forestry operations, the benefits for wildlife arising from them and the opportunity for visitors to carry out practical work and see its effect on a subsequent visit.

A predominantly long established Scots pine wood, with trees of varying ages, with larch and Douglas fir interspersed. There is a pond, originally designed as a fire dam to provide an emergency water supply in case of fire at the listed Ufton Court (c.1600) which is in the middle of the wood, providing both an attractive area for visitors and for many species of dragonfly. Alder, oak and birch grow in the gulleys leading to the pond and the large clearfelled areas, where the pine is regenerating, support a nightjar population.

HAVEN WOODLANDS
Management of woodland, hedgerow & heathland habitats. Management plans & survey.
17 Archers Road, Eastleigh, Hants, SO50 9AQ.
Tel: 01703 496715
NATURE CONSERVATION MANAGEMENT

*Rushall Woods

(W Cumber & Son (Theale) Ltd) **F** 40ha
O.S.S. 174 - SU 588 714
01734 744547

💷£1🚗20🚗2🚻U ♠ ☀ Y WC ᕁ 🍴 ☂
♿ ⚡ FP ⛲

Leave M4 at junction 12: A4 past Theale: A340 towards Pangbourne, take the first L to Bradfield. Go through Bradfield, just L towards Stanford Dingley, then first R for Rushall Farm or second R for Rushall Manor. Pond, recreational woodland walks between 1 and 5 miles long. Please keep to the marked trails. Guided visits and school visits can be arranged by appointment between 1 Mar and 30 Nov. Please give two weeks notice. To make arrangements contact John Bishop on the above number. Donations to the Forestry Trust.

Rushall Woods are mainly ancient woodland which has been brought into management over the last five years. There is a coniferous plantation which is being felled and both natural regeneration and replanting of Douglas fir and Scots pine is underway. Work in the main has been limited to underwood coppicing and ride widening. One area of hazel is being rotationally coppiced. There are new plantings in some important landscape positions. The woodlands have a good variety of species with some outstanding cherries. They are a beautifully rich area of wildlife and especially attractive in the spring. There are a number of statutory footpaths and access is encouraged except on Saturdays in the winter. The farm supports the John Simonds Trust as it seeks to encourage a love and understanding of the countryside.

Sulham Wood

(Managed by Forest Enterprise) **F** 53ha
O.S.S. 175 - SU 647 745
01296 625825

🚗12🚻 ♠ ☀ Y 📖

Take the minor road S from the A329 Pangbourne - Reading road, at 'T' junction turn L, car park on L at the top of the hill.

*Swinley and Bagshot Forest
(Crown Estate Commissioners) **F** 1000ha

O.S.S. 175 - SU 876 662

01753 860222

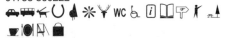

Start from the "Look Out" heritage centre on Nine Mile Ride, Bracknell, half mile to the W of the Bracknell to Bagshot dual carriageway (A322). See special feature on visitor centres at back of book.. The centre includes a schoolroom, and displays of local commerce and wildlife.

Swinley and Bagshot Forest extends is part of the much larger Windsor Forest. Scots and Corsican pine are the dominant species, grown mainly for commercial reasons. Spinneys of natural birch and elderly Scots pine are interspersed and add diversity to landscape and wildlife, which is rich and includes an SSSI in the vicinity of Mill Pond. This and other features of scenic and archaeological interest are served by waymarked trails. Principal amongst these are Caesar's Camp, dating to about 700BC, and Napoleonic redoubts.

*Ufton Park
(R H R Benyon) **A** 30ha

O.S.S. 175 - SU 626 667

01734 302504

W of Reading and S of the A4(T). From junction 12 of the M4 take the A4, Theale bypass for two miles., then take second road L to Ufton Nervet, follow signs to Ufton Court. Guided visits can be arranged. Please book for ALL visits at least 3 weeks in advance. Contact Mr K R McDiarmid on the above number. Donations made to the Forestry Trust.

A mixed wood forming part of the Englefield Estate. Mixed age compartments all in production. The wood was originally planted with oak and coppice, much of

which has been felled and replanted for the purposes of timber production and conservation. Species include oak, sweet chestnut, ash, red oak, larch, Scots pine, Corsican pine and Norway spruce. Flora and fauna include roe and fallow deer, foxes, badgers, wild flowers, butterflies, and birds including all three woodpeckers, nightjar, nightingale, various warblers and gamebirds. See also Round Oak Piece.

Westrop Wood
(Mrs S J Constantinidi Will Trust) **F** 25ha

O.S.S. 174 - SU 517 708

01761 470765

From Newbury travel east on A4; turn L in Thatcham to Cold Ash, pass through village and turn R at crossroads into Bucklebury Alley signed to Westrop Green. Entrance to wood is on R after the houses, approx. 1/2 mile.

The wood is open all year round - please observe notices when tree felling operations are underway. This is a most attractive mixed wood containing a wide variety of species. A group of very old Scots pine on the top of Westrop Hill is a fine feature protected by covenant. Bluebells and primroses in abundance.

BUCKINGHAMSHIRE

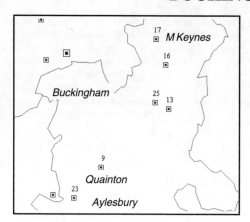

1. Bacombe Hill
2. Black Park
3. * Bottom Wood
4. Burnham Beeches
5. Captain's Wood
6. * Cockshoots
7. Common Wood
8. Dancersend
9. Finemere Wood
10. *Gomm's Wood
11.* Hockeridge & Pancake Woods
12. *Hodgemoor Wood*
13.* Howe Park Wood
14. King's Wood

15. Langley Park
16. Linford Wood
17. Little Linford Wood
18. Millfield Wood
19. Old Hanging Wood
20. * Pavis Wood
21. Piggots Wood
22. Priestfield Arboretum
23. Rushbeds Wood
24. Sandells and Netherlands
25. Shenley Wood
26. Walkwood
27. * *Wendover Woodland Park*
28. Whiteleaf Wood

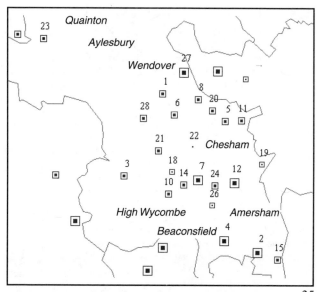

Bacombe Hill

(Buckinghamshire County Council) **F** 25ha
O.S.S. 165 - SP 864 074
01296 383394

From Wendover High Street, take Ellesborough Road past the Station. 0.5 mile up this hill on the L of the R hand is the small parking area for Bacombe Hill. Other facilities include the Ridgeway National Trail, bridleway and network of permissive paths. There is full and free access all the year.

Situated on the Chilterns scarp slope above Wendover, Bacombe Hill contains open chalk grassland, recent ash woodland, hazel coppice and scrub. The site is being managed for open public access, woodland production and nature conservation. Following the introduction of coppicing in 1990 the site now provides materials for traditional hedgelaying practices in the area.

Black Park Country Park

(Buckinghamshire County Council)
F 210ha
O.S.S. 176 - TQ 005 833
01753 511060

Signed (white and brown tourist type) off A412 trunk road Slough - Uxbridge. Car park adjacent to 5.5 hectare lake and picnic area. There is full and free access all year on foot - vehicles excluded from dusk - 0800 hours.

An attractive mixed woodland of oak, beech, sweet chestnut and Scots pine, with specimen trees, most of which were planted between 1820 and 1833 by Viscount Anson, later created Earl of Lichfield. The woodland is managed on continuous cover principles. The Shugborough estate, which is the seat of the Earls of Lichfield, comprises 400 ha of parkland, woodland and formal garden. The mansion House, county museum and working farm museum are to the public. Details from the property./₂ hectare lake and picnic area. There is full and free access all year on foot - vehicles excluded from dusk - 0800 hours.

Attractive setting, of almost completely woodland consisting mix of conifer and broadleaved. Hard rides provide good access even in wet weather. 22ha heathland to the north of the park surrounded by 25 hectares managed as a local nature reserve. Good variety of birdlife. Objectives of management are multi-purpose: timber production, nature and landscape conservation, and quiet countryside public recreation.

*Bottom Wood

(Chiltern Society) **F** 14ha
O.S.S. 165 - SU 795 949
01494 461286

Bottom Wood lies in a valley to the N of A40, 3 miles SE of Stokenchurch (Jct 5 M40) and 2.5 miles W of West Wycombe. Park at top end of Old Dashwood Hill, Studley Green, off A40. Take bridleway to valley bottom and turn L into wood - leaflet and management map available. Open Days and visits can be arranged. Donations for guided visits. Public Bridleway, which gets very muddy, runs the length of the wood.

Ancient semi-natural Chiltern beechwood with wide variety of other trees, including wild cherry, ash, oak, goat willow, whitebeam,and wych elm. The wood is managed as a nature reserve and used by the Chiltern Woodlands Project for demonstration purposes. It has a rich ancient woodland flora and also, on Toothill, a remnant of chalk downland recovered from a pine plantation. 175 species of butterflies and moths have been recorded. Old sawpits, boundary banks and terraced fields add historical interest.

Burnham Beeches

(Corporation of London) **FE** 220ha
O.S.S 175 - SU 953 850
01753 647358

S from junction 2 of the M40 and N from junction 6 of the M4. Along A355 to Farnham Common and turn into Beeches Road which takes you into the

Beeches. Many local pubs, 2 cafes (1 seasonal), picnic area - common. A few facilities for the disabled including parking bays and paths near features. Fully open access twith byways open to all traffic (daylight hours only). Guided visits by appointment, please contact Mark Frater on above number. A new guide book is available from the cafes or office.

A National Nature Reserve with ancient semi-natural woodland, mainly beech and oak with heathland, wetland, ponds, coppicing and wood pasture systems - beech pollards with rare breed ponies, cattle and pigs. Twelfth century scheduled monument. Rich social history including Mendelssohn and Jenny Lind. Varied flora, rich and diverse fauna. Ford Conservation Award for the Natural Environment, also Forest Authority Centre of Excellence Award.

JOLLY WOODMAN - An old country inn serving lunch and evening meals with real ale and good wines. Large garden with woodland walks direct from the front into the woods of Burnham Beeches. Tel: 01753 644350

Captain's Wood

(Buckinghamshire County Council) **F** 10ha
O.S.S. 165 - SP 953 032
01296 383394

From the centre of Chesham take Bellingdon Road from the A416 towards Bellingham. This road leads into Hivings Hill. Captain's Wood is on the LH side of Hivings Hill at the steepest part of the road. There is woodside parking for 3 cars, bridleway and a network of footpaths but no other facilities. Access is full and free all the year.

This ancient semi-natural woodland is a superb asset to the local community. It is predominantly beech high forest with some excellent groups of beech naturally regenerating. A multi-purpose woodland management approach is pursued, with emphasis being placed on enhancing the nature and landscape conservation value of the site. There is a diverse range of native tree and shrub species and ground flora reflecting the different soil conditions across the site.

*Cockshoots

(Sir Leonard Figg) **F** 24ha
O.S.S. 165 - SP 872 042
01494 488346

2.5 miles S of Wendover on the Amersham road (A413). Look for signs to Cockshoots Wood. Picnic site and car park.

An old beech wood of which half has been felled in the last 20 years and replanted with oak, cherry, southern beech, larch, Lawson cypress and western red cedar. The wood is well provided with footpaths leading from the car park. Bluebells and primroses are conspicuous in the spring and many species of wild flowers throughout the summer months. Muntjac and fallow deer, badgers and foxes are present.

Common Wood

(Robin Fleming) **R** 118ha
O.S.S. 175 - SU 911 943
01295 688100

Leave Beaconsfield by the B474 for Penn and Tylers Green. Pass through Penn into Tylers Green. Turn R at the crossroads in the valley bottom into Common Wood Lane. The entrance to the wood is 400m from the crossroads on the L hand side. Self guided trails open between April and September but there may be restrictions during forestry operations. Please contact Peter Hale on above number, or in writing, at Payn's House, Oxhill, Warwick, CV35 0QR, for a descriptive leaflet of the wood (£1 plus postage). Donations to the Forestry Trust.

The mature beech were planted in about 1850 partly on the site of Wycombe Heath. An active policy of regenerating them is taking place with a number of stands of hardwoods and one stand of naturally regenerated European larch. The objective is to grow good quality hardwoods as well as creating an uneven aged wood to provide a diversity of habitats.

Dancersend

(Berks, Bucks and Oxon Naturalists Trust)
F 30ha
O.S.S. 165 - SP 900 095
01296 433222

🚗3🚶🌲☀️🦋📖♿🥾

*A4011 from Wendover to Tring. Just before A41
turn sharp right to St. Leonards. After 1.5 miles, at
a sharp L hand bend, park on R verge or pull in on
L and walk up track to reserve. No charge is made
for access and the reserve is open all year. A
BBONT nature reserve and an SSSI. A leaflet
describing the reserve is available.*

The reserve lies on varying soils and dry valley slopes
and contains a rich variety of wildlife. The beech with
oak woodland was felled in the last war and colonised
by scrub. In the mid 1950s the Forestry Commission
replanted most of this area with beech, larch and
spruce. Original woodland survivors include stinking
helleborine. There is also an area of chalk grassland
carrying pyramidal, fragrant and bee orchids, clustered
bellflower, Chiltern gentian, green hairstreak and dark
green fritillary.

Finemere Wood

(Berks, Bucks and Oxon Naturalists Trust)
F 40.3ha
O.S.S. 165 - SP 720 215
01296 433222

🚗3🚶🌲🦋📖♿🥾 FP

*Travel northwest from Quainton (SP 74 20), turn
left at a T junction towards Edgcott. After 0.75mile,
just over the rise, a track goes right. Park on
nearby verge. Walk up track to reserve. A leaflet
describing a wildlife walk around the reserve is
available Further details from the above phone
number.A BBONT nature reserve and a SSSI.*

The wood is a rich mosaic of habitats resulting from its
chequered history. Much of the site was replanted with
conifers in the 1950s; this is being thinned and
managed as a productive crop but will be replaced by
native broadleaved woodland. Substantial areas of
ancient woodland survive: oak with hazel, maple and
ash coppice, as well as blackthorn and aspen.
Coppicing is being reinstated, with great benefits for

flowers and insects, and the blackthorn is being
managed for the nationally rare black hairstreak
butterfly. Woodland rides are managed for the benefit
of butterflies and flowers. This is considered one of the
best sites for butterflies in the area (including purple
emperor).

*Gomms Wood

(Wycombe District Council) F 14ha
O.S.S 175 SU 894931
01494 421827

🚗15🚶🌲☀️🦋ℹ️📖♿🥾🅿️⛺

*From High Wycombe take A40 Beaconsfield
Road. After 1 mile turn left into Cock Lane. After
1.5 miles the woodland is signposted and runs
along the L hand side of the road. Continue for .5
mile and turn left at end of wood into car park.
Waymarked trail starts from here.*

Gomm's Wood contains a rich and diverse mix of
habitats including ancient and secondary Beech woodland, young plantations of Beech, Oak, Ash Cherry and
Lime, traditionally managed Hazel coppice, native
scrubland , and species rich rich chalk grassland. A
butterfly ride, newly established hedgerows, a wild-
flower meadow and old boundary banks add further
interest. The wood is a demonstration wood, managed
in partnership with BTCV and supported by Southern
Electric. It is promoted as a model for multi purpose
management with the objectives of nature conservation, public recreation, community involvement, education landscape and timber production.

*Hockeridge and Pancake Woods

(Royal Forestry Society of England, Wales
and Northern Ireland) FE 74ha
O.S.S. 165 - SP 978 063
01442 822028

🚗20🚶♿📖🅿️🚻

*Off the A416 Chesham to Berkhamsted road at
Hockeridge Cottages on the Herts/Bucks border.
52 labelled specimen trees. Explanatory leaflets
and maps are available free on receipt of an s.a.e.
from the RFS, 102 High Street, Tring, Herts, HP23
4AF or telephone as above. The site is not really
suitable for the disabled. There are rights of way
through the woodland and self guided trails.*

Please keep to the marked trails Guided walks and group visits by appointment at other times. Please give 2 months notice. Charges for guided walks are £2 for adults and £1 for children. Donations to Forestry Trust on open days. Walkers are welcome on the permissive footpaths elsewhere in the wood. Rights of way should be adhered to.

A mixed multi purpose working woodland in the Chilterns providing a microcosm of lowland forestry, woodland types and management practices in the U.K. A demonstration woodland of how to harmonise conservation, recreation, landscape and education.

Hodgemoor Wood

(Managed by Forest Enterprise) **F** 113ha
O.S.S. 175 - SU 969 939
01296 625825

Off A355 between Amersham and Beaconsfield, take minor road - Bottrells Lane - leading to Chalfont St Giles.

This is an SSSI with forest walks.

*Howe Park Wood

(Milton Keynes Parks Trust) **F** 23.1ha
O.S.S. 152 - SP 831 345
01908 223322

Howe Park Wood is immediately S of Westcroft Roundabout at the junction of Chaffron Way and Tattenhoe Street in the SW corner of Milton Keynes. There is a car park and picnic area on the N side of the wood, off Chaffron Way. The wood is a SSSI with high value to nature conservation. We prefer visitors to keep to the paths and to keep dogs on a lead, especially during the bird nesting season. There is an excellent path and ride network, a number of seats and two interpretation panels, but no other facilities.

Howe Park Wood is an ancient semi-natural woodland, possibly a remnant of the former Royal Forest of

Whaddon Chase. Records date back to the 11th century. It has been managed as coppice with standards in the past and was part of a medieval deer park. It is a wet ash/maple/dog's mercury woodland, with stands of oak/bramble woodland on drier areas. Of special interest is the natural occurrence of small stands of hornbeam, far to the north west of its accepted East Anglian range. Aspen and willows are common in the the wet areas and the abundant blackthorn supports two colonies of the rare black hairstreak butterfly. There are also purple hairstreak, white admiral and wood white butterflies recorded. There is a very rich ground flora, with bluebells, woodrush, pendulous sedge, wood anemone, primroses, violets, yellow archangel and woodruff. At least 5 orchid species may be found and the flora is typical of ancient woodland with a long history of traditional management. About 300 species of moths have been recorded, including such scarcities as buff footman, slender brindle and pinion streaked snout. The wood is managed primarily as a nature reserve.

Kings Wood

(Chepping Wycombe Parish Council)
F 73 ha
O.S.S. 175 - SU 897 935
01494 814600

Leave Beaconsfield by B474 passing through Penn. In Tylers Green turn L at crossroads in Valley bottom into New Road At crossroads continue into Cock Lane. Entrance opposite school. Parking opposite school, by Cock Lane Cemetry, at bottom of Kingswood Road and next to Dolphin Public House, Totteridge.

An amenity wood for the use by the public. Adjoins Gomms Wood. Consists mainly of beech. Regeneration and planting taking place, and conservation projects are being undertaken. Two ponds, glades and rides are being created. There are rights of way through the wood.

Langley Park Country Park

(Buckinghamshire County Council) **F** 55ha
O.S.S. 176 - TQ 016 821
01753 511060

🚗 ◡ 🍴 ● WC ⊔ ⊥

Follow brown tourist signs off main A412 Slough - Uxbridge. Toilets open seasonally but there are full facilities in adjacent Black Park Country Park. Full and free access all year - vehicles excluded from dusk - 0800 hours.

Traditional parkland features of wood pasture - views to Windsor Castle. Recommended during April/ May/June during Azalea/ Rhododendron flowering period. Good mature oak woodland with fine avenues of Wellingtonia.

Linford Wood

(Milton Keynes Parks Trust) **F** 40ha
O.S.S. 152 - SP 845 406
01908 223322

🚗 ⊀ ● 🅿 ⊥

Linford Wood is just over 1/2 mile N of central Milton Keynes between Monks Way and Dansteed Way. There are car parks off Brecklands and Saxon Street, on the W side of the wood. The wood has a good footpath network, suitable for disabled access, with picnic areas, seats and benches. There is also a "trim trail" for fitness exercises. Visitors are requested to keep dogs on a lead, especially in the bird nesting season.

Linford Wood is a mixture of ancient wet ash/maple woodland, old secondary woodland and recent plantation. It is an important feature of the landscape of central Milton Keynes. It is also of considerable conservation importance, with a very rich flora and fauna. Most of the wood has a high mixed canopy of oak, ash and maple standards with an understorey of hawthorn, blackthorn, bramble, wild rose and crab apple plus hazel, maple and ash coppice. Historical records go back to 1283 and a fragment of a medieval wood bank and ditch remains in the SW corner of the wood. Over 200 flowering plants have been recorded and the ground flora is dominated by bluebells and dog's mercury with such rarities as herb paris, butterfly orchid, bird's nest orchid and broad leaved helleborine.

It is also an important area for recreation, used quite heavily by dog walkers, joggers, bird watchers, picnickers and horseriders.

Little Linford Wood

(Berks, Bucks and Oxon Naturalists Trust) **F** 42.5ha
O.S.S. 152 - SP 832 455
01296 433222

🚗6⊀ ● ⅄ ⊔ ⌃ ⋔ FP

Not to be confused with Linford Wood (above)! B526 from Newport Pagnell. Just before Gayhurst turn left towards Haversham. After 1/2 mile turn left along track. Reserve is 1.5 miles on, beyond M1 and Dairy Farm. A leaflet describing a wildlife walk around the reserve is available. A BBONT nature reserve.

Although an ancient woodland site, much of it was felled and replanted 100 years ago. It still remains rich in wildflowers with 130 plant species including 23 ancient woodland plants such as herb paris (flowering in May - June). Suitable timber trees are occasionally cropped, coppice crafts are being re-introduced, and charcoal is made on site.

Millfield Wood

(Berks, Bucks and Oxon Naturalists Trust) **F** 7.3ha
O.S.S. 165 - SU 870 954
01296 433222

🚗⊀ ● ✳ ⊔ ⌃ ⋔

A4128 N from Wycombe. After 1/2 mile turn L into Hughenden Manor and park. Walk back down drive, go a few yards L, cross the road and follow bridleway up hill to the reserve. A leaflet describing a wildlife walk arond the reserve is available from the above phone number. A BBONT nature reserve and an SSSI.

A rare example of a semi-natural Chiltern beechwood on chalk. Severely damaged in the great storms but producing good natural regeneration of trees (ash and beech) with areas of mixed trees (holly, yew, white-beam, field maple) and some coppiced hazel. Many spring flowers, such as goldilocks buttercup, wood anemone and a good display of herb paris.

developing a system of group regeneration, recruiting natural regeneration where possible. On the lower, less accessible slopes the thin soil over chalk has resulted in a large number of moribund standing beech - fabulous wildlife habitats.

Old Hanging Wood

(Dr J W & Mrs M A McAnuff) **F** 7ha

O.S.S. 176 - TQ 011 976

West Barn, Hall Place, Seer Green,
Beaconsfield, Bucks HP9 2YE

Follow A404 E from Little Chalfont. 1 mile from Chalfont & Latimer Station bridleway on R leads to and through the wood after 5 mins walk. Bus stops on A404 close to bridleway. Only parking 100m E of bridleway entrance.

After a series of damaging fires in 1960s this small semi-natural ancient wood is now fully stocked with an uneven-aged mixture of native hardwoods and larch. The wood is continuously worked by the present owner, with advice and occasional practical help from the Chiltern Woodlands Project. Management includes some coppicing but the main objectives are timber production and silvicultural improvement for the benefit of wildlife, amenity and landscape.

*Pavis Wood

(Buckinghamshire County Council) **F** 35ha

O.S.S. 165 - SP 914 093

01296 383394

From the S side of Tring, near the Museum, take the lane S towards Hastoe village (road passes under the A41). Bear R in Hastoe. Pavis Wood is 1/4 mile along this road opposite the next LH bend. Facilities include parking for 3 cars, bridleway (Ridgeway path) and network of footpaths. There is full and free access all the year.

Pavis Wood is a diverse ancient semi-natural woodland principally comprising broadleaf high forest with a scattering of conifers. A multi-purpose woodland management approach is pursued. New plantings are a consequence of the recent storms which ravaged the exposed escarpment. Emphasis is being placed on

HAVEN WOODLANDS
Management of woodland, hedgerow & heathland habitats. Management plans & survey.
17 Archers Road, Eastleigh, Hants, SO50 9AQ.

Piggots Wood

(Dr & Mrs Wheeler Robinson) **R** 20.3ha

O.S.S. 165 - SU 853 987

Piggotts, North Dean, High Wycombe, Bucks HP14 4MF

In Lower North Dean 4 miles N of High Wycombe park at the top of Piggotts Hill. There are no entrance charges but donations welcomed to Cystic Fibrosis Research Trust via the owner. Please keep to the paths; no access for horses; groups by appointment (schools welcomed).

20 hectares of ancient semi-natural woodland, most designated as heritage woodland by English Nature because of the interesting flora. One area of Piggotts Wood South replanted in 1993; two areas in Piggotts Wood North in 1993. Some coppicing and glades to encourage variety of habitats. Ancient boundary banks and sawpits. Copy of Eric Gill crucifix. Managed by Chiltern Woodlands Project.

Priestfield Arboretum

(Mrs A Carton) **A** 2ha

O.S.S. 175 - SU 901 992

The Dendrologist, PO Box 341, Chesham, Bucks HP5 2RD

Off Stoney Lane, Windsor Lane, Little Kingshill Nr Gt Missenden, Bucks. Little Kingshill is off the main A413. There is limited parking in Stoney Lane, but no other facilities. There is a guide book, price £2.00 incl p&p which is available from the above

address. Access is free (by appointment only through the Dendrologist) but a donation towards maintenance and planting of trees would be welcome. There are Open Days which are held in Jun and Oct.

The woodland consists of 200 unusual and rare trees including representatives of all conifer genera that can be grown in this area of Britain. The Taxodiaceae have a very good representation at Priestfield. Small growing broadleaf exotics are currently being added for interest and colour. Shrub management by volunteers with grass cutting by the owner twice a year.

Rushbeds Wood

(Berks, Bucks and Oxon Naturalists Trust)
F 45ha
O.S.S. 165 - SP 668 157
01296 433222

A41 W from Aylesbury. At Kingswood turn L towards Brill. After 1.5 miles follow road L and just before T junction turn R over bridge into car park. A leaflet describing a wildlife walk around the reserve is available from the above phone number. A BBONT nature reserve and an SSSI.

This ancient woodland has over 120 species of flowering plants, 50 fungi and 60 mosses and liverworts. Dead wood supports beetles and other invertebrates which attract numerous woodpeckers, including the greater spotted. Part of the wood is being brought back into coppice management, a large area is being left as wildwood, and an area of blackthorn is being managed for the black hairstreak butterfly. The rides have been widened for the benefit of flowers and insects.

Sandells and Netherlands

(The Earl Howe) **R** 26ha
O.S.S. 175 - SU 937 924
01295 688100

From Beaconsfield (Newtown) take Penn Road and then turn R into Ledborough Lane. Drive for

350m and turn L into Sandells Wood End. Drive for 900m and the entrance to the wood is on the R by the public footpath sign and the Penn Parish Council notice board. There is adequate street parking. There is fully open access to the wood from April to September and there are rights of way and self guided trails. There may be some restrictions to access during felling operations. Please contact Peter Hale on the above number, or in writing, at Payn's House, Oxhill, Warwick, CV35 0QR for a descriptive leaflet of the wood (£1 plus postage). Donations to the Forestry Trust.

The mature beechwoods were probably planted in about 1850. The stand has been recently thinned and some storm damage has occurred. The belt of young hardwoods are to provide a screen when final fellings and replantings take place. The objective is to grow good quality timber. An ancient boundary ditch borders part of the wood.

Shenley Wood

(Milton Keynes Parks Trust) **F** 23.4ha
O.S.S. 152 - SP 825 357
01908 223322

Shenley Wood is between Fulmer St and Tatten-hoe St on the W side of Milton Keynes, with Portway to the N and Child's Way to the S. Access is via a path from Chalkdell Drive on the NE side, or from the car park off Merlewood Drive, by the SW corner of the wood. There is a good car park and a picnic area, a network of paths and rides with several seats, but no other facilities. Shenley Wood is an important nature conservation site and visitors are asked to keep to the paths, and keep dogs on the lead, especially in the bird nesting season.

The wood is a fragment of ancient semi-natural woodland, historically associated with the nearby hamlets of Shenley Brook End and Shenley Church End, with records dating back to 1693 when it was twice as large. It contains a wide variety of trees and shrubs. Being primarily wet ash/oak woodland there is a predominance of ash, with lesser numbers of oak and field maple. Some of the large standard ash and oak are growing on very old previously coppiced bases, possibly 300-400 years old. In the 1950s small areas were planted with beech, Norway spruce, Lawson cypress and western hemlock but none of the latter and very few of the first three have survived. Hazel, field maple, aspen and goat willow dominate the shrub layer, with extensive brambles and hawthorn patches, and dense blackthorn thicket in places. Privet, dogwood and dog rose are all frequent, Guelder rose is also quite common and there are a very few wayfaring trees and purging buckthorn. The ground flora is also rich, being dominated, under the relatively light open canopy, by rough meadow grass, and bramble with dog's mercury in the drier areas; meadowsweet, ragged robin and pendulous sedge in the wet places. This rich and diverse flora and structure supports a wide variety of woodland birds, butterflies and moths, other insects and small mammals, though with the exception of a hornet moth few rare species are recorded. It is currently managed to conserve its wildlife value and as a park.

*Wendover Woodland Park

(Managed by Forest Enterprise) **F** 325ha

O.S.S. 165 - SP 889 107

01296 625825

🚌£1 🐎 ♦ ☀ ¥ 📖 ⚑ ⚶ wc ♿

From A4011 Wendover-Tring road a brown tourist sign directs visitors to the woodland entrance. Barbecues, forest trails, orienteering course, forest fitness trail. Special events programme and guided walks leaflet available.

Situated on the northern edge of the Chilterns escarpment, the woods afford some spectacular views of the Aylesbury Vale. These productive woods are now probably the most important nesting site for one of the smallest of our birds, the firecrest. Management has been adapted to conserve this bird and its habitat. Recreation is positively encouraged with a range of trails and play furniture.

Walkwood

(Beaconsfield Town Council) **F** 9ha

O.S.S. 175 SU 933 903

01494 675173

 🌳 ● ▯

Take the A40 from Beaconsfield Old Town towards Wycombe (J.2 M40) turn right into Walkwood Rise. Park at far end, take path on right into wood. Walkwood is within easy walking distance of of Beaconsfield B.R. station. Turn left from station onto B474. Take Burkes Road at second mini roundabout. Take first left, wood is down path on right.

A varied ancient broadleaved wood. Was once part of the grounds of the well known statesman and philanthropist Edmund Burke's house. Work to improve the health and condition of this amenity woodland has been carried out since 1989, to plans drawn up by the Chiltern Woodlands Project. Invasion of Laural and Rhododendron has been a problem. Storm damaged areas have been thinned or replanted with broadleaves - Beech, Oak, Wild Cherry and Hornbeam. Elm disease has affected some areas. Grey squirrels have damaged some young Beech and Oak. Further work is planned.

Whiteleaf Wood

(Buckinghamshire County Council) **F** 10ha

O.S.S. 165 - SP 824036

01296 383394

🚌20 🐎 ● ⚶

From the S end of Whiteleaf village, take Peters Lane up the escarpment towards Hampden. At the top of the hill (about 3/4 mile) Whiteleaf Wood car park (20 cars) is on the L. Facilities include bridleway, Ridgeway National Trail, network of permissive paths, picnic site. There is full and free access all year.

Whiteleaf Wood/Hill is a distinct north-south ridge on the edge of the Chilterns scarp. Recent gale damage has resulted in extensive planting of species native to the site. Whiteleaf Hill contains some fascinating archaeological features; a Neolithic long barrow, two round barrows, Whiteleaf Cross (existence first noted in 1738), a cross ridge dyke system, and First World War practice trenches. The principal management objectives are to enhance the archaeological interest and grassland conservation value by clearance and containment of scrub growth, and restoration of the storm damaged areas of the woodland to broadleaf high forest.

CAMBRIDGESHIRE

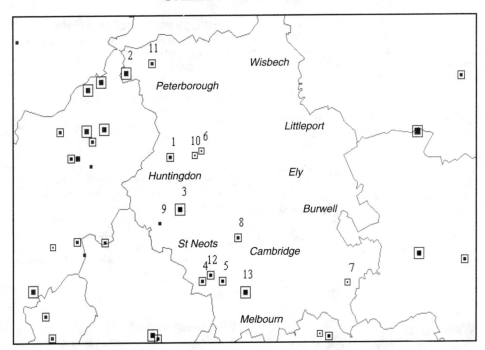

1. Aversley Wood
2. *Bedford Purlieus*
3. Brampton Wood
4. Gamlingay Wood
5. Hayley Wood
6. Lady's Wood
7. Lower Wood
8. Overhall Grove
9. *Perry Woods
10. Raveley Wood
11. *Southey Wood*
12. Waresley Wood
13. Wimpole Park

Aversley Wood

(Woodland Trust) **F** 61.5ha
O.S.S. 142 - TL 166 822
01476 74297

Take a minor road off the A1 to Sawtry village. Park off St Judith's Lane in the parish council car park.

Aversley Wood is one of the most interesting woods in Cambridgeshire. Ash and oak are the main canopy trees, along with aspen, beech and most interesting of all, the wild service tree, for which Aversley is especially important. The wood is a haven for birds. Look out for wrens and warblers; also blue, great and long-tailed tits, which have been seen and heard among the many shrubs in the wood, including hawthorn, elder, dogwood and the wayfaring tree. The rides in this wood provide habitats for many flowers including lady's smock, bugle and meadowsweet.

Bedford Purlieus

(Forest Enterprise) **R** 195ha
O.S.S. 141 - TF 045 004
01780 444394

Brampton Wood

(Wildlife Trust for Beds & Cambs) **F** 132ha
O.S.S. 153 - TL 185 698
01223 846363

The wood is on the N side of the road between Brampton and Grafham, about 1 mile W of the A1. Car park at wood entrance.

Brampton is the second largest wood in Cambridgeshire. It consists primarily of ash and field maple with hazel coppice but there are extensive blackthorn thickets, stands of recently planted conifers and many other trees and shrubs. Over 300 plant species have been recorded and it is particularly well known for butterflies, including white admiral and black hairstreak. Brampton Wood is also noted for birds

including the grasshopper warbler, nightingale, spotted flycatcher and woodcock.

Gamlingay Wood

(Wildlife Trust for Beds & Cambs) **F** 48ha
O.S.S. 153 - TL 242 535
01223 846363

From Gamlingay take B1040 towards Waresley. About 1/2 mile down the road, a track on the R leads to the reserve. Please drive carefully down track and park near wood.

Between 1949 and 1964, most of the wood was planted with a variety of conifers and oak. The rest of the wood is as it has been for hundreds of years, a mixture of coppice ash, hazel and field maple with pedunculate oak standards, some sallow and aspen. Wild service trees also grow here, a rarity in Cambridgeshire. Flora to see includes: oxlip, dog's mercury, bluebell, yellow archangel. Gamlingay is rich in mosses, fungi and insects which live only in ancient woodland.

Hayley Wood

(Wildlife Trust for Beds & Cambs) **F** 48ha
O.S.S. 153 - TL 294 534
01223 846363

Hayley Wood is on the B1046 between Great Gransden and Longstowe. The track leading to Hayley Wood is opposite a large water tower. Park on B1046 verge, W of track entrance. Please close and fasten all gates after passing through, especially those which protect the coppice plots within the wood.

The ancient Hayley Wood consists largely of tall oak standards forming a canopy above the mixed coppice and smaller trees of field maple, ash, hazel and hawthorn. Bluebell, oxlip and other beautiful spring flowers thrive in the conditions created by coppice management. Hayley is thought to have one of the largest oxlip populations in Britain and is also famous for its mosses, liverworts and fungi.

Cambridgeshire

Lady's Wood

(Wildlife Trust for Cambridgeshire)
F 6.8ha
O.S.S. 142 TL 243 826
01223 846363
🚗4🚶●👁

From Ramsey follow the road to Upwood and take the last turning on the R, into the village. Where this road turns sharply R a rough lane continues straight ahead. Follow this track towards Meadow Farm and park in the reserve car park at Upwood Meadows. Please shut the gate. A public footpath runs from Upwood Meadows to Lady's Wood, and a circular path runs through the wood.

Lady's Wood is an ancient wood which may date back to the woodland which covered most of England after the last Ice Age. Like most ancient woods in England it was once coppiced. Many of the trees in Lady's Wood were felled around 1951, but most were not removed because the timber was of poor quality. This dead wood now provides a marvellous habitat for the insects and fungi which live in and on it. The present woodland is a mixture of oak, ash (some growing from old coppice stools), and field maple, with crab apple and blackthorn. Lady's Wood is is one of the few sites in the county where ramsons or wild garlic grows, giving a strong smell of garlic in the spring. The spring flowers of ancient woodland thrive here, including bluebell, primrose and dog's mercury. Selective coppicing is carried out in parts of the wood, and new trees are occasionally planted among existing blackthorn and elm to speed the process of woodalnd recovery. Rides and paths are cut annually.

Lower Wood

(Wildlife Trust for Cambridgeshire) **F** 9ha
O.S.S. 154 - TL 626 528
01223 846363
🚶U●👁

From Linton take the B1052 to Weston Colville. The reserve is to the L of the road leading to Weston Green. Take the first turning on the L to Weston Green and continue to Three Horseshoes Farm at the end of the road. Please park in the farmyard and walk up the permissive path to the wood. Great Coven's Wood to the North of the

main ride is privately owned; please do not trespass.

Ash is the dominant tree in Lower Wood, which is an ancient wet ash/maple wood. A sinuous woodbank forms the western boundary, and pollard oaks still grow on the bank. The large bank running east-west in the northeast corner of the wood probably marked the original northern boundary of Lower Wood which is now bounded on the north by Great Coven's Wood. The edges of the rest of the wood do not have woodbanks and are truncated and linear, suggesting that part of the wood has been cleared and ploughed under to form the neighbouring arable fields (the field to the east was cleared only 30 years ago). The wood was once coppiced in the traditional manner, but this has been neglected for many years. As a result the ash coppice has grown into tall, many-stemmed trees, and the derelict hazel coppice does not thrive in the constant heavy shade cast by the ash canopy. There are some fine maiden ash and field maple. The ground flora is typical of ancient woodland, and includes oxlip, bluebell, dog's mercury and water avens. The Trust is reintroducing traditional coppice management in parts of the wood, but others will be left to grow into high forest.

Overhall Grove

(Wildlife Trust for Beds & Cambs) **F** 17ha
O.S.S. 154 - TL 337 633
01223 846363
🚗🚶●

From Cambridge take A1303 which leads on to A428. 6 miles down the A428 turn R to Knapwell; drive into the village and take track on R which leads to church. Please park by church.

Overhall Grove grows on the remains of the fields, ponds and moat of a medieval manor house, on a gentle W facing slope. Despite the slope, the wood is poorly drained and provides good habitat for many of the beautiful woodland plants that flower in the spring. Oxlip, bluebell and wood anemone grow here in profusion and there are many other botanically interesting plants, including alexanders, and a flourishing fungus population.

*Perry Woods

(A H Duberly) **P** 80ha
O.S.S. 153 - TL 133 665
01480 860305

1 mile S of Grafham Water on the B661. Roadside parking. The wood is open only on Good Friday, otherwise by appointment. No dogs please.

An excellent example of ancient woodland. SSSI. Traditionally managed with wide rides and coppiced areas.

Raveley Wood

(Wildlife Trust for Cambridgeshire) **F** 5.6ha
O.S.S. 142 - TL 244 817
01223 846363

From Ramsey take the road to Upwood and continue to Great Raveley. Take the turning to the right to Woodwalton. The reserve is on the right hand side of the road. Please park in the lay-by, do not block field entrances.

Like other nearby woods Raveley is a fragment of the prehistoric woodland which covered much of this area in Saxon times and before. The mound which runs across the glade by the entrance to the wood is thought to be part of the Saxon woodbank. The square moat on the eastern side of the wood is all that remains of an ancient manor house. Much of Raveley Wood was felled in the 1960s when mature oak, ash and elm were cut. Those not suitable for use as timber were left lying and are now an important habitat for the fungi and insects that live in dead wood (a rarity in modern managed woodland). Some of the smooth-leaved elm growing in the north and south of the wood has been coppiced, and a dense scrub of blackthorn and hawthorn has grown up in the centre of the wood. The flowering plants of ancient woodland cannot survive in the shade cast by this scrub, but Huntingdonshire woods are the last stronghold of the black hairstreak butterfly which relies on blackthorn. The trust hopes to encourage the butterfly to recolonise the wood. The ground flora is typical of ash/maple woodland in the area, bluebell, primrose, dog's mercury and goldilocks grow throughout the wood. The dense growth of scrub

in the wood provides food and shelter for a variety of birds. Mowing and raking maintain the special flora of the woodland rides. Areas where the elm was felled are now maintained as elm coppice to reduce the impact of Dutch Elm Disease, which has less effect on young trees.

Southey Wood

(Forest Enterprise) **F** 71ha
O.S.S. 142 - TF 110 025
01780 444394

From A47/A1 junction travel east approximately 1.5km and turn left (follow sign for Southorpe). Take first right about 500m, follow to wood. Picnic site, car park, forest walks. Open all year but some restrictions during forest operations.

This is a working multipurpose woodland. The car park area is situated on the site of ancient woodland and consequently has a good show of spring flowers. Throughout the wood are examples of unusual trees such as maples, hickory and Turkish hazel. A walk at any time of year will not be without some interest.

Waresley Wood

(Wildlife Trust for Cambridgeshire)
F 15ha
O.S.S. 153 - TL 263 548
01223 846363

From St. Neots take the B1046 towards Great Gransden. At edge of the village take the small road on the R running southwest towards Waresley. About 1 mile down this road there is a small bridge (Waresley Dean Bridge) over a stream. Turn L along concrete track to car park. Walk by the fence right up to the wood, which can also be reached by public footpaths from Waresley, Great Gransden and Little Gransden.

Both woods are fine examples of the ancient woodland which once covered much of the boulder clay uplands in this area. For centuries it was managed as coppice with standards and is mentioned as coppice in the Domesday Book. This management created the conditions in which woodland flowers thrive. Many ancient woods were destroyed in the years after the second world war as agricultural practices changed. Waresley and Gransden survived, although 114ha of Waresley were grubbed up between 1947 and 1973. A large part of Gransden was felled about 1929 and replanted with plantation species considered more useful than the native trees. Since 1980 some of these areas have been replanted with native species found elsewhere in the woods. Both woods are predominantly of oak and ash standards with an understorey of hazel. Oxlip flowers in spring under the field maple and hazel coppice growing on chalky boulder clay. Bluebell, primrose and wood anemone flower under the birch on the drier acidic greensand exposed in the small valley. Coppicing has been reintroduced to much of the remaining coppice woodland, which will encourage the beautiful spring flowers of these ancient woods. The rides are cut in rotation to maintain this important habitat for the flowers and insects which live in sunny, sheltered grassland.

Wimpole Park
(National Trust) **F** 112ha
O.S.S. 154 - TL 338 510
01223 207257

8 miles SW of Cambridge. Free access and parking. Open daily all year (WC's open daily). Refreshments and shop open Tues - Thur & Sat & Sun throughout year.

Beautiful landscaped park: network of waymarked footpaths lead to countryside beyond National Trust property. Map leaflet available £1.

CHESHIRE

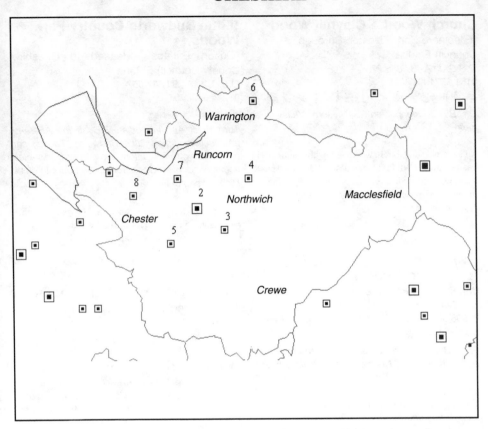

1. Church Wood & Clayhill Wood
2. *Delamere Forest Park*
3. * Little Budworth Country Park
4. * Marbury Country Park Woods
5. Primrose Hill Wood
6. *Risley Moss
7. Snidley Moor & Woodhouse Hill Wood
8. Stanney Wood

Church Wood & Clayhill Wood

(Ellesmere Port & Neston Borough
Council) **F** 40ha
O.S.S. 117 - SJ 368 775
0151 3571991

👝70🚾3🐎 🛶 WC *i* 🛠 🏇 ⛺ ⛴🅿🚻 🛥

*Off B5132 signposted to Rivacre Valley. Car
park.*

Area of oak and birch woodland with nature trail/
interpretation. Wildlife includes fox and weasel.
Meadow areas with lots of orchids and butterflies in
summer. Orienteering course, birdwatching, bluebells
in woodland in spring.

*Little Budworth Country Park Woods

(Oulton Estates - leased to Cheshire
County Council) **F** 33ha
O.S.S. 117 - SJ 587 657
01244 602845

👝🐎 WC ♿ 🛠 🏇

*Turn E off A49 immediately S off the A54/A49
intersection signed Little Budworth. Toilets, car
park, picnic area, information board, disabled
access and toilet. Open from 0830 hours to dusk.
Please keep to paths.*

The area of heathland is an SSSI. Lowland heath -
rare plants and invertebrates. Birchwood fungi.

*Delamere Forest Park

(Managed by Forest Enterprise) **F** 785ha
O.S.S. 117 - SJ 546 703
01606 882167

👝🐎 🛶 ⛲ ⛴🛥

*From Chester, take the A51 to roundabout, then
A54 to Kelsall and Northwich; after Kelsall bear L
onto A556 to Northwich, at cross roads turn L to
Delamere, turn L again in front of forest park
signs, follow track to Forest Centre. All-ability
trail, refreshments, forest walks, car parking,
Christmas tree sales centre in December. Educational facilities. Shop open 10.30-12.30, 1.30-4.00
Mon-Fri and 10.30 to 4.30 Sat-Sun. Mountain
bikers are requested to respect other visitors and
give way to pedestrians.*

Delamere Forest is the largest block of established
woodland in Cheshire. Delamere originated as a
Norman hunting ground, hence the French name
"Forest of the Meres". Many of the Meres were
drained by Napoleonic prisoners of war. Those
Meres which remained undrained are now SSSIs
because of their importance for wildlife. As the
hemlock trees on the drained Meres reach maturity
and are felled, the foresters have an interesting
opportunity to return some Meres back to their
original flooded state.

*Marbury Country Park Woods

(I.C.I.- leased to Cheshire County Council)
F 85ha
O.S.S. 118 - SJ 654 762
010606 77741

👝🐎 ◯ WC *i* 🏇

*Approx 1 mile N of Northwich. Entrance off the
Comberbach/Barnton "C" road. Brown tourist
signs off main routes. Car parking, toilets, paths,
Mere birdhide, picnic tables, link to canal, interpretative information. Opening times posted on
site, usually 0830 hours to dusk. Dog exercise
area in operation; dogs on leads in park but free
exercise in woods. Please respect fishermen and
horseriders. Birdwatching with extensive species
list of woodland and water birds.*

Historic remains of manor house. Grotto/cock fight-
ing pit. Ice house 1800's. "Elmer" - sculpture in
elm. Ghost - The White Lady. Tree Garden for
Everyman - collection of trees for the senses. Avenue
of limes. Canal. Guided walks and activities in
annual programme.

Primrose Hill Wood
(Managed by Forest Enterprise) **F** 99ha
O.S.S. 117 - SJ 537 678
01606 882167

From Tarporley take the A49 towards Northwich in 2 miles turn L at Cotebrooke towards Delamere, in 3/4 mile pass farm on R, turn L at crossroads towards Kelsall. 2 car parks on R, one in 1.5 miles, second in 3 miles.

*Risley Moss
(Chesire County Council) **R**10ha
O.S.S. 109 - SJ 665 922
01925 824339

From the M6 take M62 (eastbound) at junction 21a. Leave M62 at junction 11 onto the A574 towards Warrington. Follow signs for Risley Moss.

The woodland area comprises a path network, bird hides, observation tower and picnic areas. Glades of wildflowers, stands of oak, rowan, hawthorn, rotational coppiced areas of hazel, ash, alder, holly and birch are actively managed. Some ponds, grassland areas and mossland.

Snidley Moor and Woodhouse Hill Wood
(Woodland Trust) **F** 14ha
O.S.S. 117 - SJ 513 753
01476 74297

From Frodsham take the A56 Chester road, the B5393 (signposted to Tarvin, Alvanley and Manley). After 1 mile, turn L on to the minor road called the Ridgeway. The wood is at the end of the track running N along this road after just under 0.5 mile.

The woodland of Snidley Moor covers a west-facing slope of the central Cheshire sandstone ridge, which rises dramatically from the former marshland below. The wood contains many birch trees with some oak and rowan. A noisy, colourful bird which you are sure to come across on your walk through the wood, is the jay. The sandstone trail or Cheshire Way footpath from Frodsham follows the western edge of Snidley Moor.

Stanney Wood
(Ellesmere Port & Neston Borough Council) **F** 20ha
O.S.S. 117 - SJ 398 738
0151 3571991

On the A5117 between M53 and A41. Woodland is signposted into car park off the A5117. Car park, surfaced footpaths, information/ranger service.

Stanney Wood is an area of semi-natural ancient woodland. Birch, oak with hazel understorey. Healthy fern population. Wildlife includes foxes, squirrels, bank and field voles. Interesting and varied bird life. Circular walks and well surfaced paths suitable for prams and wheelchairs. No gradients.

CLEVELAND

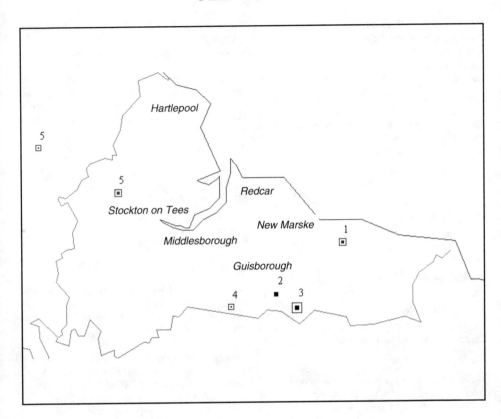

1. Errington Wood
2. *Gisborough Woods
3. *Guisborough Forest*
4. Newton Wood
5. Thorpe Wood

Errington Wood
(Langbaugh on Tees Council) **F** 80ha
O.S.S. 94 - NZ 618 203
01642 231212

⊭◡♦❊Υ╏

From A174 take Grewgrass Lane exit (signposted "New Marske"), follow road to the top of hill where the picnic site is. Car park, woodland trail and information, and 1.25 miles of footpath suitable for wheelchairs starting from the picnic site.

A mature mainly conifer wood managed for wildlife and amenity value. One of the oldest conifer woodlands in the NE (planted 1773). Unsurpassable views of the Tees Bay and beyond from its highest point.

*Gisborough Woods
(Lord Gisborough) **A** 150ha
O.S.S. 94 - NZ 598 141
Gisborough House, Cleveland

⊭❮♦Υ╏ ♒◉❚

Meeting point is at Gisborough Hall Hotel off the A171 at Guisborough.

A varied woodland aiming to produce high quality hard and softwoods. Visits by appointment only.

Guisborough Forest
(Forest Enterprise) **F** 230ha
O.S.S. 94 - NZ 600 136
01751 472771

Either from Pinchinthorpe Station car park, turn R off Gt Aylton to Guisborough road A173 at Pinchinthorpe or S from the A171 to Hutton Village through Hutton Gate.

Newton Wood
(National Trust) **F** 8.1ha
O.S.S. 93 - NZ 575 126
01751 460396

⬤

8 miles SE of Middlesbrough, 2 miles SE of Great Ayton. Access by public footpath from Great Ayton and from the National Park car park at Newton under Roseberry.

Newton Wood is a broadleaved woodland flanking the SW slope of Roseberry Topping, the famous Cleveland landmark. A semi-natural acid oak woodland botanically rich with good bird and mammal life. Spectacular displays of bluebells. Good area for walkers especially as the Cleveland Way crosses nearby Newton Moor.

Thorpe Wood
(Cleveland County Council) **F** 17ha
O.S.S. 93 - NZ 401 246
01740 630011

⛟⛟❮●wc ♿ ⓘ ⬛ ╏ FP ⏚ ■ ⚑ 🛍

The wood is part of Castle Eden Walkway Country Park. Access off A177, Stockton-on-Tees to Sedgefield road, opposite Thorpe Thewles village. There are circular walks, and ponds. The wood is open during daylight hours. The visitor centre is open 8.30 am-4.30 pm Mon-Fri, 9 am-4.30 pm weekends (closed Sat except Jul & Aug) No cycling allowed in woodland. Access is not possible by wheelchair due to steep gradients.

Thorpe Wood is a relic of the ancient woodland which once covered this country. It retains the distinctive flora of ancient semi-natural woodland with fine spring displays of flowers such as wood anemone. The pond within the woodland is also home to great crested newts. Thorpe Wood has undergone a variety of types of management over the centuries. The present policy is to retain what is left of older coppice and to manage for sustainable timber production with an emphasis on wildlife conservation. Traditional skills such as charcoal making and bodging, ''green wood turning for chairs'' are being revived. The woodland is used to demonstrate traditional woodland management techniques with associated ''Woodcraft Weekend'' events (2 per year). These may be of interest for educational visits. Please discuss with Warden - Bruce Ferguson.

CORNWALL

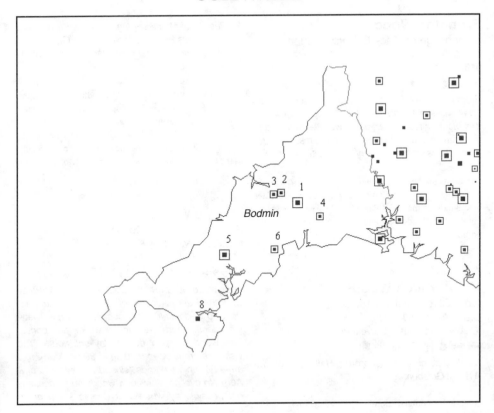

1. *Cardinham Woods*
2. Costislost and Polgeel Woods
3. Gaff and Undertown Woods
4. Horse Wood
5. *Idless Woods*
6. Kings Wood
7. Mt Edgcumbe Country Park
8. *Trelowarren

Cardinham Woods
(Managed by Forest Enterprise) **F** 264ha
O.S.S. 200 - SX 099 667
01208 72577 or 01409 221692

🚗(£0.50)🥢⏣ ⚑ ※ WC 👤 *i* ⛱ 🦌 ⚑
🍴🎨👁

From Bodmin take the A38 for 2 miles. 400 yards beyond roundabout turn L, in 600 yards go round sharp bend, turn L into forest. Car parks, cafe, cycle hire, children's play trail, all ability trail and forest walks.

The Forestry Commission has managed the woods at Cardinham since 1922. Today their fertile soils produce fine timber with impressive old Douglas fir. Four walks explore the natural beauty of the forest; one of the walks which follows the stream is suitable for people of all abilities.

Costislost and Polgeel Woods
(Pencarrow Estate) **R** 53ha
O.S.S. 200   SX 032 702

🚗🥢⏣●⚑

On the A389 from Bodmin to Wadebridge. The woods border the road just north of Washaway on the south side.

Broadleaved woodland of mixed age, situated in the Camel Valley, actively managed for amenity and nature conservation. Replanting with generally native species has been undertaken and oak coppice is being brought back into management. Permitted paths through the woodlands provide an interesting extension to the Camel Trail and give an interesting insight into the positive management of previously neglected broadleaved woodlands.

Gaff and Undertown Woods
(Pencarrow Estate) **R** 12ha
O.S.S. 200   SX 015 696

🚗3🥢●

From Wadebridge take the A389 towards Bodmin. As you leave Sladesbridge (1 mile) turn R, signed Tredannick. Go straight across next cross

roads, signed Polbrock. After a further 2/3 mile you will find a small parking area and information board on R at entrance to track.

These adjoining small semi-natural ancient coppice woodlands, mostly of oak, are particularly lovely in the early spring with their typical woodland flowers. Unworked since 1820 until recently small coupes are now being taken annually, aiming at restoring the traditional 20 year rotation. A permissive public footpath runs through both woods, connecting at the NW end with the very popular Camel Trail and in the SE, via a short length of public highway, with the bridleway through Polgeel and Costislost Woods.

Horse Wood
(Duchy of Cornwall) **F** 27ha
O.S.S. 201 - SX 161 613
01579 343149

🚗 WC 🥢 ⚑ *i* 🍴🦌

Follow the signs on the A390 to "Duchy of Cornwall Nursery" between West Taphouse and Lostwithiel. Car parking, picnic area, retail tree nursery, information leaflet, drinks and WC available in the nursery.

This is a commercial woodland situated in the picturesque Fowey Valley with views of Restormel Castle and plantings of Douglas fir, larch, hemlock, cedar and broadleaved species. A small pinetum has been created and specimen broadleaves planted at intervals around the trail. A pond has been dug out with some adjacent ornamental planting. School parties and groups welcome. Contact Brian Wilson on above number.

Idless Woods
(Managed by Forest Enterprise) **F** 114ha
O.S.S. 204 - SW 822 477
01409 221692

🚗🥢⚑⏣

2 miles N of Truro. Car park and forest walk.

Kings Wood
(Woodland Trust) **F** 59ha
O.S.S. 204 - SX 007 493
01476 74297

Take the B3273 S from St Austell. After 1.25 miles pass through the village of London Apprentice and just after a road to the R towards Polgooth, turn L on to a track. Follow the track over the bridge, around to the R and park either in a lay-by here or at the far end of the track.

Kingswood is situated on the steep SW facing hillside of the Pentewan Valley and according to ancient maps has been in existence since at least 1600AD. The slopes above the valley bottom are dominated by oak, beech and ash. In spring bluebells appear on the slope, as well as wood sorrel and primroses. The wet valley bottom provides an ideal habitat for alder, sedge and gypsywort. You may spot butterflies such as holly blue and orange tip along with many common woodland birds.

Mount Edgcumbe Country Park
(Plymouth City Council & Cornwall County Council) **F** 350ha
O.S.S. 201 - SX 453 533
01752 822236

From Plymouth, Cremyll Foot Ferry from Admirals Hard, Durnford Street. Vehicles, Torpoint Ferry. Follow A374 then B3247 to Mount Edgcumbe. From Cornwall A38 to Trerule Foot then A374 then B3247. Toilets including facilities for disabled by Orangery within the formal gardens at Cremyll.. No admission fee for formal gardens, woodland and parkland which are open all year. Mount Edgcumbe House and Earls Garden open April 1 until Oct 31, Wed to Sun, for which there is an admission charge. Car park with map and information boards located at Cremyll OS Ref. SX 453533 (three other car parks at Barrow Park OS Ref SX 450526, Maker OS Ref SX 446521 and Rame Head OS Ref. SX 420488).

Mount Edgcumbe is a rare example of an intact 18th century landscape. Almost surrounded by Plymouth Sound and the sea. The opportunities for parkland and coastal walks are endless. There are gardens in the English, French and Italian styles which are over 200 years old. Tree species include gingkos, tulip trees, giant hedges of holm oak, and cork oaks, including the largest in Britain. In addition there are extensive mixed woodlands which are home to a herd of wild fallow deer.

*Trelowarren
(The Vyvyan family, and the Trelowarren Woodlands Trust) **A** 117ha
O.S.S. 203 - SW 720 239
01736 731846

3.75 miles SE of Helston. Take the B3293 SE from Helston, turning L into the Trelowarren Estate at the village of Garras. In the central estate complex, close to the car park and WCs there is a bistro/cafe and small gift shop. Visits can be arranged but there must at least 10 people booking for any one visit. All visits must be made by prior appointment only. For further information please write to Dr S P G Perry, Woodland Manager, Stile Cottage, Trevithal, Paul, Penzance, Cornwall, TR19 6UQ or ring the above number. Donations to the Forestry Trust.

The majority of Trelowarren woodlands were established by the Forestry Commission during the period 1958-67, following the felling of acres of mature broadleaves. The woodlands are a complex mixture of conifer and broadleaved elements with the former predominant. The principle conifers are Douglas fir, Sitka spruce, western hemlock, lodgepole pine and larch, with smaller areas of less common species. The main broadleaved species are sweet chestnut, beech, ash, alder and sycamore. Geology, soils and topography over the woodlands vary considerably from the serpentine clays of the Lizard plateau areas, whilst the valleys have more typically woodland ground floras. The woodlands provide habitat for a wide range of bird species.

CUMBRIA

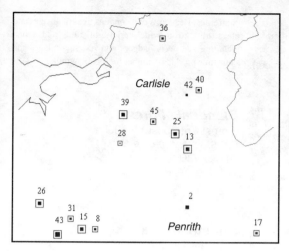

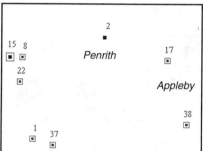

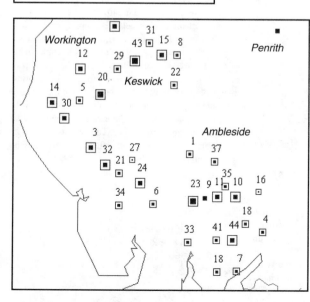

1. Baysbrown Wood
2. *Beacon Wood
3. *Blengdale Forest*
4. Brigsteer Park
5. *Broadmoor*
6. *Broughton Moor*
7. Brown Robin
8. *Brundholme
9. Bryerswood Woodlands
10. *Chapel House*
11. *Claife Woods*
12. *Cogra*
13. *Coombs Wood*
14. *Dent Fell*
15. *Dodd Wood*
16. Dorothy Farrers Spring Wood
17. Dufton Ghyll Wood
18. Durham Bridge Wood
19. *Eggerslack Wood*
20. *Ennerdale Forest*
21. *Giggle Alley*
22. Great Wood
23. *Grizedale Forest Park*
24. Hardknott Forest
25. High Stand
26. *Higham & Setmurthy*
27. Hows Wood
28. Hutton-in-the-Forest Grove
29. Lanthwaite
30. *Lowther Park & Sillathwaite*
31. *Mirehouse & Catstocks Woods
32. *Miterdale Forest*
33. *Old Hall Wood*
34. *Rainsbarrow*
35. Rayrigg
36. Shank Wood
37. Skelghyll Wood
38. Smardale Gill
39. Sowerby Wood
40. Talkin Wood
41. Thornphinsty & Crag Wood
42. Whinhill
43. *Whinlatter Forest Park*
44. Witherslack Wood
45. Wreay Woods

Baysbrown Wood
(Langdale Green Slate Co Ltd) **F** 87.6ha
O.S.S. 90 - NV 326 044
 Langdale Green Slate Co Ltd (Windermere),
Beresford Road, Windermere. LA23 2JG

⟿∪●❋🐾🐗🐗

Elterwater Village is west of Ambleside, on the
A593 for Coniston. After 2.5 miles turn R at
Skelwith Bridge towards Langdale Valley, after 2
miles turn L into Elterwater. There is parking,
accommodation and a pub in Elterwater. A circular
route to the wood starts by crossing Elterwater
Bridge and following the lane up the hill, take R
fork and then turn R again.

An attractive mixed broadleaved woodland on an
ancient woodland site on the lower slopes of Lingmoor
Fell. The main block of woodland consisting of
Sawrey's Wood, Baysbrown and Hag Woods is mainly
mature oak with open grassy glades that have been
traditionally grazed by Herdwick sheep. There are
scattered fine old Scots pine and larch and mixed small
areas of Scots pine and larch planted in the 1930s, and
pure European larch on the higher ground. Baysbrown
Wood is an SSSI containing a diverse flora of mosses
and liverworts as well as most common species typical
of an upland oak wood. The wood has been
professionally managed for timber production for over
30 years whilst maintaining its landscape and special
natural interest.

*Beacon Wood
(Lord Lonsdale) **R** 126ha
O.S.S. 90 - NY 520 311
01931 712577

⟿🐾▲❋

Take the A6 through Penrith, turn R towards
Lazonby and R again towards Langwathby past
the church and the path is on the L. Limited
parking.

The permissive path to Beacon Pike (open all year)
runs through productive woodland where particular
attention is paid to the landscape value of this
prominent hillside. The view from the Pike encom-
passes the town itself, the Lakeland hills to the W and
the Eden Valley and Pennines to the E. Predominantly
coniferous, Beacon Wood contains trees of all ages and
plays host to a wide variety of flora and fauna
including roe deer, badgers and red squirrels, at the
same time producing timber for local sawmills.

Blengdale Forest
(Forest Enterprise) **F** 480ha
O.S.S. 89 - NY 109 059
017687 78660

⟿∪▲❋🐗

Brigsteer Park
(National Trust) **F** 34ha
O.S.S. 97 - SD 489 877
015395 60723

🚗10🐾▲ⓘ⛺

Approach from the Levens village to Brigsteer
village road. Parking at several lay-bys through-
out the wood. There is full free access. Main
access point "3 Beeches" at the S end of the
wood. Information signs at various points.

Ancient semi-natural woodland. On ground varying
from limestone scree and escarpment to peat moss. 16
ha were cleared of hazel/ash coppice in the late
1960/1970s and replanted with a conifer/broadleaf
mixture. Remaining area was left as old coppice with
standards. At present a long term plan to create
diversity and conserve species through: (1) restoring
mixed plantations to ash/hazel dominated woodland
(2) restoring old coppice to a small scale coppice cycle
(3) ride management (4) retaining non-intervention
areas, is being carried out. The wood is rich in
invertebrates especially butterflies, flowering plant
species and native shrubs.

Broadmoor
(Forest Enterprise) **F** 39ha
O.S.S. 89 - NY 082 159
017687 78660

🚗20🐾▲❋

Cumbria

Broughton Moor
(Forest Enterprise) **F** 79ha
O.S.S. 96 - SD 246 936
01229 860373

Brown Robin
(Cumbria Wildlife Trust) **F** 26ha
O.S.S. 97 - 411 792
015394 32476

From Grange BR station walk up the drive of The Netherwood Hotel taking farm track off to L. Alternatively, park on B5271 at above grid ref. and walk up slope. Limited parking on roadside. A trail around the reserve is marked by white topped posts. A leaflet is also available from the above.

The woodland contains some fine specimens of native and naturalised trees with a ground flora including bluebell, violet, wild daffodil and primrose. A wide variety of woodland birds can be seen, as can both red and grey squirrels. The woodland is being managed sustainably for timber and wildlife. Thinning, coppicing and deer fencing are being carried out at present.

*Brundholme
(John Fryer-Spedding) **F** 84ha
O.S.S. 90 - NX 267 242
017687 72287

Follow Brundholme Road out of Keswick centre to car park at Briar Rigg. A leaflet will be available from National Park Information Offices.

The woods are in the main ancient semi-natural but interspersed with young plantations of hybrid larch and sitka spruce landscaped with gean, ash and sessile oak. The ancient coppiced oak woods of the Manor of Brundholme provided bark for local tanneries. The Lake District National Park Authority has constructed

a scenic walk through the woods from which exciting views of the northern fells can be enjoyed. The woods provide a habitat for badgers, red squirrels and many birds including flycatchers and, on the River Greta, river birds.

Bryerswood Woodlands
(Mrs P E Naylor) **P** 138ha
O.S.S. 97 - SD 382 952
015394 43528

(a) From Windermere Ferry landing (W side) follow road B5285 to top of Ferry Hill and turn in at first gates on R, immediately turn R into woodyard. (b) From Hawkshead follow B5285 towards Ferry; after passing Far Sawrey (2.5 miles) entrance gates (black) are ahead; after entering gates immediately turn R into woodyard. Village shop and Sawrey Hotel nearby. Guided tour will be held on Sun 24 Sept 1995, start. 2pm (2 hours min.). Charges £2 per adult and £1 per child to be donated to the Forestry Trust.

The Bryerswood Estate Woodlands (300 to 700 feet above sea level) are managed as commercial woodland with main priorities: (1) production of wood (2) conservation of woodland (some ancient woodland sites) (3) enhancement of landscapes (4) maintaining a reserve of capital.. Provision of employment and creation of wildlife habitats are also important. 2/3 coniferous, mainly spruce and larch but also Scots pine and western hemlock. 1/3 broadleaved, mainly oak, but some beech, alder and birch. Good views. Mammals: red and roe deer, red squirrels. Birds: buzzards, ravens etc. SSSI. In the Lake District National Park.

Chapel House
(Forest Enterprise) **F** 333ha
O.S.S.96/97 - SD 393 858
01229 860373

Claife Woods
(National Trust) **F** 230ha
O.S.S. 97 - SD 388 954
015394 46534
🚗20�》🎣☀🌲

Approach (S end) on the B5285 Hawkshead to
Windermere Ferry road. National Trust car park
at the foot of Ferry Hill.   Approach (N end) on
road from High Wray village to the lake, car park
at Red Nab.

Claife Woods are mixed uneven aged woodlands
stretching from near Ferry Nab on the W shore of
Windermere to Wray Castle. The majority of the
woodlands are on the steep slopes rising from the lake.
There is an excellent network of footpaths, including a
lakeside walk through the woods, plus splendid views
of the Lakeland fells from the higher paths. The whole
area is rich in wildlife including red and roe deer and
red squirrel. National Trust policy is to ensure the
continuity of the woodlands as an important backcloth
to the lake. This involves continuous small scale timber
operations which do not intrude on the landscape.

Cogra
(Forest Enterprise) **F** 192ha
O. S.S. 89 - NY105 207
017687 78660
🚶‍U🎣🌲

Coombs Wood
(Forest Enterprise) **F** 101ha
O.S.S. 86 - NY 511 449
01229 860373

Dent Fell
(Forest Enterprise) **F** 180ha
O.S.S. 89 - NY 042 136
017687 78660
🚗10🚶‍U🎣☀🌲

Dodd Wood
(Managed by Forest Enterprise) **F** 260ha
O.S.S. 89/90 - NY 245 279
017687 78660
🚗50🚶‍U🎣☀🌲 wc 👤 🔧 🗑🍴

Dorothy Farrers Spring Wood
(Cumbria Wildlife Trust) **F** 2.6ha
O.S.S. 97 - GR 480 963
Cumbria Wildlife Trust, Church St, Ambleside,
Cumbria. LA22 0BU
🚶🌳🌲

The reserve lies on a minor road between
Staveley and Bowston. There are daily British
Rail services to Burneside and Staveley. Parking
is available where the public footpath leaves the
road.

This small area of ancient semi-natural woodland has
been coppiced in the past to produce timber for
bobbins, charcoal and basket making. Near the
entrance the remains of a charcoal "pit" can be seen.
Coppicing is currently being reinstated. By periodi-
cally opening up the canopy, the ground flora benefits
from the increased amount of light available. In spring
you can see early purple orchid, primrose, dog's
mercury and bluebell. A variety of fungi inhabit the
stacks of cut timber including black bulgur, many
zoned polypore and honey fungus. Long tailed tit,
goldcrest, treecreeper, great spotted woodpecker and
sparrowhawk can be seen in the wood.

Dufton Ghyll Wood
(Woodland Trust) **F** 10.11ha
O.S.S. 91 - NH 687 250
01476 74297

Dufton Ghyll is situated 3.5 miles N of Appleby
on the western edge of the Pennines. From the
A66 and B6542 in Appleby, follow the road signs
to Dufton village. It is best to park at Dufton
village green and take the footpath signposted to
Ghyll, which leaves the village near the post

office. Paths can be wet in winter and stout footwear is advisable.

Dufton Ghyll is a sheltered, steep-sided valley. The ground flora is diverse and in spring and summer an array of various brightly coloured flowers such as anemone, bluebell, pignut and angelica carpet the ground. At the E edge some large beech and sweet chestnut can be seen which may be up to 200 years old. 3,000 trees such as oak, hawthorn and ash were planted by the Trust between 1981 and 1983 to recreate the woodland lost when many mature trees were felled.

Durham Bridge Wood
(M S Argles) **F** 14ha
O.S.S. 97 - SD 449 895
015395 63323

From A590 (M6 to Barrow) turn up Lyth Valley on A5074 at Gilpin Bridge. After 3 miles turn L to Row. Bear R at top of hamlet. Gate into wood by house on right 700 yards. Parking for 2-3 cars at lane side.

The wood is always open and there is a public footpath through it. Other rides may be used. The wood is part of the Whitbarrow SSSI on limestone. Standards (mainly oak) with ash and hazel coppice. Unmanaged for 50 years. Work started 1992/93 to attempt coppice regeneration by cutting overgrowth to stool, leaving young maiden trees and shrub species. 6 hectares now attractive woodland. Produce - hedging stakes, firewood and charcoal burning on site.

Eggerslack Wood
(Forest Enterprise) **F** 47ha
O.S.S. 96/97 - SD 407 791
01229 860373

Ennerdale Forest
(Forest Enterprise) **F** 2603ha
O.S.S. 89 - NY 110 153
017687 78660

Minor road from Ennerdale Bridge, 9 miles E of Whitehaven. Toilets, refreshments - In summer only. No charges.

Enjoy the forests of the Ennerdale Valley. Views of the Lakeland peaks and Ennerdale Lake. Abundant birdlife and botanical interest. Marvellous autumn colours from the varied tree species.

Giggle Alley
(Forest Enterprise) **F** 10ha
O.S.S. 89 - NY 140 002
017687 78660

Great Wood
(National Trust) **F** 95.5ha
O.S.S. 89 - NY 271 213
017687 74296

1 mile S of Keswick on the B5289 Borrowdale road is a large car park on the L (East) side of the road within the wood. Full open access to the wood although certain areas may be closed for safety reasons during timber operations over the winter months. Car parking fee is £1.20 - £2.40.

This is a mixed wood on the W facing slopes of Walla Crag near Keswick. An important conservation area, 45 ha of the wood, is an SSSI due to the valuable bryophytes and lichens. Great Wood is part of the important group of woodlands in the Borrowdale valley. Being at the drier end of the valley it is markedly different to the woods further up the valley. The N end of the wood is predominantly conifer, planted in the 1930s and 1950s, while the southern part has many native broadleaves of mixed ages.

Grizedale Forest Park
(Forest Enterprise) **FC** 2400ha
O.S.S. 96 - SD335 945
01229 860010
🚗140(£1)🚐3(£3)🦌◯ ⚑ ☀ ⛾ wc
♿ ⓘ 🏩 ⛾ 🧺 ⚑ 🚩 🍴 ⛰ 🏚 💼

*3 miles S of Hawkshead and midway between
Lake Windermere and Coniston Water, the
Forest Park Centre is signposted off the A590 at
Haverthwaite and the B5285 at Hawkshead.
Facilities as above plus exhibition, trails, sculp-
ture, orienteering, art gallery, cycle hire. Educa-
tional groups please book in advance, coaches
please telephone for access route.*

Grizedale is a working forest with a history of
supplying the needs of industry and communities for
over 1000 years. Today the Forest Park is seen as a role
model for others on how successfully to meet the
challenges of multi-purpose management. Annually an
estimated 300,000 visitors come to Grizedale whilst
25,000 tonnes of timber are sent to customers
throughout the north of England and south Scotland.
Conservation of wildlife and archaeological features is
an important aspect of management, with Grizedale
being home to the only native herd of woodland red
deer in England and the site of numerous features
which illustrate the long history of coppice management.

Hardknott Forest
(Forest Enterprise) **F** 629ha
O.S.S. 96 - SD 219 984
01229 860373
🚗20🦌◯ ⚑ ☀ ⛾ 🧺

High Stand
(Forest Enterprise) **F** 261ha
O.S.S. 86 - NY 490 485
017687 78660
🦌◯ ⚑ ⛾

Higham and Setmurthy
(Forest Enterprise) **F** 159ha
O.S.S. 89 - NY 161 319
017687 78660
🦌◯ ⚑ ⛾

Hows Wood
(Friends of the Lake District) **R** 8ha
O.S.S. 89 - NY 180 010
01539 720788
🦌 ⚑ ☀ 🏚

*On S edge of road between Woolpack Inn and
Boot hamlet in Eskdale valley. Please do not
park on the road.*

An ancient semi-natural woodland that was extensively
re-planted in 1967 by the Forestry Commission. The
FLD acquired the wood in 1987 to return it to a native
woodland as the site forms an important visual element
in the valley floor. Access to the wood is by
permissive footpath.

Hutton-in-the-Forest
(Lord Inglewood) **R** 4.6ha
O.S.S. 85 - NY 357 460
017684 84449
🚗40🦌 ⚑ wc ⓘ ⛾ 🧺

*3 miles NW of junction 41 on the M6. On the
B5306, Penrith to Wigton Road. WCs and tea
room when house open. Open every day except
Sat and Christmas day from 11am to 5pm.*

Hutton-in-the-Forest includes both ornamental and
forest trees in a garden and forest setting. There are
three generations of planting. First, a number of
over-mature hardwoods planted by Henry Fletcher in
the mid 18th century; secondly coniferous planting by
Sir Henry Vane in the second part of the 19th century;
and finally 20th century planting by the 1st Lord
Inglewood.

Lanthwaite Wood
(National Trust) **F** 28ha
O.S.S. 89 - NY 150 216
01900 85312

🚗25🐄 🚶 ❄️🔲

Take the B5289 from Cockermouth through Lorton towards Loweswater. Car park on L just past Scale Hill. Car parking charge is £1.20 - £2.40 depending on length of stay. Specific paths may be closed temporarily due to timber operations. Parts of the wood are accessible for wheelchairs.

Lanthwaite is a mixed woodland on the N shore of Crummock Water. Chiefly uneven-aged mixed conifer with a significant broadleaf element. There is considerable natural regeneration of most species which is encouraged. Roe deer and red squirrel are present.

Lowther Park and Sillathwaite
(Forest Enterprise) **F** 156ha
O.S.S. 89 - NY 050 122
01229 860373

🚗10🐄 ○ 🚶 Ψ

*Mirehouse and Catstocks Woods
(John Fryer-Spedding) **F** 13ha
O.S.S. 90 - NY 236 282
017687 72287

🅱️(£1)🚗100🚌2🐄 🚶 ❄️Ψ WC ♿ ℹ️
🍽️🔲♨️🚻🍴🅿️🚂🚩

From A66(T) Keswick Bypass follow historic house signs to Mirehouse car park. There is a tea room in an old sawmill. Adults £1, children 80p (includes access to Mirehouse grounds and adventure playground). Open 1st Apr to 31 Oct.

Mirehouse Wood is made up of stands of Scots pine planted in 1784 and European larch planted in 1825, interspersed with sessile oak. There is a good population of red squirrels and badgers and a wide variety of birds especially woodpeckers, tree creepers and nuthatches. Catstocks Wood is an ancient semi-natural woodland on the lake shore, part SSSI. The wood consists of 200 year old sessile oak with younger planting of oak, beech, thuja and Norway spruce with a belt of hazel and alder scrub on the lake shore, widely used by water birds for nesting.

Miterdale Forest
(Forest Enterprise) **F** 336ha
O.S.S. 89 - NY 141 022
017687 78660

🚗20🐄 ○ 🚶 ❄️Ψ

Old Hall Wood
(Forest Enterprise) **F** 36ha
O.S.S. 96/97 - SD 323 855
01229 860373

🐄 ○ 🚶 Ψ

Rainsbarrow
(Forest Enterprise) **F** 50ha
O.S.S. 96 - SD 190 933
01229 860373

🚗5🐄 🚶 Ψ🅿️

Rayrigg Wood
(Pattinsons (Windermere) Ltd) **F** 14.3ha
O.S.S. 97 - SD 404 975
Pattinsons (Windermere) Ltd, Beresford Road, Windermere, LA23 2JG.

🐄 ● Ψ🍺

NW edge of Windermere town, accessible from the main street, Lake Road, turn N onto Longlands Road, past rugby football ground, entering wood through pillars. Within easy walking distance of the car park and toilets at Rayrigg meadow, via Birthwaite Road or Millbeckstock.

An attractive semi-natural mixed broadleaved wood on the northern edge of suburban Windermere. There are fine looking old oak, with spreading crowns, also a few large beech, ash, wych elm, sycamore, wild cherry, lime, birch, aspen, goat willow and alder, with scattered European larch and Scots pine. A good area for most common woodland birds and animals including roe deer and red squirrels, woodpeckers and nuthatch. Managed under a special management agreement with the Forestry Authority, under a group selection system, with small scale timber production, mainly for the owners use in their own house building and repair business and supplying firewood for the Steamboat Museum boats.

No coach access. See O.S. Outdoor Leisure Map 7 for footpaths and area of wood owned by NT.

Situated on the lower slopes of Wansfell, above Stagshaw Gardens, with views from Jenkin's Crag, a viewpoint within the wood, out to Windermere Lake and the Lake District fells. The terrain is steep in parts but the wood has a good network of footpaths. Ancient semi-natural woodland, mainly oak singled from coppice, with old charcoal pitsteads scattered through the area. The lower slope adjacent to Stagshaw, was planted with many American conifers and other exotic species in the 1800s. These now tower above the broadleaved canopy of the wood - some of the tallest trees in the Lake District. Red squirrel and roe deer are found in the wood.

Shank Wood
(Robert Carr) **R** 28ha
O.S.S. 76 - NY 457 708
01228 791281

Turn NE of M6 junction 44 Longtown. Turn R at Graham Arms Hotel. 1 mile turn R signed Solport. Proceed 4 miles. Farm on L with 2 large towers. Visitors should call at farm to collect a guide sheet. 4 miles of permissive waymarked paths.

Shank Wood is the central section of the Lower Lyne Woods SSSI. A very ancient river gorge wood with diverse soil types ranging from acid to neutral creating habitat for over 300 species of plants. No management had been undertaken for 100 years until 1985. The present owner has done some selective felling and replanting and restored the ancient tracks and roads. Wildlife conservation is a priority - most species of native birds and mammals are present.

Skelghyll Wood
(The National Trust) **F** 38ha
O.S.S. 90 - NY 380 028
01539 446534

1/2 mile south of Ambleside on the A591, turn L up to Stagshaw Gardens (NT, open April-June), very limited parking - access dangerous, visitor could park at Waterhead and walk to wood on footpaths.

Smardale Gill
(Cumbria Wildlife Trust) **R** 40ha
O.S.S. 91 - NY 738 083
Church St, Ambleside, Cumbria. LA22 DBU

10 🚗 ♿ ❄ 🦌

Take the minor road from A685 signposted Waitby + Smardale. Go over railway line and disused line at Smardale Hall. Turn L by cottages to free car park. A permit is required to visit the sections of wood above and below the railway but these can be adequately viewed from the line.

At Smardale, Scandal Beck has carved a deep gill through the carboniferous limestone. Woodland covers much of the steep easterly slope of the gill but there are also important grasslands dominated by blue moor grass. Perched half-way up the slope is a disused railway line, once part of the Tebay - Darlington route, now a very pleasant path with fine views up and down the valley. The line crosses Scandal Beck on a huge viaduct which has recently been renovated by the Northern Viaduct Trust. Over 20 species of butterfly have been seen on the reserve including the scotch argus which feeds on blue moor grass. Breeding birds include redstart, pied flycatcher, treecreeper and sparrowhawk.

Sowerby Wood
(Malcom Wright) **R** 110ha
O.S.S. 85 - NY 364 530
01556 502 754
⚡🜨🌿❄

The wood is to be found 3 miles SW of Carlisle on the A595T.

This is a lowland site (150' - 180'). The predominant species is Scots pine (80%) most of which was planted between 1958-62. A regular thinning regime is being followed. A pond and area of natural regeneration has been created.

Talkin Wood
(Cumbria County Council) **F** 16ha
O.S.S. 85 - NY 545 587
01697 73129
🏔60🍴5⚡🌿❄🦌 WC 🚻 ℹ️ 📖 ⛳🦽
🚶♿🚣🍴🚗🛶⛺🛍️

Leave M6 at junction 43, go E on A69 towards Newcastle. At first roundabout on the outskirts of Brampton take second exit and fork R after 150 yards (B6413). At crossroads turn R and follow brown tourist signs for Talkin Tarn (2 miles). The Country Park is open all year from dawn to dusk but many of the facilities are seasonal. A ranger service operates to advise and assist visitors. Guided walks by prior arrangement. Rowing boats and canoes are available for hire, windsurfing with own equipment by arrangement.

Talkin Wood is an ancient semi-natural woodland around Talkin Tarn, a remnant of a large glacial lake. Mature beech dominates alongside Scots pine and oak. The shrub layer is well developed together with prolific natural regeneration of rowan and birch. 150 species of fungi, 250 species of flowering plants and 120 species of birds have been recorded. Roe deer and red squirrel are also present. The woodland, soon to be under Woodland Grant Scheme, is managed as a landscape, educational and wildlife resource.

Thornphinsty and Crag Wood
(C F M Rawlinson) **R** 20ha
O.S.S. 97 - SD 410 860
015242 72249
🚗3🦌🍴Y

From A590 Barrow road turn up through High Newton and take the Cartmel Fell road. The wood is 2 miles along the road on the RH side. Car parking for 3 cars on timber loading lay-by. Open at all times but the wood is used for shooting Oct-Feb and care should be taken during this period.

The top of the wood is stocked with 30 year old spruce, Scots pine and larch. There is plenty of evidence of red and roe deer. The lower area, Crag Wood, has been deer fenced to allow regeneration of over mature hardwoods. Conifers have been planted in mixture but these will be removed as thinnings. The middle area has been planted with mixed hardwoods in tree shelters over the last seven years. There are signed public footpaths.

Whinhill
(E C Graham) **A** 19ha
O.S.S. 86 - NY 517 576
01228 70555
🚗3🦌🍴Y ℹ️⛳📱

2.5 miles SSW of Brampton. 0.5 mile E of Hayton village. The grid ref above is a house close to the wood.

As the name implies this hill used to be rough pasture. Then, between 1938 and 1948 the NE was planted with Scots pine, Japanese and European larch, Douglas fir, Norway and Sitka spruce in pure stands of each species. The SE was planted in 1962 with Scots pine European larch, beech and oak in mixture for the most part. The SW was planted in 1971 similarly but with the addition of Abies, Norway spruce and Spanish chestnut. In the NW there is mature oak and recently (1990) planted pine, larch, oak and beech in mixture. In the centre a block of Japanese larch was planted in 1987. Red squirrels and roe deer are inhabitants.

Whinlatter Forest Park
(Forest Enterprise) **FE** 1200ha
O.S.S. 89 - NY 206 245
017687 78469

➡120(£1)🚍5(£3)↝∪ ⚡ ☀ ⛄ WC
♿ ⓘ 📖 🗭 🗃.🌲 ⛲🎯 🏞 🏪

*4 miles W of Keswick on the B5292 between
Braithwaite and Lorton. Cycle hire, orienteering,
open Feb - mid Dec, 10am - 5pm. Educational
groups please book in advance.*

Whinlatter is England's only mountain forest with
plantations extending to the 500 metre contour; the
fertility of the soils varies greatly resulting in a wide
variety of tree species and wildlife habitats. The
numerous view points overlook the Northern Fells and
are ideal locations for interpreting the effects of
glaciation.

Witherslack Wood
(The Stanley Family) **F** 400ha
O.S.S. 97 - SD 433 862
015395 52252
🦌∪⛲⛄ FP

*Turn N off the A590 (M6 to Barrow in Furness) at
Derby Arms. Go straight through Witherslack to
Bowland Bridge. The woods surround Witherslack
Hall school. There is access through the wood on
rights of way, bridleways and a public road. Guided
walks are occasionally held by the Lake District
Rangers; contact them for details on above
telephone number.*

Wreay Woods
(Cumbria County Council) **R** 18ha
O.S.S. 85 - NY 435 513 or NY 450 497
015394 32476

*On the A6 at Scalesceugh Hall, Wreay village, or
from the N from the picnic area beside the M6.
Open to the public at all times. A reserve leaflet can
be obtained from the Cumbria Wildlife Trust. The*

W bank of the river is closed to all visitors.

Wreay Woods lie in a gorge formed by the River
Petteril just S of Carlisle. Although it is a site of ancient
woodland much of the old wood has been felled at
some time in the past so there are not many mature
trees in evidence. The ground flora, however, is of
interest with species such as moschatel or ''town hall
clock'', bluebell, wood sorrel, dog's mercury and
ramsons. As well as woodland birds, river bank species
such as dipper, grey wagtail, heron and even kingfisher
can be seen.

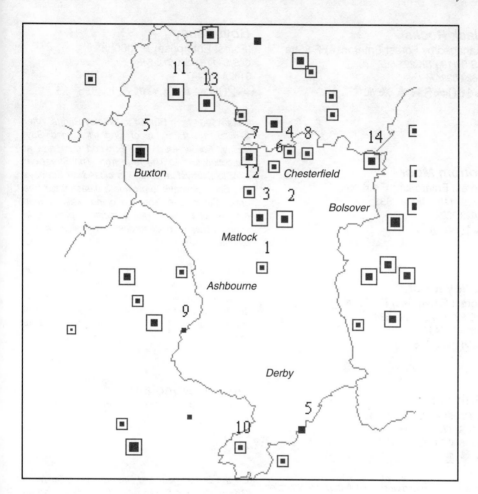

1. *Black Rocks*
2. *Bottom Moor*
3. Farley Moor
4. Firth Wood
5. *Goyt Valley*
6. Linacre Woodlands
7. Longshaw Estate

8. Nor Wood, Cook Spring & Owler Wood
9. Norbury Estate Woodlands
10. *Rosliston Farm Forest*
11. *Snake Pass*
12. *Stand Wood
13. Upper Derwent Woods
14. *Whitwell Wood*

Black Rocks
(Managed by Forest Enterprise) **F** 85ha
O.S.S 119 - SK 291 557
01623 82247
🚗100🚽5🚻 ⛺ ☀ WC 🪧 🔥

Bottom Moor
(Forest Enterprise) **F** 112ha
O.S.S. 119 - SK 321 633
01623 822447
🚗10🚻 ⛺ 🦌

Farley Moor
(Forest Enterprise) **F** 171ha
O.S.S. 119 - SK 299 634
01623 822447
🚗20🚻 ⭕ ⛺ ☀ 🦌

Firth Wood
(Derbyshire County Council) **F** 14ha
O.S.S. 119 - SK 368 788
01246 433186
🚻 ● 🏛

Between Dronfield and Coal Aston, off Stonelow/ Firthwood roads. Car parking on road.

An ancient semi-natural woodland on sloping ground at the edge of the old parish boundaries. The southern area is the most varied with some hazel coppice remaining and a good ground flora beneath an oak/sycamore/ash canopy. Much of the wood was planted as high forest in the nineteenth century, with beech a favoured tree. Some of the old oak coppice has grown to become a part of the canopy. A small area of larch adds extra variety, planted in the 1930s. A small pond and area of grassland are also within the woodland boundary.

Goyt Valley
(Forest Enterprise) **F** 1000ha
O.S.S. 119 - SK 012 748
01623 822447
🚗200🚻 ⛺ ☀ 🦌 WC ♿ ℹ 📖 🪧 🔥

Take A5004 from Buxton to Whaley Bridge. After 2 miles turn L at top of long hill signed Goyt Valley. Follow road over Errwood dam and at T-junction turn L. The road from The Street car park to Derbyshire Bridge is closed on Sundays and Bank Holidays to provide a pleasant car free area. Picnic site and woodland walk around remains of Errwood Hall particularly pleasing in spring when rhododendrons and azaleas are in bloom.

The woodland comprises pine, larch, oak plantations (circa 1850) and remnant broadleaves in the numerous cloughs within the valley. Above the tree line lie large areas of heather moorland and acid grassland, most of which has been designated an SSSI.

Linacre Woodlands
(Severn Trent Water Limited) **FE** 88ha
O.S.S. 120 - SK 336 729
01629 540696
🚻 ⛺ WC ℹ

Off the B6150 near Old Brampton, 3 miles W of Chesterfield. Extensive footpaths, some accessible to wheelchairs. WCs (not disabled), nature trail.

A wide variety of woodland types and species around three small reservoirs just W of Chesterfield. Much work has been done, and continues, on improvements to the network of footpaths, some of which are suitable for wheelchairs. The woodlands contain a wide range of bird species and the bluebells are spectacular in spring.

Longshaw Estate
(National Trust) **F** 444ha
O.S.S. 119 - SK 266 800
01433 631708
WC [i] ☕ 🛍

10 miles W of Sheffield on A625.

Large area of moor and woodland.

Nor Wood, Cook Spring and Owler Wood
(Woodland Trust) **F** 30.75ha
O.S.S. 110 - SK 368 805
01476 74297

Take the A61 S from Sheffield for about 5 miles: then turn L onto the B6057 to Jordonthorpe. The woods are easily reached by footpaths from Jordonthorpe and Dronfield.

Some parts of these woods date back at least to the Middle Ages. The main tree species are oak, beech and ash, with understorey of hazel, cherry, aspen and alder. There is a rich variety of flora to be found including creeping soft grass, buckler fern and dog's mercury. Fox and hare are also present. Look and listen for birds such as the great spotted woodpecker, cuckoo and tawny owl.

Norbury Estate Woodlands
(T W Clowes) **A** 22ha
O.S.S. 119/128 - SK 125 414
01335 324225
🚌10🚐1✕ 🔥 ⚑

Meeting point is at Norbury Hall. Take A515 Ashbourne/Lichfield road. 3 miles out of Ashbourne turn sharp L down B5033 at signpost pointing to Norbury and Ellestone. After 2.5 miles from turning turn L after 2nd footbridge over road (5 miles SW Ashbourne). No entrance fee but donations to local church and Forestry Trust

welcomed. All visits by appointment between months Mar to Oct inclusive. Apply to owner giving 4 weeks notice. Strong footwear advised. Walking necessary. Duration of visit between 1 and 2 hours.

About 55 acres of private woods varying in size from 1/2 acre to 12 acres. The woods are managed by the owner and his brother for amenity, sporting and commercial purposes. The commercial considerations are secondary. Age of trees varies from 100 years to 1 year. The woods are mostly hardwood/softwood mixtures. Oak is the predominant hardwood. Birdlife is encouraged. The woods are regularly used by the local hunt. About 500 pheasants are reared yearly.

Rosliston Farm Forest
(Managed by Forest Enterprise)
R 56ha
O.S.S. 128 - SK 244 170
01889 - 586593

Rosliston Farm Forest is managed by Forest Enterprise in partnership with S Derbyshire District Council and the National Forest. Parking is in the village with access via the footpath through the churchyard at Rosliston.

Rosliston Farm was acquired by the Forestry Commission in 1993 for planting as a community woodland under the National Forest initiative. The wood will be planted over the next 5 years in conjunction with the local community. This is a rare opportunity to follow the development of a wood from bare fields. Agricultural crops are still being grown and visitors are kindly requested to keep to the paths and headlands.

Snake Pass
(Managed by Forest Enterprise) **F** 140ha
O.S.S. 110 - SK 109 915
01623 - 822447
🚌50🚐5✕ 🔥 ✳ ⚑ ☂ 🎒

*Stand Wood
(Chatsworth House Trust) **R** 89ha
O.S.S. 119 - SK 263 705
01246 - 582204

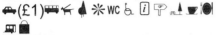

From Rowsley, Baslow or Bakewell follow signs to Chatsworth. The visiting season is from Easter to the end of Oct, 10.30-16.30hrs. The wood is adjacent to Chatsworth House, garden and farmyard. Shops and restaurant are open during the visitor season. There are marked trails through the wood (please keep to these). A limited number of guided visits can be arranged throughout the year. For details of these and to make group visit bookings please contact Mr S Seligman on the above telephone number.

Stand Wood occupies a W facing escarpment in the Derwent Valley. It is the backdrop to Chatsworth House and prior to the first plantings of 1750 was a bare hillside. Some originally planted trees are still growing but there has been continuing felling and replanting by the Cavendish family since the early 19th century. This has produced an interesting mix of age, class and species together with some exotics. It is a wood of great interest to people as well as wildlife. Timber production is a low priority. The surrounding commercial woodlands help to finance this conservation management.

Upper Derwent Woodlands
(Severn Trent Water Limited) **FE** 830ha
O.S.S. 110 - SK 173 893
01629 85696
∪ ♠ WC ᵬ 🛈

Off A57 Sheffield - Manchester road. 12 miles W of Sheffield. Cycle hire (charge), way-marked walks, ranger service. Please keep to the extensive path network.

Most of the forestry around the Upper Derwent Reservoirs is between 50 and 80 years old. Whilst the appearance is of extensive coniferous plantations,

there are areas of mixed and ancient semi-natural woodland. Access is particularly encouraged on the extensive networks of footpaths and bridleways in the area, some leading to open moorland beyond. Road closures, and a minibus service on busy days, together wtih cycle hire facilities all add to visitors' access opportunities and enjoyment. Wildlife includes goshawk, crossbills, herons and the occasional red squirrel. An extensive programme of thinning and felling operations over the next few years will produce a more diverse and interesting forest that fits better into the landscape. A Centre of Excellence Award winner in 1993.

Whitwell Wood
(Managed by Forest Enterprise) **F** 171ha
O.S.S. 120 - SK 527 773
01623 822447
🚗20🚌2⛓ ♥ ⛩ 🗷↕ ☙ 🍺

DEVON

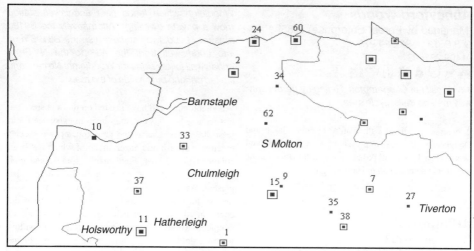

1 Abbeyford. 2 Arlington. 3 Avon. 4 Birch/Alder Arboretum. 5* Bovey Donn. 6 Burrator. 7 Buzzards.
8 Castle Drogo. 9 Chawleigh Barton. 10 Clovelly. 11 *Cookworthy.* 12 Dart Valley Woods. 13
Dunsford Wood. 14* Eastcottdown. 15 *Eggesford.* 16 *Fernworthy.* 17* Gatherley N. 18* Gatherley
S. 19 Harcombe. 20 Hardwick. 21* Harpford. 22* Heath. 23* Heathercombe. 24 Heddon Valley.
25 Hembury. 26 Higher Combe. 27* Hillersdon. 28 Hilltown. 29.Holne(1). 30 *Holne(2). 31 Holyford.
32 Hunting Park. 33* Huntshaw. 34* Kedworthy. 35* Kennerleigh. 36 *Kiddens.* 37* Knotts &
Parsonage. 38 Lower Broxford 39 *Lukesland. 40 *Lydford.* 41 Manor. 42 Marridge. 43 Milber. 44
Occombe. 45 Parke. 46 *Pool Down. 47 *Quicke. 48 *Riding Park. 49 Roadford. 50 Salcombe. 51
Scadson. 52 Shaptor. 53* Shute Hill. 54* Stoke(1). 55 Stoke(2). 56 *Tavistock. 57 Teign Valley. 58
Torquay. 59* Townleigh. 60 Watersmeet. 61* West Bowerland. 62* Whitehills. 63 Whitleigh. 64 Wray

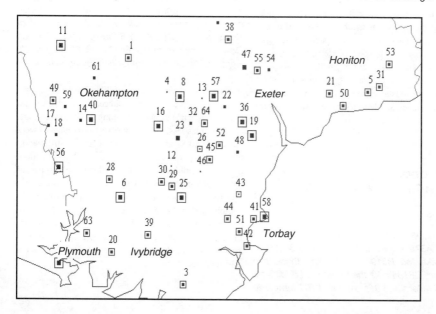

Abbeyford Woods
(Managed by Forest Enterprise) **F** 85ha
O.S.S. 191 - SX 589 975
01409 221692

🚗🐕🅾🚶☀️ *i* ⛺📷♨️

*1.5 miles N of Okehampton. Riding by permit only,
way marked trails, cycle area.*

A diverse woodland with mature conifers, larch and
Douglas fir, and some impressive 100 year old oak and
beech. The Tarka trail passes through the wood on the
way from Okehampton to Hatherleigh.

Arlington
(National Trust) **F** 200ha
O.S.S. 180 - SS 611 405
01271 850348

🚗50🚌4🏕🚶☀️🦌 WC ♿ *i* 📖⛺📷
♨️🍴🅾🏪

*7 miles NE of Barnstaple on E side of A39.
(Summer only for disabled WC). All facilities at
Arlington Court. No caravans. 1 April to 31
October. Extensive paths in the park and the
woods are freely open all year.*

Arlington is a mixed woodland on valley sides
surrounding the Arlington Court parkland. Managed
on a sustained basis of mixed species and ages.
Maintained as oak-beech woods. Extensive level paths
through woods and park. Herd of Shetland ponies and
Jacob sheep. Buzzards and ravens nest in woods. Also
pied flycatcher, redstart, woodpeckers, red and roe
deer. Wildlife haven and heronry by lake sanctuary for
wildfowl. Valuable lichen and invertebrate site.

Avon Woods
(Woodland Trust) **F** 39ha
O.S.S. 202 - SX 732 486
01476 74297

🐕🅾

*From the A379 from Modbury or the A381 from
Totnes, take the B3194 which joins these two
roads. From B3194 take the turning to Loddiswell.
Approx. 1 mile along this road is a RH turning to*

*Woodleigh which leads past Loddiswell station
(now a private dwelling). Alternatively the B3196
runs into Loddiswell station; also the B3196 runs
into Loddiswell from the A38 to the N. From
Loddiswell follow signs for Woodleigh. No car park,
limited parking by the side of the road.*

Woodland may well have existed on this site since the
last ice age and has certainly been in existence for at
least 300 years. Oak is the predominant tree species
together with ash and hazel, much of which has been
coppiced in the past. Field maple, spindle and crab
apple, which are less common in Devon are also
present. Avon Woods are home to a wide variety of
insects, birds and mammals. Of special interest is the
common dormouse which favours the areas of
coppiced woodland. The spotted flycatcher, willow
warbler, goldcrest and nuthatch are just some of the
thirty or so bird species seen in this wood.

Birch/Alder Arboretum
(Mr & Mrs Ashburner) **R** 5ha
O.S.S. 191 - 709909
01647 231311

🅿️£2🚗20🏕 🅾 ☀️ *i* ⛺♨️🏪

*Just S of the lane connecting Whiddon Down
with Drewsteignton; on a soiuthward branch
continuing down the hill to the A382 just N of
Sanly Park. About 1.5 miles from Whiddon
Down. Open from 2 - 6pm from 26 May to 23
Sept. 1995, or at any other time by appointment.*

A collection of wild-origin birch and alder seedlings,
with usually several provenances of each species.
Each provenance grown in a clump of 10-20 seedlings,
or sometimes less. The majority of provenances were
planted 1980-84 and they have now grown sufficiently
to give a park-like atmosphere to the collection.
Sculpture exhibitions are now held in the oldest part of
the arboretum every summer. The birch stems are very
effective now, particularly in winter and spring when
combined with the emerging fresh leaves. In spring
too (and late winter) the alder atkins are very striking.
In summer the shade from the trees creates a special
atmosphere, and the foliage of many birches and alders
is handsome.

*Bovey Down & Bovey Warren
(Clinton Devon Estates) **F** 43ha
O.S.S. 192 - SY 203 912
01395 443881

Take A3052 Exeter/Lyme Regis road. Turn N at Hangman's Stone opposite B3174 to Beer. Parking in lay-by on A3052 at Hangman's Stone.

2 young commercial woodlands divided by public road running N/S. A SE border of hardwoods adjoins to an area of Japanese larch, Scots pine, Corsican pine and sitka spruce, giving an impressive array of colours during spring and autumn. Inhabited by many varieties of woodland wildlife including roe deer and badgers. Several rides suitable for walking.

Burrator Wood
(South West Water Services Ltd) **F** 392 ha
O.S.S 201/202 - SX 550 680
01822 852435

At the cross roads by the Burrator Inn in Dousland, take the road to Meavy. On the edge of the village fork L over cattle grid to Burrator Dam. There is informal car parking and picnic areas all round the reservoir and in the woods. WC facilities, including disabled, at Burrator Dam: these are, however, closed between October and March. Fishing is available at Burrator Reservoir (charges available on request), ice creams and refreshments are available from a vendor at the dam. Fully open access to the woods throughout the year, with permissive paths and a bridlepath. There are also byways, open to all traffic, through the wood. Guided walks and open days can be arranged by appointment. Contact John Griffiths, Head Forester on the above telephone number. Burrator Woods, surrounded by hills and tors, has a centrepiece - Burrator Reservoir. The woodlands range from mature conifer plantations to newly planted broadleaved woods. A 40 acre arboretum is being established with special access for wheelchairs. Many walks in the woods and beside the reservoir. The interplay of woods, water and tors creates a magnificent natural setting.

Buzzards
(National Trust) **F** 67ha
O.S.S. 181/192 - SS 909 117
01392 881691

3 miles W of Tiverton on B3137. At far end of Withleigh take L fork with 'No through road' sign. No other facilities. Good views of mid-Devon landscape. Quiet and isolated for those who wish to get away from it all. A network of paths freely open all year. Not for the faint-hearted. Steep climb to car park, otherwise fairly level paths.

Mixed broadleaved woodland of varying ages. Some overgrown hazel coppice. Network of meadows in bottom of valley of Little Dart River, a tributary of the River Exe. Some broadleaved replanting took place in 1980s and is showing good growth. Plots of cherry and oak. Small plot of new hazel coppice being established. Called ''Buzzards'' because they can always be seen. Other woodland birds. Red and roe deer are resident.

Castle Drogo
(National Trust) **F** 329ha
O.S.S. 191 - SX 723 903
01647 433563

At Drewsteignton 4 miles S of A30, via Crockernwell. There is parking for 100 cars and 4 coaches. WC (including disabled), shop, information and tearoom in the castle. Extensive paths, rights of way and bridlepaths through the woods. Freely open all year. Castle open 1 April to 31 October. Pub and parking at Fingle Bridge all year round.

Mixed conifer and broadleaved plantations of all ages. Straddles River Teign in the Dartmoor National Park. Extensive paths with marvellous views of the moor. Castle Drogo completed 1932. Ancient granite walled deer park with rare lichens and invertebrates. Some large areas of sessile oak woods derived from coppice system of last century. Prestonbury hill fort can be viewed from paths, also River Teign. Hunters' path and Fishermans' path are definitive public footpaths. Some paths are linked to woods at Steps Bridge (6 miles).

Chawleigh Barton Wood

(Mr J A Sibley) **P** 29ha
O.S.S. 180 - SS 714 126
01365 866305

The village of Chawleigh is on the B3042 which connects Eggesford Station (A3777) to Witheridge (on old A373). Park in the village, and walk 300m along the road leading NE out of the village towards the bridge over the Little Dart River. The entrance gate is on the L. There are paths through the wood. Visits can be made on Sat and Sun, 0800-1800 hrs, between 4 April and 3 October. The Forest Manager is Mr W J C Blight and in the event of an emergency telephone the above number.

This delightful mature oak woodland has a very good show of bluebells in the spring, when red deer can occasionally be seen in the fields across the Little Dart River. At the far end of the wood a magnificent mature crop of Douglas fir (120 - 130ft high at 65 years old) in a sheltered dingle was felled in 1988 and, hoping for a repeat performance the area was replanted with the same type of tree. As it is a dry, stony slope, Douglas fir was also planted on the old pasture next to the road. As spruce thrives on wetter sites this species was selected for planting in the two clay fields next to the river, which is a notable feature along the N boundary. This woodland provides a very pleasant walk with interesting variety.

Clovelly Wood

(John Rous) **A** 200ha
O.S.S. 180/190 - SS 315 245
01237 431200

Take the A39 to Clovelly Cross, then the B3237 to Clovelly. After <1 mile the road swings to the R; carry straight on through lodge gates to estate office by parish church. For larger parties with coaches there is Clovelly's main car park. Facilities here include WC, coach park, cafeteria, film theatre, etc. There is a bridleway running through the wood. Visits are by appointment only. For further details please telephone the above number. Access is restricted during the period Oct-Jan,

when there are shoots.

An ancient semi-natural woodland fringing a NE facing coast. This woodland has early 19th century carriageways and paths through sessile oak, ash, beech and sycamore. The understorey includes hazel, holly and hawthorn.. Bridging streams with deeply incised valleys, the carriageway leads past vistas of Bideford Bay to the top of the famous cobbled street. From here it proceeds to dramatic headlands (350ft) and down to intimate valleys. There are abundant ferns including scaly male fern, male fern and broad buckler fern. 120 different lichen varieties thrive here which has resulted in the site being notified as an SSSI.

Cookworthy Forest

(Managed by Forest Enterprise) **F** 640ha
O.S.S. 190 - SX 416 014
01409 221692

Signposted off the A3079 Okehampton to Holsworthy road near Halwill junction. Please book educational visits at least 6 weeks in advance. Riding by permit issued from office.

Dart Valley Woods

Spitchwick Manor Estate (managed by Devon Wildlife Trust) **F** 290ha
O.S.S. 191/202 - SX 680 727
Devon Wildlife Trust, 188 Sidwell Street, Exeter EX4 6RD

Take the B3357 Ashburton to Princetown road. Park either at New Bridge or Dartmeet where there are large public car parks. Access to the entire site is permitted. Footpaths follow the river from New Bridge to Dartmeet (c5 miles). Stout footwear essential as the foopaths are very rough.

Spectacular area of woodland and moorland with valley bottom marshes, riverside scrub and various moorland habitats. Woodland almost entirely oak with extremely rich flora and fauna. Probably now the most important British site for the rare high brown fritillary. The river supports dippers, grey wagtails and goosanders, whilst the woods abound with pied flycatchers, wood warblers, buzzards, ravens and all three woodpeckers.

Dunsford Wood
National Trust (Managed by Devon Wildlife Trust) **F** 57ha
O.S.S. 191 - SX 798 875
Devon Wildlife Trust, 188 Sidwell Street, Exeter EX4 6RD
🚗30🚌�🚻🏕⛺♿ⓘ 🎣🎠🐕🏠

Dunsford Wood Nature Reserve lies 8 miles W of Exeter. Take the B3212 Exeter to Moretonhampstead road. Car parking is available at Steps Bridge in the Dartmoor National Park car park. A public footpath leads visitors through the reserve from Steps Bridge to Clifford Bridge (c1.5 miles) along the bank of the River Teign.

Large areas of oak woodland with smaller valley bottom ash woods. Several large clearings with spectacular show of spring flowers especially daffodils. The site is very important for invertebrates including many scarce butterflies. Wood warblers, pied flycatchers, buzzards and all three woodpeckers breed here and the site also supports several nationally scarce plants.

*Eastcottdown Plantation
(Mr P T L Newman) **A** 50ha
O.S.S. 201 - SX 468 847
01566 783202
🚗10🚌1🚻 🎣

Approximately 8 miles from Tavistock via Chillaton (3 miles); 15 miles from Okehampton via Lewdown or Lydford (5 miles) and 9 miles from Launceston via Lewdown (3 miles). There is parking for 10 cars and 1 coach in the farmyard behind park cottage; a WC at the site, use by permission of the forge. Visits to the wood are by appointment only, throughout the year. There are self guided trails and guided visits can be arranged. Guided visits will be charged for at £2 for adults and £1 for children. For appointments and further details please contact Mr Newman at the Manor House,

Coryton, Okehampton, Devon EX20 4PG, or on the above telephone number. Donations to the Forestry Trust.

The wood is located on a lower carboniferous chert ridge, with a steep southern escarpment. The site was planted in about 1840 with a mix of beech, oak, sweet chestnut, silver fir, larch, spruce and pine. This is now being felled and replanted over a 30 year period. Planting includes Douglas fir, larch, red cedar, grand fir, southern beech and cherry, with some natural regeneration of northern beech and chestnut. Rhododendron is rampant in parts of the wood. Old manganese, slate and lime mines/quarries can be seen around the site.

Eggesford Woods
(Managed by Forest Enterprise) **F** 222ha
O.S.S. 191 - SS 694 106
01409 221692
🚗🚌🎣🚻🏕⛺♿🚻 ⓘ 🎠🌲

Take the A377 N from Crediton, drive through Lapford, the forest car park is 2 miles further on to the R. Riding by permit only. Cycle hire is available at the Eggesford Garden Centre which provides all ability access with toilets and restaurant. Can be approached by rail on Tarka line from Exeter and Barnstaple.

The Forestry Commission's first plantings in 1919 are commemorated. A beech avenue was planted after 50 years of Commission planting, Her Majesty the Queen and the Duke of Edinburgh helped to plant an oak grove when the Commission had planted over one million acres nationally. Walks lead through the arboretum and past a Norman motte and bailey castle. The picnic area is located under the towering Douglas fir. The woodland is a fine habitat for butterflies, deer and a host of birds of prey.

Fernworthy Wood
(Managed by Forest Enterprise) **F** 590ha
O.S.S. 191 - SX 668 838
01392 832262
🚗🚻 🏕⛺🌲

65

From A382 take the road to Chagford. Turn R at the square in Chagford, follow signs to Fernworthy. Car parking, toilets, picnic area. Educational visits can be arranged in advance, please allow 6 weeks notice.

This woodland is an excellent example of a commercial, timber producing forest within the Dartmoor National Park. Intensive work has been undertaken on landscape design, incorporating the management of the many ancient monuments, streams and open moor into one design plan. The proliferation of sitka spruce natural regeneration is of professional interest, and the tranquillity of the reservoir will ensure a relaxing visit.

*Gatherley North

(J B Dyhouse, managed by Fountain Forestry) **A** 23ha
O.S.S. 201 - SX 384 836
01364 3316

🚗3 ♦ ❋ ❦

From Launceston, through Lifton into Leat Road. Go over river and take first R, signposted Gatherley, wood is 1.5 miles on the R. There is parking for 3 cars. All visits by appointment only. For further details and appointments please contact Fountain Forestry Ltd, Poundsgate, Newton Abbot, Devon TQ13 7PA or ring above number.

Originally a broadleaved woodland, it was largely felled in World War Two. It is now predominantly conifer plantation with some broadleaf in retentions and new planting. Attractive views across Lyd Valley towards Launceston Castle. Roe and red deer. Main timber species are Douglas fir and Japanese larch.

*Gatherley South

(J N Kirkman, managed by Fountain Forestry) **A** 22.5ha
O.S.S. 201 - SX 384 836
01364 3316

🚗 ❋ ❦

Launceston to Lifton (old A30) R turn after Arundel

Arms into Leat Road. Take 1st R signposted Gatherley, wood is 1.5 miles on the R. Small parking area. Visits by appointment only. For further details and appointments please contact Fountain Forestry Ltd, Poundsgate, Newton Abbot, Devon TQ13 7PA or telephone above number.

Bordered by the River Ramor. Good views over the neighbouring countryside. Young plantations of Douglas fir, Japanese larch and Sitka spruce. Ash retention blocks. New plantings of broadleaf varieties mainly oak. Roe and red deer have been seen.

Harcombe Estate

(Fire Services National Benevolent Fund)
RE 60ha
O.S.S. 192 - SX 888 818
01626 853639

🚗5 ❦ ♦ ❦ ⛺ ⚑

From the N - leave S carriageway of A38 at top of Haldon Hill, turn L into lane 100 yds past Exeter racecourse. Approx. 1 mile down lane to main entrance. Donations to Fire Services National Benevolent Fund and Forestry Trust. Access to the estate - check at reception. Open Mon, Tues and Wed 9am - 5pm. Closed mid Dec to mid Jan. There is a public right of way through the estate, also self guiding marked trails. Please keep to trails. Maps available.

160 acres of mixed secondary woodland including new pure and mixed broadleaf and broadleaf/conifer plantings. Areas of pure oak, beech, ash and birch woodland, with stream running down to a series of lakes used for private fishing. Centre of Excellence award for lakeside plantation notable in early summer for profusion of various rare orchids as well as base-rich species. Small stands of recently thinned alder and pruned hardwoods including cherry and sweet chestnut.. There is extensive heathland on the upper edges of the estate, where a number of Bronze Age Tumuli can be seen.

Hardwick Wood
(Woodland Trust) **F** 21ha
O.S.S. 201 - SX 528 556
01476 74297

Hardwick Wood adjoins the Plympton to Plymstock road, which crosses the A38 to the E of Saltram House. There is limited parking at the wood but no other facilities.

Hardwick Wood covers an area of prominent hilltop on the edge of Plymouth, which has been covered by woodland for at least 300 years. It is one of the largest blocks of mature woodland in the area. The predominant tree species are oak, ash and beech with at least one small leaved lime tree, a rare native tree in this area. Hardwick is home for large numbers of plants and animals, including the bluebell, campion, creeping buttercup, wild garlic, woodpecker, goldcrest and fox.

*Harpford Wood
(Clinton Devon Estates) **F** 63ha
O.S.S. 192 - SY 104 908
01395 443881
🚗10 �️

A3052 Exeter/Lyme Regis road. Turn N at Bowd on B3176 Ottery St Mary road. Park 1/2 mile on L in lay-by beside recycling centre.

A most attractive mixed wood in two parts divided by former railway line. Very steep in parts. The wood contains oak, beech, chestnut and other broadleaves and some fine stands of Douglas fir, Japanese larch together with other softwoods including western hemlock, Norway and Sitka spruce ranging in age from 1812 to 1993. There are many rides throughout the wood and two routes, a short (red) and a green (long) are marked starting at the car park.

*Heath Wood
(Mrs D Harper) **A** 40ha
O.S.S. 191 - SX 812 879
Woodlands Farm, Bridford, Exeter, Devon EX6 7EW
🚗4 �️ 🚶

From Exeter take the B3212 towards Dunsford. After about 6 miles, at the bottom of a steep hill, turn L onto the B3193. Follow the river on the R. Cross the river and take the R turning as the road bends to the L. Follow the road up the hill and take the first R. Carry on for 1 mile to the meeting point. There is parking for 4 cars. Guided visits can be arranged by appointment only. Please give 30 days notice for any visit. Charges for guided walks will be £2 for adults and £1.50 for children, group visits by negotiation. Donations to the Forestry Trust. For details contact Mrs Harper at the above address.

There has been a wood on this site for over 600 years. The wood consists of a large and diverse range of habitats, from wetland to steep shaly slopes. At the highest point of the woodland there are commanding views over the upper River Teign. With so many different habitats there is a large bird and insect population, such as buzzards, sparrowhawks and woodcock. The flora in parts of the wood include rare species found in only a few localities in England. The wood has no defined paths or tracks, and so suitable footwear should be worn. The wood is not suitable for visits by persons with limited mobility.

*Heathercombe Wood
(C D Pike) **A** 150ha
O.S.S. 191 - SX 719 810
Weekend/0164722 347
🚗20🚶�️🚻

Through Manaton, Bovey Tracey - about 1 mile to T junction (not L turn) turn L and keep straight on through Henttree Cross, signposts will then show Heathercombe. Only medium size buses can be accommodated. The meeting place is at Manwood, down the drive, as indicated by the signpost at the bottom of Heathercombe valley. Woodland paths and picnic area. Limited WC facilities. There is one footpath and one bridleway through the wood. Visits by appointment 1 month in advance by contacting Mr Pike on above telephone number. Donations made to the Forestry Trust. A book on the history of the valley is available for sale.

Heathercombe is an estate in the woodland valley on

the side of Dartmoor. It is dedicated to forestry, and contains an arboretum planted over the past 25 years. The forestry dates back about 100 years. There are some fine 100 year old trees but most of the planting has taken place since 1950. There are woodland rides and paths throughout the estate. The estate also includes Bronze Age settlements, a post war chalet bungalow and a medieval longhouse. Within the woodland snowdrops, daffodils, bluebells, rhododendrons and azaleas may be found. The estate is fully planted. During the next 20 years the development will take the form of thinning and main crop felling, mostly on a selective basis.

.

The woodland is located 2 miles N of Buckfastleigh, 1 mile W of the A38. There is parking for 20 cars. Picnic area; level paths for the disabled and extensive paths through the woodlands by the River Dart.

A mainly oak woodland with adjoining heathland. Managed in the last century for charcoal and tanbark; the trees have now been singled out to high forest. There are small areas of beech and mixed conifer. This woodland is an SSSI and within the Dartmoor National Park. An Iron Age hill fort on the crest of a hill gives good views of the surrounding area.

Heddon Valley
(National Trust) **F** 380ha
O.S.S. 180 - SS 655 481
01271 850560 (evenings)

Approximately 2.5 miles E of Blackmoor Gate (A39) turn L signed Heddon's Mouth and Hunter's Inn. Free car park in 1.25 miles. All in Exmoor National Park. Hunter's Inn public house open all year; in normal hours serves food and drink. Small souvenir and ice cream shop in summer months.

Woodlands are predominantly sessile oak woods of coppice originally for charcoal, tanbark and lime burning in last century. Remains of lime kiln at Heddon's Mouth. Now being singled to high forest. Mostly timber goes for firewood, pulpwood or estate repairs. Many paths - open all year. Some suitable for wheelchairs. Woodlands on steep slopes but paths gentle. Good area for birds; flycatchers, treecreepers, buzzards and woodpeckers. Red deer, badgers and otters have been seen. Paths link to coastal path with spectacular views. Guided walks by arrangement with the Warden on the above telephone number.

Hembury Wood
(National Trust) **FE** 150ha
O.S.S. 202 - SX 729 680

Higher Combe Wood
(Elliot Bialick) **F** 8ha
O.S.S 191 - SX 774 825
016477 257

Park in Lustleigh village as this is the nearest place to park. Follow public footpath through village orchard past Middle Combe. Higher Combe Woods are reached before Sanduck. Access is freely available under a voluntary access scheme promoted by the Countryside Commission and supported by the land-owner.

One area of the wood is semi-ancient oak woodland with hazel coppice. The two further compartments were planted with a 'natural' mix of indigenous native deciduous species in 1992. These provide an interesting opportunity of seeing the development of a new woodland from its beginning.

*Hillersdon Woods
(Mrs E N A Hadwen, managed by Fountain Forestry) **A** 23.6ha
O.S.S.192 - SS 984 078
013643 316

From Cullompton take the minor road N towards Tiverton. After 2 miles at Butterleigh Cross turn L. Take next L at `Birchen Oak'. After 1/2 mile entrance on L. No WCs on site. Guided visits can be arranged at weekends between Mar and Oct.

Please book at least 21 days in advance; contact Fountain Forestry on the above telephone number. Donations to the Forestry Trust.

Hillersdon Woods are found on high ground overlooking Cullompton. There may have been woodland on this site for more than 400 years. The majority of the broadleaved woodland is dominated by beech dating from the 19th century and probably established for shooting purposes. Recent planting includes larch, fir and spruce. The woodlands are very diverse in species and age and include examples of a number of trends in woodland management and establishment. There is also an archaeological site in the centre of the wood.

Hilltown and Quercus Walk
(Nicholas Collier) **R** 25ha
O.S.S. 201 - SX 540 718
01822 852122

🏠2🚗12⛺ ●

Woodtown is 4.5 miles from Tavistock and 2 miles from Horrabridge. Follow the signs to Sampford Spiney. It lies deep in the Walkham valley near Ward Bridge, and is signposted within the last mile. Continue through the entrance gate and down the drive to park in the estate yard. The wood is open to the public, throughout the week, between 1 April and 31 October, 10am - 5pm. All group visits are by appointment only and must be made at least 2 weeks in advance. Guided visits can be arranged and self guided trails are being developed (please allow 1.5 hours to complete the woodland walk). Donations to the Forestry Trust. For further details and any enquiries please contact Nicholas Collier on the above number or at Woodtown, Sampford Spiney, Yelverton, Devon PL20 6LJ.

Hilltown Wood stands at the centre of an important western oak wood system in the Walkham Valley, on the SW edge of Dartmoor. It is part of a major SSSI. The woodland character is predominantly high forest, dominated by pedunculate oak. Ash, alder and sycamore occur on the valley floor and there is some invasion of beech. The understorey contains abundant hazel, holly and sallow. Moss and fern communities are well developed in the more humid conditions by

the streams. In response to the long history of woodland continuity and the pollution-free oceanic climate, an interesting range of lichens has developed. The River Walkham, clean and well oxygenated, is a major spawning ground for salmon and sea trout; the site as a whole provides suitable habitat for a diverse bird community, and is rich in butterflies, flora and fauna. Badger setts and evidence of deer and otters are to be found. The Quercus Walk at Woodtown is an interesting Victorian perambulation of at least eight different species of mature oaks.

Holne Woods (1)
(National Trust) **F** 68ha
O.S.S. 191/202 - SX 702 703
01626 821527 (evenings)

🚗10⛺ ● ☀ 🦌 🍽 ♨ 🏛

3.5 miles W of Ashburton, S of B3357. Free car park at New Bridge. In Dartmoor National Park. No facilities, nearest 1 mile at Poundsgate - public house, shop and garage.

Woodland on W side of picturesque River Dart. Predominantly oak woods of coppice origin for charcoal and tanbark in the last century - now cut for pulpwood to make cardboard and small timber for fencing and gates. Riverside path fairly level, with splendid views of Dartmoor. Paths extend 2 miles and out on to open moor. Small areas of semi-mature conifers grown for timber. Woodland birds - pied flycatchers, treecreepers, woodpeckers. Sea trout and salmon in river in due season.

*Holne Woods (2)
(Dartmoor National Park) **F** 66ha
O.S.S 202 - SX 685 713
01626 832093

🚗50⛺ ● ☀-WC ♿ 🚶

Take Princetown road out of Ashburton. Fork L on Newbridge Hill to Holne. Follow this road not turning off into Holne until you pass over Vennford Dam. Car park on R. S of wood (N of road). There are WCs (including disabled) but they are closed in winter. Please lock valuables out of sight in cars. Please do not climb over regeneration fences.

Year round open access via common land. A guided visit will be held during 1995 (details in Dartmoor Visitor). Donations to the Forestry Trust.

Holne Woods are ancient oak woodlands of coppice origin with untouched areas and regeneration compartments. Woodland is well known for its bryophyte and lichen communities and upland birds including pied flycatchers, redstarts and many warblers. It is a SSSI.

Hunting Park and Sanduck are principally broadleaved woods. There is some sycamore which is being removed and the larch is gradually being felled. Mature oaks are retained to provide a rich habitat, in some cases until the trees die. The woods are being managed for butterflies and dragonflies in particular. Red and roe deer have been recorded in the woods as has the dormouse. There is an old ruined long house in Sanduck. The wood is prominent in the landscape and this is the principal object of management.

Holyford Wood

(South West Water Services) **F** 25ha
O.S.S. 192 - SY 233 924
01822 852435

From Exeter take the A3052 (or from Axminster take the A358 then turn R onto the A3052) towards Seaton. Turn N off the A3052 at Seaton for Holyford and then left at Holyford after 1/2 mile for Holyford Woods. There is limited parking. There is full open access to the wood with a public footpath crossing it from N to S. Requests for guided visits should be made to John Griffiths, Head Forester at Burrator Lodge, Sheepstor, Yelverton, Devon, or telephone above number.

The woods form part of a water catchment leading to a small water treatment works. The N side of the valley contains ancient woodland with oaks.

Hunting Park and Sanduck

(Dartmoor National Park) **A** 18ha
O.S.S. 191 - SX 772 842
01626 832093

1.4 miles S of Moretonhampstead on A382, 400 yards S of Wray Barton layby (E side of road) almost opposite entrance to old railway. No WCs. Guided visits can be arranged for groups of 10 or more, by appointment. Cost £2 for adults and 50p for children. Please give one month's notice to: Mr Lane, Dartmoor National Park, Parke, Haytor Road, Bovey Tracey, Newton Abbot, Devon TQ13 9IQ, or telephone the above number.

*Huntshaw

(Clinton Devon Estates) **F** 84ha
O.S.S. 180 - SS 503 224
01395 443881

B3232 from Great Torrington (3 miles) turn L at Huntshaw Cross. Parking for up to 3 cars on public road at Foxes Cross.

This group of commercial woodlands contains a variety of hardwoods and softwoods planted between 1874 and 1993. Near to the E perimeter is part of a scheduled Ancient Monument known as Berry Camp. The wood is home to many varieties of typical woodland wildlife including roe and fallow deer. The wood contains many rides suitable for walking and a stream meanders E to W.

*Kedworthy Wood

(David Miller) **R** 17.7ha
O.S.S. 180 - SS 705 373
01271 860800

The wood is found 1.25 miles N of Brayford, off the A399. Open Jan-May and Sept-Dec. Group/ guided visits by appointment only. Please ring David Miller on the above telephone number. Please give one week's notice for visits. Donations to the Forestry Trust.

Kedworthy Wood is a small mixed broadleaf and conifer woodland, just inside the Exmoor National

Park. It has been a woodland site for at least 100 years. A delightful moorland stream runs the length of the wood. Main timber species are oak, alder, Douglas fir with some Japanese larch.

*Kennerleigh Wood
(Paul Orchard-Lisle, managed by Fountain Forestry) **A** 45ha
O.S.S. 191 - SS 819 063
01364 3316
🚗4🦌 ♣ ⚘

N from Crediton through Sandford on minor road. Approximately 3 miles on and 1/2 mile before Kennerleigh village the woods will be found, on the L with an open entrance/loading bay signposted `Kennerleigh Wood'. Guided visits can be arranged for weekends except between 1 Nov and 1 Feb. All visits by appointment only, please give 2-3 weeks notice. For further details contact A J Sandels of Fountain Forestry, Poundsgate, Newton Abbot, Devon, TQ13 7PA, or telephone above number.

Kennerleigh Woods are a very fine example of productive, high timber quality mixed conifer plantation. The wood is predominantly Douglas fir and larch but with some spruce and beech plantations. There are some very interesting areas of red oak. In addition there are stream habitats, hazel coppice, old oak coppice and young ash coppice, now thinned to single stems. A tour of Kennerleigh Wood gives a good insight into forest silviculture, woodland conservation and the use of woods for recreation and sport.

*Kiddens Wood - (Bullers Hill)
(Managed by Forest Enterprise) **FC** 500ha
O.S.S. 192 - SX 882 847
01392 832262
🚗 ♣ WC ♿ ♀

From Exeter take the A38 to the top of Haldon Hill. Take the exit signposted "Forest Walks". Car Park 1.5 miles from junction. As well as a car park there are toilets, forest trails (including disabled trail)

butterfly trail, and the Bird of Prey Viewpoint where there is an honesty box. Educational visits can be arranged in advance. Please allow 6 weeks notice.

Kiddens Wood is situated on the Haldon Hills, near Exeter. Tremendous views of the city, and Dartmoor make this forest an ideal place for bird watching. The Haldon Bird of Prey Viewpoint was created to provide birdwatchers with easy access to one of the best viewpoints, thereby reducing pressure on nesting raptors elsewhere in the forest. The most notable visitor to the forest is the honey buzzard, but sparrowhawks, goshawks and kestrels can also be sighted, along with 34 species of butterfly, 13 species of dragonfly - the list is endless. Part of the wood is a forest nature reserve, with SSSI status.

*Knott's & Parsonage Woods
(Dr Derek A Wolfe) **R** 12.5ha
O.S.S. 190 - SS 407 112
01409 281454
🚗🦌 ● ❄ ♀ 🛈 ♀ ⚏

Travelling SW along the A388 (main Torrington-Holsworthy road) from Woodford Bridge, take the road on the L just before the top of the hill, signposted Thornbury. The third lane to the L leads to Buttermoor Farm, where cars may be parked. For this the farmer may ask a small fee. Turning R from here on foot, the first farm gate on the L gives access to a cart track which after 260m stops at the boundary of two fields. Following this boundary for a further 160m it meets the boundary of Knott's Wood. The entrance gate is 75m along the side of the wood. Picnics are allowed by permission only. No charges but donations are invited for the Forestry Trust. All year access, but limited to organised parties or groups, with prior permission, and a recognised individual fully responsible for all members of the group. A copy of Permission and Conditions for visit will be provided on request. Guides are available by arrangement.

These ancient semi-natural woodlands include a derelict farm complex and a wet area where alder and goat willow were earlier coppiced. The stream which once supplied the farm now has a hydram pump to water cattle on the woodland fields. Changing seasons bring bluebell, blackberry and wild mushrooms.

Devon

Wildlife includes fox, badger, red and roe deer and several species of bats. Kingfisher, dipper, woodcock and barn owl are all to be seen and there are butterflies, dragonflies, mosses and lichens. The woods border on both a 7ha water meadow and the River Torridge, with their own flora and fauna.

Lower Broxfords Wood

(Mr P Norman) **R** 24ha
O.S.S. 192 - SS 844 026
01363 866305

Take A3072 from Crediton to Tiverton. After about 1 mile cross over Creedy Bridge and then take first L to Upton Hellions. The entrance to the wood is on the R as the small village is approached. There are no facilities but the wood is open Sat, Sun and Bank Hols. Tracks and paths will be closed for forestry operations.

A working conifer woodland with crops dating from about 1960. Natural seedlings are appearing. Volunteer broadleaves have been nurtured. A very long wood that has many tracks suitable for walking. The woodland provides shelter for a range of wildlife in a predominantly fertile farming area.

*Lukesland Cleave

(B N Howell) **F** 17ha
O.S.S. 202 - SX 640 575
01752 893390

The entrance is midway between Ivybridge and Harford. From the A38 exit on the W edge of Ivybridge, proceed up the main street and immediately after crossing the river turn L. Proceed up the hill (paper mill on the L) across the staggered cross roads. The Wood is on the left after Ermewood House. There are no WC facilities on the site. There is fully open access to the wood on every day of the year except Saturdays. There are self-guided trails. Group visits by appointment only, rates by negotiation, please give one months

notice. Donations to the Forestry Trust. For further details please contact Mr Howell on above telephone number.

In Dartmoor National Park, the woodlands extend a mile along the river Erme. Mainly replanted 1954-1965 with Douglas fir, larch, western red cedar, beech and American oak. Some fine redwoods (Wellingtonia), of about 140ft, large Douglas and noble firs and an incense cedar are left from a planting of 1880. Fallow deer, badgers, buzzards, ravens, woodcock, dippers and many other birds.

Lydford Wood

(Forest Enterprise) **F** 154ha
O.S.S. 191/201 - SX 495 850
01409 221692

From Okehampton follow the A30, then A386 to Lydford. Turn as for Lydford and take first turning on R after the railway bridge. Follow the L hand fork 10m after the junction. Follow this road until you see the entrance sign for Lydford Woods on the L. There is fully open access to the wood for walkers, subject only to considerations of safety and conservation when areas may be closed off. Horse riding by permit only. Guided walks for groups are possible by prior arrangement for which a charge of £25 will be made, except for school parties which are free. More specialised forms of recreation are catered for by a permit system. For information leaflets and further details ring the Forest Enterprise District Office.

Lydford was an oak coppice woodland until the 1920s. Under Forestry Commission management the woods have been converted, in the main, to conifers. Woodland walks lead through mature stands of larch, Douglas fir and Corsican pine, younger stands and a seed orchard. At several points walkers can enjoy beautiful vistas across the valley and may glimpse birds of prey. Management at Lydford is aimed particularly at increasing conservation value. The Forest Enterprise is working hand in hand with conservation organisations to further develop butterfly habitats, open space and water habitats. Two forts on site are scheduled ancient monuments.

72

Manor Woods

(Torbay Borough Council) **F** 15ha
O.S.S. 202 - SX 930 632 / 934 640
01803 218848

W entrance is off Hesketh Road, Torquay and the N entrance is off Lincombe Drive, Torquay. Two grid references are given for separate entrances at each end of wood. Other public entrances also exist. There is a network of paths. Open all year, all day.

The wood is on a steep coastal site, and includes a Victorian woodland garden with some impressive exotic tree specimens and an extensive footpath network. In addition there is a stand of naturally regenerated native hardwoods, partly secondary, with an exceptionally fine pollard oak. Woodland management comprises selective thinning of compartments, in rotation..

Marridge/Elberry/The Grove Woods

(Torbay Borough Council) **F** 46.5ha
O.S.S. 202 - SX 895 572 / 905 563
01803 218848

N entrance from Broadsands car park, go SE along Elberry Lane to junction with Churston golf course; entrance to wood is on L before golf course. S entrance is off Bascombe Road, Churston, at end of long stone-surfaced lane. Woodland is also on SW coast path. Two grid references are given for separate entrances at each end of wood. Other public entrances also exist. Open all year, all day.

A long relatively narrow coastal woodland on land sloping steeply down to cliffs, combes and beaches, with a magnificent series of long-abandoned quarries (the "seven quarries"), running into a large ancient semi-natural woodland (The Grove) partly replanted as a larch/sweet chestnut plantation in the 1930s. Good specimens of both larch and native broadleaved trees, some wonderful views and a very good variety of

native species, including sorbus species with an extremely restricted distribution. An extensive footpath network crosses the site. Species include ash, sweet chestnut, beech, oak, extensive coastal sycamore, with a wide range of understorey/herb layer species including orchids, spurge laurel, and good displays of bluebells. Woodland management comprises of felling moderate sizedn coupes, with replanting, together with selective thinning of compartments in rotation, and the opening out of view points.

Milber Wood

(Teignbridge District Council) **F** 7.3ha
O.S.S. 202 - SX 875 705
01626 61101

1 mile E of Newton Abbot. Take road signposted "Milber" from Penn Inn roundabout on A380, then 1st R. Entrance on R after 100m. Open all year round. Occasional guided walks, picnic table, seats.

Wood originally part of large estate owned by the Carew family at nearby Haccombe House. Originally known as "Penninn Plantation" it was purchased as a local amenity in 1924. The higher land, including a public footpath, is dominated by mature oak, beech and Scots pine. The sloping land was planted by local children soon after clearance during the 1st World War. Species include larch, black and Scots pine, birch, spruce, sycamore and cherry. Management is designed to retain the visual quality and for nature conservation.

Occombe Wood

(Torbay Borough Council) **F** 27.5ha
O.S.S. 202 - SX 874 631 / SX 890 623
01803 218848

W entrance is off Preston Down Road, E entrance is off Langdon Road, Paignton. Open all year, all day. Two grid references are given for each end of wood; other public entrances exist.

An ancient semi-natural woodland at its W end,

merging into an oak/chestnut/pine plantation to the E. W section surrounds steep valleys with streams at foot, and has some very good native specimens and high quality wildlife habitat, a wide range of species. There is an extensive path network with good views of the sea and surrounding landscape from the E section. Tree species include oak (sessile and pedunculate) ash, beech, chestnut, field maple, sycamore, hazel, with a native calcareous understorey/herb layer including viburnum, spindle, woodspurge, "town hall clock" medick and dog's mercury.

Parke Estate

(National Trust) **F** 36.9ha
O.S.S. 191 - SX 808 783
01626 832093

Take the A38 from Exeter to Plymouth road. Turn off at Drumbridges Junction, 22km from Exeter onto the A382 to Bovey Tracey. Parke House is 1km W of Bovey Tracey. There is an independently run shop, tea room, rare breeds centre and information centre. These are open between 1 Apr and 31 Oct. The woodlands are freely accessible all year round as is the picnic and play area.

The wood is just outside the Dartmoor National Park. A selection of large old trees in the park. The woodland is predominantly broadleave trees of mixed ages, although there are some fine Douglas fir. There is an extensive network of riverside woodland paths. One footpath follows the route of the old Moretonhampstead railway line. There is a variety of woodland birds. The house on the estate is the headquarters of the Dartmoor National Park Authority.

*Pool Down Wood

(Mike Smith) **A** 7ha
O.S.S. 191 - SX 799 755
01626 821465 (daytime)/01626 833099 (evenings)
➡15➡1 ♣ WC ⛺ ⸸ 🛍

Take the A382 W from Newton Abbot to Drumbridges roundabout over the A38. Take the

second exit towards Liverton, Ilsington. After 300m turn R, pass through Liverton, and Pool Farm is one third of a mile from the village centre. Guided visits can be arranged but will need 3 weeks notice. Charges for visits are 50p for children and £1 for adults, non guided, and £1 for children and £2 for adults, guided. For further details please ring Mike Smith on the above number.

Thirty years ago the wood, a mixture of oak, ash and Scots pine, was clearfelled and replanted with Douglas fir, Japanese larch and western hemlock, with naturally regenerating birch, ash, Scots pine and oak. The 1976 drought, plus intensive blackthorn competition, killed the larch in the central part, and this was replanted with Douglas fir and Corsican pine, with naturally invading ash also present. The current policy is to develop a high yielding temperate 'rainforest' with mixed species, varied ages, a high rate of carbon capture, yet with great wildlife value; in short, an example of woodland permaculture.

*Quicke Estate Woodlands

(Dr J Quicke) **AC** 375ha
O.S.S. 192 - SX 877 977
01392 851627
➡3⸸ ♣ 🦌

South of the A377 from Exeter. Limited car parking. Please do not obstruct roads or tracks. Visits by appointment only. Please ring above number or write to Dr J Quicke at Venny Cleave, Newton St Cyres, Exeter, Devon EX5 5BT.

Woodlands are in several separate areas, such as Scrawthorne (near to Newton St Cyres), Crooklake, Blackdown and the main larger areas of Newton Wood, Whitestowe and Whiptail Woods to the south (the latter two are managed by the Forest Enterprise). Resident population of roe, fallow and red deer.

*Riding Parks and Lawelldown Woods

(The Clifford Estate Co Ltd) **A** 12.7ha
O.S.S. 191/192 - SX 870 780
01626 852179
➡2✕⋃♥ ✳ 🍺

From Chudleigh follow the signs to Ugbrooke Park. Go up Tower Hill and take the sharp R at Biddlecombe Cross. All visits must be arranged in writing to the above address.

Riding Parks and Lawelldown Woods are of interest as a site in the national context. They have been classified by Dr George Peterken as an ash/wych elm woodland, of which ten were known to him in 1983, Riding Parks being the most southerly example. The small-leaved lime and the wild service tree regenerate naturally. As a diverse calcareous based woodland and for the quantity of lime trees present, it is unique in Devon and rare W of the Mendips. Much of the woodland is classified as ancient semi-natural. The site is centred on an outcrop of Devonian limestone. Species include ash, small-leaved lime, wych elm, field maple, pedunculate oak, some beech, sycamore and mountain ash with an underwood of hazel and hawthorn. The ground vegetation possesses a rich flora, characteristic of ancient woodland on base rich soils: dog's mercury, ransoms and wood anemone being abundant.

Roadford Lake Woods

(South West Water Services Ltd) **F** 62ha
O.S.S. 190 - SX 414 890
01822 852435

� 🚶 WC 🏇

Follow the signs on A30 between Lewdown and Lifton. The site is to the N of the A30. A charge will be made at the main Roadford Dam car park. There is open access to the wood on permissive paths. Guided visits can be arranged. For further details contact John Griffiths, Head Forester at Burrator Lodge, Sheepstor, Yelverton, Devon on the above telephone number.

This site is made up of three separate woods by the new Roadford Reservoir. Slew Wood and East Banbury Wood form a backdrop to the new dam. The woods are managed primarily for amenity and wildlife, the plan being ultimately to convert the whole wood to broadleaved trees.

Salcombe Hill

(National Trust) **F** 37ha
O.S.S. 192 - SY 140 882
01395 578107

🚶 20 🏇 🚶 ☼ ⛺ 📷 ♨ 🏁

1 mile E of Sidmouth. Free car park adjoining Norman Lockyer Observatory. No other facilities. Public houses, hotels and shops at Sidmouth one mile.

AONB woodland on S side of road. Extensive network of paths - some level, some steep - linked to coastal path with spectacular views from cliff tops over the whole of Lyme Bay. Some mixed broadleaves but larger area of mixed conifers planted in 1960s. Thinned out on a 4 year rotation and to be changed to broadleaves by about 55 years old. Some small areas blown down in 1990 storm already cleared and replanted with oak, ash, beech and sweet chestnut.

Scadson/Ten Acre Brake

(Torbay Borough Council) **F** 35ha
O.S.S 202 - SX 884 634/SX 895 627
01803 218848

🚶 10 🏇 ∪ 🚶 ☼ ⓘ ⛺ 🏇 🏁

NW entrance off Cockington Lane, Paignton, SE entrance off Old Paignton Rd. Grid references given for entrances at each end of wood, other public entrances also exist. There is a footpath network which is open all year, all day.

A long, linear woodland running down a steep sided valley with a stream in the bottom; part ancient semi-natural woodland, part plantation. Has some good specimen hardwood trees, extensive coppice with standards and a good range of native species. N compartments of the wood were severely storm damaged in 1990, and have been cleared and replanted; aim is to improve the timber quality on site by an ongoing management programme; provide coppice underwood for the local thatching market, for charcoal and firewood, and maintain a valuable wildlife habitat. Trees include stands of oaks, ash, beech, a larch/Douglas fir plantation, sycamore, and hazel with a herb layer including ivy and dog's mercury, with a good bryophyte/fern component.

Shaptor and Furzeleigh Wood
(Woodland Trust) **F** 78ha
O.S.S. 191 - SX 818 794
01476 74297

From Bovey Tracey take the A382 towards Moretonhampstead, then almost immediately turn R onto the steep minor road by the hospital. There is limited parking and no facilities. It is advisable to keep to the paths as unknown mine shafts may still be present. Fully open access.

Shaptor and Furzeleigh woods form an important woodland in the valley between Bovey Tracey and Moretonhampstead, with Shaptor Wood having had continuous cover for at least 300 years. Oak, ash and birch are the predominant tree species, with honeysuckle and spindle common in the understorey. These woods are particularly rich in plant life with a total of 92 woodland species recorded including wood anemone and epiphytic ferns. The wet areas support distinctive wetland plants. Spotted flycatchers, wood warblers, redstarts and foxes are among the wealth of animal life to be seen in the wood.

*Shute Hill
(W A Nicholls & Sons, managed by Fountain Forestry) **R** 47.6 ha
O.S.S 192 - SY 257 973
01626 834491

⇔6⊨ ⚹ ❈ ⥀ ↑

From Shute village take minor road leading up past church and school. The entrance and car park are on the L after 0.3 mile. Rights of way and permitted paths. Guided walks may be arranged.

This woodland was damaged in the storms of 1989/90 and was largely replanted, with attention to environmental considerations as well as timber production. The exposed southern end of Shute Hill is planted with Corsican pine and a hardwood belt over the top of the hill will finally dominate the skyline. The other new planting is primarily Sitka spruce and Douglas fir with older mixed conifers which survived the storms. There is a stone Armada beacon on the property, and the surrounding area has been landscaped with funding assistance from Devon County Council and help from local community groups.

*Tavistock Woodlands
(The Right Honourable The 7th Earl of Bradford) **RC** 475 ha
O.S.S. 201 - SX 426 736
01822 832131

⇔15⥀3 ⚹ ⥀ ↑

Find the Devon Great Consols Chimney Stack at grid reference SX 426736 (about 4 miles W of Tavistock). There is parking for 15 cars and 3 coaches. Visits are possible on any day between 1700 hours to dusk (ie outside working hours) with prior permission being gained from Mr Timmis on the above telephone number. Group visits can also be arranged through the above contact, please give at least 8 weeks notice. Charges for guided visits will be £2 for adults, £1 for children; group charges by negotiation. Donations to the Forestry Trust.

A unique block of woodland in the S Tamar and Tavy valleys with a forest cover that dates back to pre Domesday and which has been moulded by practical human requirements right up to the avant garde Bradford Plan continuous cover system of today. Extraordinary growth rates are displayed by both exotic conifers and broadleaves, such as Douglas fir and Nothofagus. There are some fine stands of beech and areas of ancient oak coppice. A truly diverse and functioning forest area supporting red and roe deer as well as most other British mammals There is a wide range of other fauna and flora.

Teign Valley Woods
(National Trust) **F** 129ha
O.S.S. 191 - SX 809 884
01837 53406 (evenings)

⇔30⥀3 ⚹ ❈ WC ⓘ ⏚ ⛰ ⛺ ⛱⥀

From Exeter take the B3212 Moretonhampstead Road W for 12km. Look for the Steps Bridge Hotel. During the summer months there is a private hotel, bar and tearoom open. There is also a short path for the use of disabled visitors but most of the woodland is on hilly terrain.

A spectacular hanging oakwood, consisting of mainly old oak coppice. The woodland is an SSSI in the Dartmoor National Park. The site is of high landscape value and famed for its profusion of daffodils. Birds found on the site include buzzards, pied flycatchers, marsh tits, three species of woodpeckers and dippers on the stream.

From Stowford Cross on A30 between Okehampton and Launceston take the road marked "Kennels". Visits by appointment.

Townleigh Wood is part of a modern dairy farm where a lot of new planting has been done over the last 17 years to try and make the farm look attractive. New woods round the farm buildings join up with old woodland that goes down to the River Thrushel. There are also commercial woods of larch, Sitka, and Douglas fir in various states of management.

Torquay Coastal Woodlands
(Torbay Borough Council) **F** 108ha
O.S.S. 202 - SX 941 639 / SX 924 673
01803 218848

🚗80↖🌳❄WC [i] ⛺ 🏇 ⛰ 💧

S entrance is off Ilsham Marine Drive, Torquay. N entrance is off Watcombe Beach Road. The SW Coastal footpath runs through the site end to end. Free access all year, all day. Footpath network. Grid references are given for separate entrances at each end of wood, other public entrances also exist.

An extensive stretch of coastal woodland, with outliers N and S of the listed section, comprising a mixture of ancient semi-natural, secondary semi-natural and a small amount of plantation woodland, interspersed with cliffs, beaches, narrow combes, and some open land. The area has no outstanding stands of timber, but is very rich in native species and in wildlife, especially birds. Tree species include ash, sycamore, elm, field maple, thorn, with occasional small-leaved lime; understorey/herb layer includes hazel, spindle, woodspurge, spurge laurel, butcher's broom, cowslips, and purple gromwell. There is a good population of raptors and other birds and fine displays of bluebells in spring.

*Townleigh Wood
(R L Nicholson) **A** 14ha
O.S.S. 190 - SX 428 878
01566 83277
↟

Watersmeet Wood
(National Trust) **F** 233ha
O.S.S. 180 - SS 744 486
01596 52648

🚗40🚌2🚶🌳❄🦌WC [i]⛺⛰💧🍽️
💧

The wood occupies both sides of the A29 SE of Lynmouth. Full access to the woodland paths throughout the year. Car park is above Watersmeet House, where between 1 Apr and 31 Oct the shop, tea room and picnic area are open. The paths by the river are not recommended for the disabled.

The woodland clothes the steep valleys by E and W Lyn rivers. The wood is old coppice, once used by the tanning and charcoal industries. The extensive path system, which also links to open moorland, radiates from Watersmeet House. A point of interest is the Iron Age linear earthworks known as Countisbury Camp. The wood is of great landscape and scenic value. Further information at Watersmeet House.

*West Bowerland
(Mr A J Burgess, managed by Fountain Forestry) **A** 58 ha
O.S.S. 191 - SX 533 940
01364 3316
🚗3 ↟

Take A3079 from Okehampton to Holsworthy. West Bowerland is 4 miles from Okehampton on L just after disused railway.

This is an area of new woodland created in the early 1970s by planting some wet low grade agricultural land. A range of coniferous species were used with Sitka spruce being the dominant one. Other species include Japanese larch, Norway spruce and Corsican pine. Old hedgerows were retained to give diversity and two small ponds have been excavated and support rare species of dragonfly. The wood is thought to be the haunt of a black panther!

*Whitehills Plantation
(Lady Margaret Fortescue) **A** 44ha
01598 760336
Ṟ

Directions on application. There are no facilities at the wood. Visits by appointment only. For further details and appointments please write to H R Thomas, resident land agent, Estate Office, Castle Hill Filleigh, Barnstaple, Devon EX32 0RA or ring the above number. School parties, one visit per term. Two weeks notice is required for group visits. Donations to the Forestry Trust.

Whitleigh Wood
(Woodland Trust) **F** 20ha
O.S.S. 201 - SX 477604
01476 74297
🚗🐎●

From the A38 follows signs for the A386 to Tavistock. From the A386 turn W towards the B3373 to Tamerton Foliot. After proceeding straight across at the next roundabout, turn R onto the Tamerton Foliot road. Whitleigh Wood is on the L a short way up the road, but it is better to continue as far as the island in the road centre and then turn L into Borrowdale Close. There is limited parking and no other facilities. Full open access to the wood.

The site on which Whitleigh Wood stands has been tree covered for at least 150 years and has an important amenity value in an otherwise built up area. Oak, birch, field maple and sweet chestnut are the main tree species present along with hazel, blackthorn and young

ash saplings making up the understorey. The wood supports a rich plant and animal community including grey wagtail and redpoll, heath speedwell, creeping jenny and hart's tongue fern. Numerous fungi species including fly agaric and shaggy inkcap can be found in this wood.

Wray Cleave
(Dartmoor National Park) **R** 31ha
O.S.S. 191 - SX 774 837
01626 832093
🚗3🚌1🏃●☀️🌿Ṟ

Half way between Moretonhampstead and Bovey Tracey on the A382. Public rights of way link up with permitted path to form circular walk. Guided walk will take place on 3 May 95 (2.5 hrs). Cost of guided walks is £2 for adults and 50p for children. Donations to the Forestry Trust.

Wray Cleave is an ancient and semi-natural wood. There are micaceous haematite mine workings in the wood which were abandoned in 1926. Deer frequent the site. Landscape, wildlife and archaeological aspects feature prominently in the management plans. The principal species being retained is oak.

DORSET

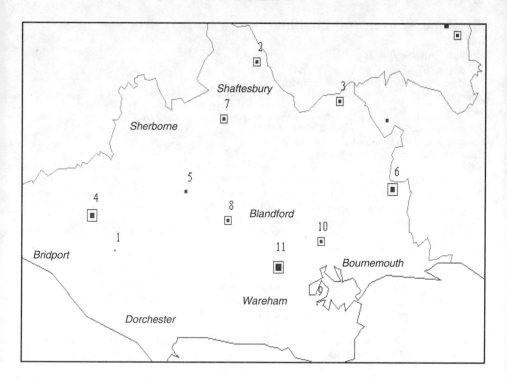

1. *Belstone, Warren & Chaffins Copse
2. Duncliffe Wood
3. Garston Wood
4. *Hooke Park
5. Melcombe Park
6. *Moors Valley Forest*
7. Piddleswood
8. Ruins Plantation
9. *Slepe Wood
10. *Stony Down
11. *Wareham Forest*

*Belstone, Warren and Chaffins Copse
(William Crutchley) **A** 7ha
O.S.S. 194 - SY 530 943
Mappercombe Manor, Powerstock, Bridport,
Dorset DT6 3SS

Get to Powerstock 3 miles NE of Bridport. From Powerstock Church take S road to T junction, turn L towards Nettlecombe, passing Marquis of Lorne Inn. Leaving Nettlecombe on L. 0.25 mile to cross roads, turn L after 1/2 mile leave Marsh Farm on L. Further 1/2 mile up No Through Road to rendezvous. Park where conditions allow by road. Groups of young people are especially welcome. Appointments by letter only. Donations to Farms for City Children and Forestry Trust.

Three adjacent broadleaved woodlands totalling 7 hectares demonstrating three methods of attempting to establish viable crops. The plantings vary in age from 50 year sweet chestnut to current natural regeneration of ash and a planting saved late by Belgian thinning. Under western edge of Eggardon Hill, fine scenery, plenty of flora and fauna.

Duncliffe Wood
(Woodland Trust) **F** 86ha
O.S.S. 183 - ST 825 225
01476 74297

Take the A30 W from Shaftesbury towards E Stour. After about 3 miles turn L onto a minor road towards Stour Row. Duncliffe Wood is to the L of this road 0.74 of a mile after turning onto the minor road a track leads off to the L into Duncliffe Wood. Park along this track.

Duncliffe Wood is one of the largest areas of woodland in N Dorset. It is set like a saddle on top of two hills and offers superb views of the surrounding area and contains a pollarded tree which is perhaps the oldest living thing in Dorset. Oak and ash dominate the deciduous areas, but intermingled with them are wild cherry, rowan and hazel coppice. Butterflies, including white admiral, purple hairstreak and silver washed fritillaries, still breed in profusion

in the wide rides of the wood, feeding on the sun-loving plants that grow here.

Garston Wood
(RSPB) **R** 34ha
O.S.S. 184 - SU 004 194
01929 550969

Turn off A354 Blandford - Salisbury road to Sixpenny Handley. From Sixpenny Handley take the road North to Broad Chalke. Car park is about a mile along this road. Leaflet available in car park. The reserve is open at all times - access via car park or public footpath from Deanland. No charges but donations welcome. Open days including free guided walks will be held in May and July 1995. Telephone above for actual dates. Visitors are asked to stay on woodland paths and dogs must be kept under close control.

Garston Wood is an ancient woodland that has played an important part in the local economy for hundreds of years. Hazel, with mainly oak/ash standards, has traditionally been coppiced. In recent years this has been neglected. The RSPB has begun to reinstate the coppice cycle over 27ha (leaving 7ha as high forest). April/May is the best time for flowers when bluebells and wood anemones carpet recently coppiced areas. 200 species of vascular plants have been recorded . Silver washed fritillary butterflies are on the wing in July and the wood provides habitat for nightingale, turtle dove and dormouse. Roe and fallow deer may be seen.

*Hooke Park
(Parnham Trust) **R** 135ha
O.S.S. 194 - ST 526 002
01308 863130

30 3

From Beaminster take B3163 signed Dorchester, Maiden Newton, Evershot. After 2 miles turn R signposted Hooke. After 1.5 miles turn R into Hooke Park through main entrance bounded by large wooden rings. There is parking for 30 cars and 3 coaches. The woodland is open 7 days a week throughout the year. There are rights of way and self guided trails - please keep to the marked trails. There is no charge to walk the woodland but there is a small charge for car parking. Guided, specialist and educational tours of the woodland and of Hooke Park College's award winning buildings can be arranged by appointment. Contact above telephone number for details and charges. Please book at least one month in advance.

Hooke Park is situated on an ancient site. The famous Dorset coast in only 6 miles away. There is a network of old boundary banks with neglected pollards to be found throughout the Park. Replanted in the 1950s by the Forestry Commission after clearance of the then principal species of oak, ash and alder. Even age with a distribution of species, predominantly beech and Norway spruce and oak/spruce mixtures. Resident population of roe and fallow deer.

Melcombe Park
(M C Woodhouse) **A** 60ha
O.S.S. 194 - ST 750 040
Higher Melcombe, Dorchester, Dorset DT2 7PB
 (£1)←6✈ ▲ ▯

From village of Melcombe Bingham, follow signpost to Melcombe Park Farm. Village 3 miles W of Milton Abbas in central Dorset. No facilities. Car parking limited to 6 cars or 1 coach. Public House, Fox Inn, Ansty, 1 mile. Written appointment only - for guided tour only, (May to August) please contact Lt Col J M Woodhouse, Estate Manager at above address. Charges £1 per head for adults (to Charity), children free.

Replanted ancient woodland. Softwood planting 1946 - 60 being replaced now by hardwoods. Mainly oak and ash with varied softwoods remaining. Clay subsoil. Wildlife includes deer, and foxes.

Moors Valley Forest
(Managed by Forest Enterprise in conjunction with E Dorset District Council)
R 500ha
O.S.S. 195 - SU 110 045
01929 551811

The Forest and Country Park are signposted from the roundabout on the A31 one mile W of Ringwood. Car park charges vary from 50p to a maximum of £3 in peak season. The charge covers whole day parking. See Information Point and Visitor Centre in car park for information on the Forest.

A productive forest which adjoins Moors Valley Country Park. The forest teems with wildlife and whilst it is very popular with visitors it is easy to find quiet areas to stop and look. A play trail with snakes and ladders, tree top trail and the Loggosaurus, to name a few, have been built from forest timber to entertain the children. The mainly pine forest is host to nightjars, goldcrests, roe deer, sand lizards and adders amongst others.

Piddleswood
(G A Pitt-Rivers) **F** 71ha
O.S.S. 194 - ST 801 135
←▲

A357 Blandford - Sherborne road 2 miles E of Sturminster Newton. Car park 1/4 mile N of main road signed Fiddleford Mill where there is car parking. There are no charges and access is unrestricted, except for camping which is not allowed.

An SSSI, mainly oak with coppice, also larch and Douglas fir plantations. 16 hectares are managed by Dorset Trust for Nature Conservation as a nature reserve.

Ruins Plantation

(Ruins Plantation Trust) **R** 22ha

O.S.S. 194 - ST 790 023

Kitt Hill House, Sherborne, Dorset, DT9 3PL

From Milborne St Andrew on the A354 from Blandford to Dorchester take the road N to Milton Abbas. At the bottom of the village (just over 3 miles) take the road to Hilton past the Milton Abbey school for one mile and turn down the track through the beech avenue planted for Lady Caroline Sackville West. There are no facilities and no charges. Open Saturdays and Sundays. Parking is sometimes allowed in the beech avenue but the land does not belong to the woodland. Educational visits should be arranged in writing to Mr M Gill at the above address.

The wood was part of the Milton Abbey Estate which was once a favourite retreat for royalty. The beech woods on the steep N slope were felled during the war for making gliders and aeroplanes. The area was replanted mostly with beech between 1950 and 1965 but there has been good regeneration of ash. Grey squirrel damage has greatly reduced the amount of beech. Sycamore, oak, chestnut, horse chestnut, Douglas fir, Thuja, Tsuga, larch and Lawson cypress are also present.

*Slepe Wood

(W Bond) **A** 5ha

O.S.S. 195 - SY 961 871

01929 463301

The wood is off the unclassified road from Stoborough, nr Wareham, to Arne. As it is part of a nature reserve exact details will only be given on application. Limited roadside parking is available. There are no charges.

This small but varied wood offers examples of commercial timber production, natural woodland and conservation practice within the RSPB reserve at Arne. The sensitive nature of the wood makes it especially suitable for education, but inappropriate for informal recreation.

*Stony Down

(F W & P Myerscough) **R** 54ha

O.S.S. 195 - SY 970 960

01202 887628

5 miles from Poole on A350 towards Blandford turn right into Rushall Lane by petrol station. After 1000 yards park car in Rushall Lane and walk northwards on bridlepath into wood. Access is limited to the bridleway which traverses the wood and is marked with blue arrows. More extensive visits by appointment.

A working wood of Scots pine, Corsican pine, Douglas fir, Western hemlock, larch, sweet chestnut, birch and other hardwoods and scrub. Wildlife typical of the area.

*Wareham Forest

(Managed by Forest Enterprise) **F** 2000ha

O.S.S. 194/195 - SY 900 920

01929 551811

N W of Wareham on the Wareham to Bere Regis road. Main car park, signposted Sika Trail, other small parking areas available at forest gateways.

Wareham Forest is a mainly pine forest with Scots and Corsican pine the main species planted. Heathland is an important feature and contains many rare species which can be observed in the forest, e.g. nightjar. Woolsbarrow is an Iron Age Hill Fort and provides good views over the forest - follow signs.

DURHAM

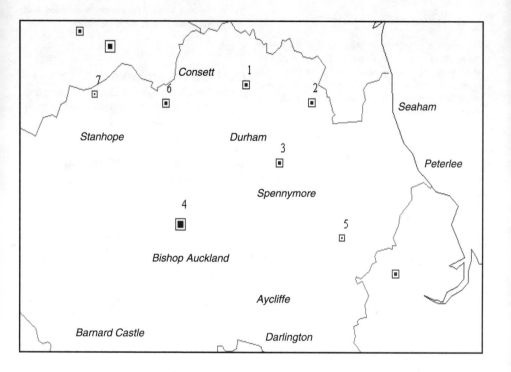

1. Carrickshill Wood
2. Cocken Wood Picnic Site
3. Durham Riverbanks
4. *Hamsterley Forest*
5. Hardwick Hall Fen Carr
6. Pontburn Wood
7. West Plantation

Carrickshill Wood

(Durham County Council) **F** 10ha

O.S.S. 88 - NZ 204 546

0191 383 4028

The wood is situated 1 mile to the N of Stanley at the western end of the Beamish Estate. It can be approached via minor roads leading from the A693 or A6076. Park at Beamish Burn picnic area and cross the bridge into the wood. There are no charges and the wood is open at all times.

An ancient woodland site which is thought to have been continuously wooded since medieval times. The public footpath formed part of a "Ladies Drive" used for horseback riding in the last century. Comprising mixed deciduous woodland there is active regeneration and a well developed shrub and herb layer. A stand of mature birch, with abundant honeysuckle, is a particularly attractive feature at the western end of the wood. Growing in wet hollows is a range of herbs of interest including bugle, yellow pimpernel, valerian and water avens.

Cocken Wood Picnic Site

(Durham County Council) **F** 10ha

O.S.S. 88 - NZ 297 473

0191 383 4028

The picnic site is 4 miles to the N of Durham City on the right bank of the River Wear. If travelling from Durham take the A690 N and turn L to Leamside village. There is a lay-by on the minor road on the N side of the river. Light refreshments are available at the (now ruined) Finchale Priory on the opposite side of the river. There is free and full access. The river cliffs are steep and dangerous in places and visitors should keep to approved paths.

An area of ancient woodland and a designated County Wildlife Site comprising mixed deciduous woodland including oak, beech, ash, elm, sycamore and birch with an understorey of hawthorn, hazel, yew and holly. The ground flora is characteristic of acid woodland in the region with abundant giant woodrush. Species of interest include moschatel, toothwort and, where mineral rich flushes occur,

opposite-leaved golden saxifrage. Roe deer and red squirrel are recorded from the wood. A footbridge across the river connects the site with Finchale Priory which was built in the 11th century and ruined at the time of the dissolution of the monasteries.

Durham Riverbanks

(The Dean & Chapter of Durham Cathedral, Durham University & Durham City Council) **F** 10ha

O.S.S. 88 - NZ 277 423

0191 384 1690

(£0.60) (£5) ☂ ☀ [i] ☕

Several signed access points from the city centre. Open all year round during daylight hours.

Mainly native broadleaved woodland clothing the banks of the River Wear around the peninsular on which the World Heritage site of Durham Cathedral and Castle stand. A masterly setting for a magnificent Norman development. Continuous cover forestry is being attempted. The woodland sculpture of the last supper known as "The Upper Room" and the view from Prebends Bridge are noteworthy.

Hamsterley Forest

(Forest Enterprise) **F** 2500ha

O.S.S. 92 - NZ 092 313

01669 20569

(£1.50) ☂ [i] WC ♿ ⚑

Turn W off A68 between Toft Hill and Witton le Wear and follow signposts to Hamsterley. Follow brown signs from Hamsterley to Hamsterley Forest. There is a small visitor centre selling leaflets, maps, books, and souvenirs. There are WCs with baby changing facilities and provision for the wheelchair user. There are also forest drives, picnic places, walks and cycle trails. Car parking charge is £1.50. Coaches, by appointment only, £15.00. Guided tours, also by appointment, are £10.00 per hour. The forest is open all year from 0730 hours to 2030 hours. Special provisions are made for school parties and educational groups.

The largest forest block in County Durham, with attractive riverside car parks and picnic places. The forest drive enables visitors to drive into the heart of the forest whilst waymarked walks, cycle and horse trails enable them to explore the woodlands which vary from old mature trees in the valley to newly replanted upland forest areas in the hinterland.

Hardwick Hall Fen Carr
(Durham County Council) **F** 2ha
O.S.S. 93 - NZ 346 292
0191 383 4028

Part of Hardwick Hall Country Park, situated to the W of the A177, 1 mile to the W of Sedgefield. From the car park cross the Serpentine Lake and follow the signs for the Nature Trail. Facilities include a boardwalk, interpretative signs and a resource pack for teachers available from Land and Property Dept, Durham County Council, County Hall, Durham DH1 5UH, price £2.75. Free and full access is available at all times.

An area of willow and birch carr woodland with some ash, with a ground flora including tussock sedge, the uncommon blunt flowered rush, and in the most marshy sections, plants such as bogbean, bottle sedge and ragged robin. A raised boardwalk, built by conservation volunteers in 1981, enables visitors to see the woodland and its wildlife without getting their feet wet and provides an excellent opportunity to view plant succession from marsh to mature woodland. A bird hide overlooks the carr from which many of the birds of interest, including warblers, tits, spotted flycatchers and woodcock, may be seen.

Pontburn Wood
(Woodland Trust) **F** 24ha
O.S.S. 81/88 - NZ 147 562
01476 74297

These woods are situated at Hamsterley Mill, 7 miles SW of Newcastle and 4 miles NE of Consett, County Durham. Park at Pontburn bridge on the B6310, or on the A694 at the end of Mill Farm road. There are no facilities. No charge is made to walk in the wood and it is open at all times of the year.

Pontburn Wood has an interesting variety of wildlife. Red squirrels are common in the wood, but are shy and quite difficult to spot. Look out for pine and spruce cones nibbled to the stalk littering the woodland floor. Sparrowhawk, goldcrest and kestrel can also be seen, along with bats in the summer. Oak, silver birch, and some fine old rowan are just some of the trees found there. In springtime the woodland has a lovely cover of wild flowers, including celandine, bluebell, wood sorrel and wood sanicle.

West Plantation
(David Manners) **F** 8ha
O.S.S.87 - NY 945 495
01429 265641

$\mathbb{N}$ 30 ■ 2 ← ♠ ☀ ⚔ WC ¶ ⚘ ☕ ◉ ▯ 🛍

From A68 turn W on B6278. Signposted Derwent Reservoir and Blanchland. Car park is 50 yards beyond Abbey Church (continues straight on at crossroads). An easy waymarked right of way traverses the wood from Blanchland to Baybridge. A return walk on another right of way is located on the north side of the River Derwent. Some notice is necessary for guided tours.

A mixed woodland bordering the River Derwent containing small compartments of Norway spruce, Sitka spruce, larch planted between 1942 and 1959 and mature mixed broadleaves along the river bank with recently planted areas of mainly Douglas fir interspersed with broadleaves. There has been woodland on this site since medieval times when the wood was established and worked by the monks of nearby Blanchland Abbey. The compartment of mixed birch and oak in the centre of the wood is probably ancient natural woodland much as it would have been in 1500. Wildlife is plentiful and deer, kingfishers, herons and woodpeckers are often observed. There is an interesting waterfall at the end of the wood.

Essex

ESSEX

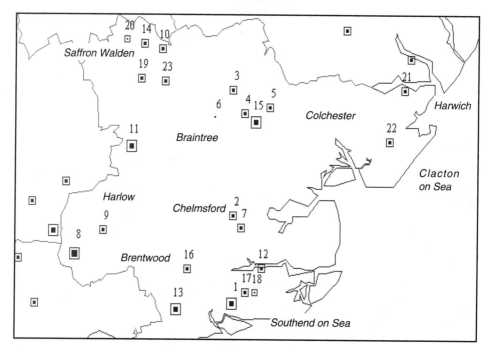

1. Belfairs
2. Blakes Wood
3. *Broaks Walk*
4. Brookes Reserve
5. *Chalkney Wood*
6. Cow Wood
7. Danbury Common
8. Epping Forest
9. Gernon Bushes
10. *Great & Little Bendysh Wood*
11. Hatfield Forest
12. *Hockley Woods

13. Langdon Reserve
14. Littlehales Wood
15. * Marks Hall Estate
16. *Norsey Wood
17. Pound Wood
18. Rawreth Hall Wood
19. *Rowney Wood*
20. Shadwell Wood
21. *Stour Wood
22. Weeleyhall Wood
23. West Wood

Belfairs
(Southend-on-Sea Borough Council)
F 121ha
O.S.S. 178 - TQ 834 876
01702 215618

Take the A127 towards Southend. On entering the signposted borough boundary, at the first set of traffic lights, turn R into The Fairway. Proceed to the next set of traffic lights and turn R into Eastwood Road. Entrance to park and car parks is approx. 100 yards on RH side. There are toilets and a cafe. Woodland open at all times, other facilities subject to park's opening and closing times.

The site comprises 85 ha of ancient woodland and parkland on which an 18 hole golf course has been laid out. Bowls, horse riding and field sports are all catered for and the woodland is used extensively for recreation. A further 36ha (a designated SSSI) is actively managed as traditional coppice with standard woodland. Over 400 species of flowering plants, 130 bird species and 500 fungi have been recorded. Wide rides provide easy access and support healthy butterfly populations.

Blakes Wood
(National Trust) **F** 43ha
O.S.S.167 - TL 775 065
01284 735480

SSSI and ASNW. Free access and parking. For further information telephone above number.

Ancient semi-natural woodland.

Broaks Walk
(Forest Enterprise) **F** 62ha
O.S.S. 167 - TL 784 316
01394 450164

Off the A1017 between Gosfield and Sible

Hedingham - 1 mile from turning to Halstead.

Mixed broadleaf and conifer woodland much of ancient woodland origin. There is a waymarked trail with an interpretative board at the start. The wood is being slowly reverted to broadleaf high forest with coppice-with-standard areas.

The Brookes Reserve, Tumblers Green
(Essex Wildlife Trust) **F** 24ha
O.S.S. 168 - TL 813 267
01206 729678

Off the A120 take the road to Stisted and from there to Greenstead Green. The reserve is on the L after about 1.5 miles. Limited parking on this corner, but a small car park is planned. Free access.

A varied reserve, comprising over 40 acres of SSSI ancient woodland and 18 acres of former arable fields. The largely hazel woodland also has small leaved lime and hornbeam, numerous ponds and a network of historic green lanes one of which is a bridleway. Primrose and various orchids are found. The huge population of fallow deer will necessitate fencing or other protection once coppicing resumes. The outer fields are to be developed as woodland and the inner as a sheltered meadow.

Chalkney Wood
(Forest Enterprise) **F** 49ha
O.S.S. 168 - TL 872 280
01394 450164

From A604 in Earls Colne turn southeast onto Tey Road (beside Coachman Inn) after 1/2 mile a sign to Chalkney Trail is on the left. Car park, way marked trail with interpretation. Open all year but some areas may occasionally be closed during forestry operations. For details of events and guided walks contact the above number.

This ancient woodland site, SSSI and Forest Nature

Reserve contains predominantly mixed broadleaved woodland and coniferous high forest planted by the Forestry Commission in the 1950s and 1960s. In recent years the policy has been to revert to site native species through heavy thinning, ride widening and the reintroduction of coppice coupes. The wood is notable for a natural graduation from small leaved lime to hornbeam; wet flushes rich in bryophytes; diverse ancient woodland flora (best seen in spring); an intact boundary bank and a probably pre-Roman hollow-way. The wood features significantly in several publications by Oliver Rackham who opened the nature trail there in 1992.

Cow Wood
(Lucy Tabor, Miss H Tabor, Mrs T Clarke) **A** 6ha
O.S.S. 167 - TL 742 258
01376 550944

From A131 N of Braintree take B1053 to Shalford, turn R after passing Towerlands Equestrian Centre, entrance to wood about 0.25 miles further on, on L. School visits £1 per half day. Open weekdays all year round. Parking by arrange- ment with owner.

Ancient semi-natural woodland which has coppiced hornbean and hazel with oak standards. Coppiced material currently used for thatching products and beansticks. Hazel hurdle on display. Other tree species include the wild service tree and a turkey oak. Good ground flora.

Danbury Common
(National Trust) **F** 73ha
O.S.S. 168 - TL 781 045
01245 222669

SSSI and ASNW. Free access. 50p car parking. For further information telephone the above number.

Semi-natural woodland. Largest area of common land in Essex outside Epping Forest. Heathland

regeneration scheme.

Epping Forest
(Corporation of London) **F** 2400ha
O.S.S. 167 - TQ 412 983
0181 508 0028

British Rail, Liverpool Street - Chingford line gives access to the W of the forest. The Central Line Station gives access to the E of the forest. Buses also serve the fringes of the forest. There is fulll open access to the forest via rights of way. Guided visits can be arranged by contacting the Information Centre on the above number. Please book 4 weeks in advance. Charges are by negotiation.

Bordered by undulating Essex farmland, the extensive woodlands of the forest enable visitors to contrast old pollarded trees with those growing in a small mixed plantation. Epping Forest contains the largest tract of ancient woodland in the Home Counties and its venerable pollards and maiden trees of beech, oak and hornbeam provide habitats for typical woodland birds as well as unique collections of fungi and beetles. Black fallow deer shelter in the holly undergrowth. Relict heathlands, grassy plains and ponds enhance this large area of open space owned and managed by the Corporation of London.

Gernon Bushes
(Essex Wildlife Trust) **F** 32ha
O.S.S. 167 - TL 478 030
0181 508 1593

Turn off the B181 NE of Epping towards Coopersale. Turn L on to Garnon Mead 200m after passing under the railway bridge. There are no facilities. A leaflet is available from Epping District Council.

A historic hornbeam pollard woodland with rich bogs and streams, whose notable plants include marsh fern, lady fern, bogbean, and kingcup. Re-pollarding is rejuvenating areas allowing natural regeneration.

Gravel extraction in the N created sphagnum bogs. Hawfinch and sparrowhawk are among the many species of birds recorded for the reserve. The Essex Way crosses the site.

Great and Little Bendysh Wood
(Forest Enterprise) **F** 92ha
O.S.S. 154 - TL 618 398
01394 450164

Enter woods from Radwinter End off minor road from Radwinter to Ashdon - lies between Saffron Walden and Haverhill.

Mixed conifer/broadleaf woodland undergoing phased reversion to broadleaf forest. Splendid ride flora.

Hatfield Forest
(National Trust) **F** 240ha
O.S.S. 167 - TL 547 202
01279 870678

🚗(£2.40)WC ⛺🅿️ ●

Off the M11 motorway take junction 8 the A120 Stansted exit. Follow A120 to Takeley village where Hatfield Forest is signposted - car park is 1 mile S of the village. There is a seasonal charge for the car park of £2.40 per car, between Easter and end of October when the cafe is also open. The wood, toilets and waymarked nature trail is open year round. There are two routes suitable for wheelchairs. (Battery operated vehicle available - please book in advance). Baby changing facilities. Children's Fun Day, 5 August. There is an 18th century Shell House with information boards. Leaflets are available on sale for self guided routes around the property.

Hatfield is the last surviving piece of medieval Royal Forest complete with its associated "plains" and coppices. The Forest is of national and international importance in terms of its biological interest and historical ecology. It is listed as a Grade 2 Nature Conservation Review site, an SSSI and an ancient semi-natural woodland. The forest is particularly

known for its pollards, dead wood invertebrates and coppiced areas.

*Hockley Woods
(Rochford District Council) **F** 96ha
O.S.S. 178 - TQ 833 924
01752 546366
🚗🐎 ● WC ⛺📖

Leave A127 to Southend at Rayleigh Weir, follow signs to Hockley. Turn R at Bull public house, Main Road, Hockley. Facilities include WCs, Awareness Centre, nature trails, leaflets, rustic products, sculptures, and educational section. Access is free. Small areas are dead hedged to prevent access onto heath fritillary breeding areas.

Hockley Woods has an ancient woodland flora and fauna, including wild service trees, bluebells etc with cow wheat, heath fritillary butterflies, nightingales. There are self guided trails, permissive horse route, guided walks and talks each week. Annual Open Days. Volunteer work parties.

The Langdon Reserve
(Essex Wildlife Trust) **F** 186ha
O.S.S. 177 - TQ 659 874
01268 419095

Take the B1007 off the A127 nr Basildon, entrance is about 1/2mile on L after passing under railway bridge. Large car park. Visitor centre is planned. There is full access to the reserve. The Plotland Museum opens 1 Apr to end Sept, Sundays 2-5pm, Bank Holidays 10am-5pm.

A huge reserve, divided into 4 main areas with their own character. Woods, plantations and scrub along with meadows and ponds form a rich mosaic. Woods are both ancient and secondary and are managed by coppicing and thinning. Miles of paths and bridleways cross the reserve, which was plotland from the turn of the century, reaching its heyday in the 1940s. No one has lived there since the 1970s and the reserve is an invaluable wildlife area on the urban fringe.

Littlehales Wood

(Forest Enterprise) **F** 16ha
O.S.S. 154 - TL 575 408
01394 450164

On minor road from Saffron Walden to Ashdon, 2 miles from Saffron Walden.

Small wood, probably of ancient woodland origin, undergoing phased reversion to broadleaved woodland.

*Marks Hall Estate

(Thomas Phillips Price Trust) **R** 200ha
O.S.S. 168 - TL 841 252
01376 563796

Take B1024 off the A120 Coggeshall bypass. Estate is signed off B1024 onto Marks Hall Road (about 1 mile from A120). Fully signed off all local roads. Normal opening hours 10.30 - 4.30 weekdays, 10.30 - 6.00 weekends/Bank holidays. Closed Mondays except Bank holidays.

Ancient woodland, predominantly small leaved lime, oak, hazel, ash, birch covers some 140 acres. A further 360 acres of mixed conifer plantings including Corsican and Scots pine, larch, Douglas fir, oak and beech. Approx 120 acres including formal grounds and parkland with a fledgling arboretum under establishment. Mature avenues of oak, lime, horse chestnut. Part of the woodland leased to Forest Enterprise. Management objectives include timber production, landscape and wildlife conservation. Coppicing has been reintroduced to the ancient woodland areas. A wide variety of plant and animal life in this rich mix of woods, glades, trackways, ponds and parkland.

*Norsey Wood

(Basildon District Council) **F** 75ha
O.S.S. 167 - TQ 680 951
01277 624553

The wood is located to the NE of Billericay via Norsey Road from the High Street. There is a car park which is always open, Information Centre (closed on Sundays), toilets, disabled facilities and guided walks.

Norsey Wood is an ancient coppice woodland with the main species being sweet chestnut, hazel, oak, alder and larch. Coppicing is still being carried out with a patchwork of clearings being created. The site is also a scheduled Ancient Monument containing Bronze Age tumulus, Roman industrial area and an extensive earthbank known as "Deerbank".

Pound Wood

(Essex Wildlife Trust) **F** 22ha
O.S.S. 178 - TQ 818 886
01206 729678

Take Daws Heath Road from the A129, S of Rayleigh Weir. Parking is limited on adjacent streets off Bramble Road. There are no facilities.

A large wood with complex geology reflected in the mosaic of hornbeam and sweet chestnut woodland. Wild service tree is locally abundant and bluebells carpet large areas. Wood ants are noticeable. Several streams cross the wood. Recoppicing has produced a vibrant show of flora, insects and birds. There are fine early medieval woodbanks, a dam, several ponds and dells.

Rawreth Hall Wood

(Anglian Water Services Ltd) **F** 2.41ha
O.S.S. 178 - TQ 830 905
01223 372612

Coming into Rayleigh from the N, on the A129, follow the road under the railway onto the A1015. Take the left into Connaught Road and park at the entrance to the sewage works. Follow the path over the footbridge and take a right after 200 yards to reach Rawreth Hall Woods. PLEASE DO NOT OBSTUCT THE ENTRANCE TO THE SEWAGE WORKS.

This ancient woodland adjoins the northern boundary of the Rayleigh East Sewage Treatment Works. The wood is uniformly stocked with hornbeam coppice and oak standards (pendunculate and sessile). Hornbeam coppice has a limited geographical distribution and is mainly found in Essex and Hertfordshire. The wood is a relic of the Rawreth Hall Estate woods which were owned by St. Johns College, Cambridge until the 19th century. The hornbeam was used primarily as firewood, having excellent burning qualities. Anglian Water has restored the coppicing regime and hence improved the conservation value of the site. Continuing the traditional management of the area will result in the production of firewood from coppice working and, over a larger period, timber from standards.

Rowney Wood
(Forest Enterprise) **F** 84ha
O.S.S. 154 - TL 568 339
01394 450164

Midway between Saffron Walden and Thaxted on the B184, 1 mile W of Howlett End. Entrance on minor road opposite barracks at Elder Street.

Mixed woodland undergoing phased reversion to site native broadleaf species.

Shadwell Wood
(Essex Wildlife Trust) **F** 7.1ha
O.S.S. 154 - TL 573 412
01206 729678

The reserve is on the W of the road from Saffron Walden to Ashdon, about 1 mile before Ashdon. Entrance is the track leading beside "Barleycroft". Limited parking at the side of the track on the opposite side of the road. There are no facilities.

A small but rich ancient ash, maple, hazel wood, with a secondary oak woodland on old meadow, and rich ride flora. Now back in a coppice rotation, deer fencing is needed to exclude fallow deer. Oxlips are a feature, with orchids and bluebells. Cowslip, primrose and adder's tongue fern are present in a glade in the old meadow. Dormice are present and many woodland butterflies.

*Stour Wood
(Woodland Trust; leased to RSPB) **F** 54ha
O.S.S. 169 - TM 191 310
01255 886043

Approx. 5 miles W of Harwich on B1352 (Harwich to Manningtree Road), close to Wrabness village. Bold entrance sign. Car park, observation hides overlooking adjacent estuary, marked trails, entire reserve area totals 317ha. Access is free but a donation to RSPB would be appreciated. Regular guided walks - reserve leaflet available from warden 35p (telephone as above). Warden available for lectures. 1 mile wheelchair trail available in drier seasons of the year.

Stour Wood is an extensive area of sweet chestnut with a long history of coppice management. In parts of the reserve woodland tumbles down to the sea at Copperas Bay (Stour Estuary). The woodland supports a range of breeding birds including the nightingale, 25 species of butterfly, including the white admiral - its only site in Essex. Plants include the wild service tree, a wonderful showing of wood anemones and paths arched with pendulous sedge. The nearby estuarine sections of the reserve support large numbers of waterfowl between Aug and Apr. The woodland is very much a 'working' wood supplying timber needs for other RSPB reserves in the region.

Weeleyhall Wood
(Essex Wildlife Trust) **F** 32ha
O.S.S. 168 - TM 156 212
01206 729678

The reserve lies off a private road leading from the A133 SE of Weeley. Limited parking by the church. There are no facilities.

A large non-intervention area has been left from the 1987 storm. It contains dangerous trees and must not be entered. One of the largest woods in Tendring, largely oak high forest with areas of sweet chestnut and hazel coppice, and a Scots and Corsican pine plantation. Also a stream with alder coppice and rich ground flora including moschatel. Bluebells carpet much of the wood which is visually at its best in May. Nightingales and dormice are recorded, other birds and woodland butterflies are well represented. Natural regeneration is rapidly healing the scars of the 1987 storm clearance. Coppicing and thinning are also carried out.

West Wood

(Essex Wildlife Trust) **F** 24ha
O.S.S. 167 - TL 624 332
01206 729678

The reserve is midway between Thaxted and Great Sampford off the B1051. A track (bridleway) leads from the road, 1 mile NE of Thaxted. There is limited parking but no other facilities, and no charges.

A wet ash, maple, hazel wood on chalky boulder clay with abundant oxlips and orchids. Formerly extensively planted with Norway spruce; remaining blocks are being thinned. Recoppicing in progress to rejuvenate hazel coppice, involving brushwood deer fencing to exclude fallow deer. Dormice are present, and birds include goldcrest, redpoll and several species of warbler.

GLOUCESTERSHIRE

Gloucestershire

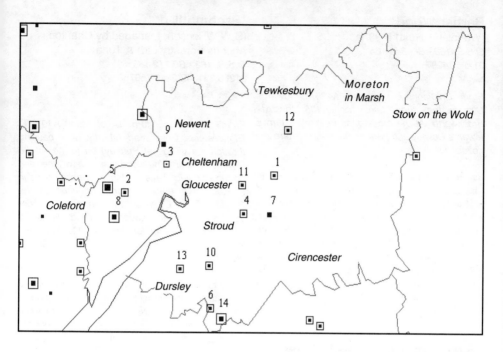

1. Barber Wood
2. *Beechenhurst*
3. *Broomhill
4. Frith
5. *High Meadow Woodlands*
6. Midger
7. *Miserden Estate Woodlands
8. Nagshead Nature Reserve
9. *Newent Woods
10. *Owlpen Estate
11. Popes Wood
12. *Queens Wood -Southam
13. Stancombe Wood
14. *Westonbirt Arboretum*

Barber Wood

(Woodland Trust) **F** 39ha
O.S.S. 163 - SO 946 164
01476 74297

From Cheltenham take the A435 S towards Cirencester, then take the A436 towards Brockworth. At the crossroads in 2 miles turn L towards Cowley and park on the verge. There are no facilities.

Barber Wood lies midway between Gloucester and Cheltenham and affords wonderful views of the Forest of Dean to the W, and the Malvern Hills to the NW. It is a Woodland Creation project and over 2800 trees, including ash, field maple and oak have already been planted. A variety of species including spindle and guelder rose will be planted to form a shrub layer. The grassland at the S side is of importance for the conservation value of species such as devil's bit scabious and quaking grass.

*Beechenhurst: Forest of Dean

(Forest Enterprise) **R** 10ha
O.S.S. 162 - SO 614 120
01594 833057

£1 WC

Beechenhurst Lodge is signposted off the B4226 between Coleford and Cinderford in the heart of the forest near the Speech House. Hotel. Car parking (£1), toilets with disabled access, forest cafe and shop, picnic area, barbecues, forest trails. The cafe is open 364 days per year. Educational groups should book well in advance.

The Forest of Dean is a working forest producing 70,000 cubic metres of timber each year. Beechenhurst Lodge sits at the heart of the forest. People, sheep and deer wander at will. The internationally known sculpture trail starts here. The sculptors were invited to the Dean to create works inspired by the forest, its industrial heritage and its wildlife. The result is a delight for the artist and layman alike. The Beechenhurst area also has large open areas for games and quiet enjoyment. The Cannop Ponds nature reserve is a short stroll away, as is Russells Inclosure.

*Broomhill

(S W Wilkinson, managed by Charlton Abbotts Forestry Ltd) **A** 10ha
O.S.S. 162 - SO 712 185
01285 831342/0249 750758

From Gloucester turn L off the A40 (T) Gloucester - Ross road (shortly after passing through the village of Huntley) on to the A4136 Monmouth road. The wood is mile down the road on the RH side. Teas in Huntley, public house in Blaisdon. No entrance fee; donations to the Forestry Trust. Open on 1st Sunday in October 1994, 1130am to 3.30pm. Guided walks by Woodland Manager starting at 11.30am and 2.00pm. School visits (by appointment) will be welcomed.

Broomhill Wood is an ancient, semi-natural woodland containing a wide range of crop types including stored coppice, chestnut coppice, larch, pine, coastal redwood stands, mature oak compartments, mid rotation oak and ash, areas of natural regeneration .

Frith

(Gloucestershire Wildlife Trust) **F** 25ha
O.S.S. 162 - SO 878 088
01452 383333

Beside the B4070 at Bulls Cross between Stroud and Birdlip. Car parking for 20 cars or 2 coaches. No other facilities. There is fully open access to the wood via right of ways and bridleways. Guided visits can be arranged by contacting Dr McGlone on the above telephone number. Please book well in advance.

A beautiful beech wood in spectacular Cotswold (AONB) country opposite Painswick and above the Slad Valley. Miles of good level tracks and views, an SSSI with a good range of wildlife associated with limestone habitat. Plants, including fungi, invertebrates and the usual range of animals.

High Meadow Woods: Forest of Dean/Wye Valley
(Forest Enterprise) **F** 1425ha
O.S.S. 162 - SO 563 160
01594 833057
🚗 🍴 WC ♿ ☕

Follow B4432 from Christchurch near Coleford. Facilities include car parking (Symonds Yat £1), toilets, orienteering course, disabled access, cafe, shop, forest trails. Please do not pass the fence in front of the cliff at Symonds Yat Rock; the cliffs are dangerous.

The ancient Forest of Dean is a working forest producing some 70,000 cubic metres of timber each year. High Meadow is a mixed broadleaved and conifer area alongside the River Wye. Symonds Yat Rock provides the focus with excellent views from the cliff tops. Peregrine falcons nest regularly on the cliffs adjacent to the rock. Forest trails wind through the forest offering the chance to spot a host of wild animals and plants.

Midger
(Gloucestershire Wildlife Trust) **F** 41ha
O.S.S. 162 - ST 794 892
01452 383333
🚗5 ⬤ ℹ

From M4 junction 18 go N on A46 for about 6 miles. Turn L 1 mile after Starveall. The car park is some 600m on the L. the wood is in the R. Please keep to the waymarked paths.

Ancient woodland of ash, oak and field maple, with some wych elm, crab apple and holly. Hazel dominates a dense understorey, which also contains goat willow, dogwood, privet, wayfaring tree and guelder rose. Many flowering plants and ferns. 29 species of butterfly and excellent bird life.

*Miserden Estate Woodlands
(Major M T N H Wills) **AD** 300ha
O.S.S. 163 - SO 938 088
01285 821303

🚗20 🍴 ☀ ☂ 🏕 🏠

Follow signs to Miserden off A417 Cirencester - Gloucester road or off B4070 Stroud - Birdlip road. There is parking for 20 cars, there are no WC facilities. The garden is open Tues, Wed and Thurs, 9.30 - 4.30, 1 Apr - 30 Sept. The garden nurseries are open daily, except Mon. There is access through the wood via rights of way, bridleways and a self guided trail (please keep to the marked trail). An illustrated pamphlet (50p) covering the trail is available at the estate office or from the village shop. Please give 1 weeks notice for group visits. There will be a charge of £2 for guided visits (children free), £1.80 for group bookings. Donations to the Forestry Trust. For further details and bookings please contact the estate office at Miserden Park, Stroud Glos, GL6 7JA, or telephone above number.

The woodland straddles the banks of the River Frome, a tributary of the River Severn which runs N to S. All the woodland is on steep or sloping ground. The woodland, predominantly pure beech, was clear felled during World War 2. Pockets of mature trees still exist although 80% of the woodland has been planted post 1945, with planting continuing until 1967. Small areas have been planted more recently, principal species being beech, sycamore, ash, European larch, Norway spruce and Scots pine. Some fine Douglas fir are to be seen. The Estate won the Dulverton Flagon for best managed woodland in 1989.

Nagshead Nature Reserve: Forest of Dean
(RSPB/Forest Enterprise) **F** 308ha
O.S.S. 162 - SO 607 085
01595 562852
🚗30 🍴2 ☂ 🏠

The reserve entrance is signposted on the B4431 immediately W of Parkend village. An information centre is open at weekends and Bank Holidays from mid-April to the end of August.

Nagshead has been an RSPB reserve since 1974 and is also an SSSI. The bird population is outstanding, featuring birds of both upland and lowland broadleaved woodland, including pied flycatcher, buzzard, wood warbler, hawfinch and turtle dove. Over half the reserve is 19th century oak plantation, the remainder being young broadleaves and some conifer stands.

*Newent Woods

(Mrs Torill Freeman) **A** 280ha

O.S.S. 162 - S0 705 227

01452 830209

From Newent drive for 2 miles along the B4216 (signposted to Huntley) to take 3rd turning on R (signposted May Hill/Glasshouse). Drive for 1.5 miles to T junction, turn R, carry on for 1/2 mile. There are rights of way through the wood and guided visits can be arranged by appointment with Mr Simons. Write to Huntley Estate, Woodend Farm, Huntley, Glos, GL19 3EY or telephone above number. (Alternative Numbers 01452 831349 and 01860 586418). Notice is required for visits. Newent Wood is approximately 10 miles W of Gloucester, on the NE slope of May Hill.

The present mixed woodland rises from the 250 ft contour to the 900 ft contour in its 1.5 mile length and occupies an ancient semi-natural woodland site. Its numerous springs and streams help to create many varied and interesting habitats for indigenous flora and fauna. Predominant tree species include oak, Douglas fir, sweet chestnut, and larch species. Although a commercial woodland, compartments of different aged trees are undergoing various silvicultural treatments, including many acres of worked sweet chestnut coppice, to produce high quality timber and rich wildlife habitats.

*Owlpen Estate

(C N Mander) **R** 55ha

O.S.S. 162 - ST 804 984

01453 860261

The hamlet of Owlpen is 1/2 mile E of Uley, off the B4066 3 miles E of Dursley. There is a licensed restaurant at the manor when the house is open.

Adequate parking. 9 holiday cottages. Two public footpaths lead through the woods from the vicinity of the manor house. The manor is open to the public Apr - Sept, Sun, Tues, & Thurs and Bank Hol. Mons, also Wed in July and Aug. Information, educational materials and plans available at the manor. Stroud District Council publish maps with recommended walks through the woods.

Traditional Cotswold edge beech woodland and associated limestone flora. The boundaries of the woodland today are much the same as in the earliest 18th century records, and they have been long managed for the production of quality beech and for conservation. After heavy felling during the two wars, there is good regeneration of mature beech in uneven-aged woods now being actively thinned to provide diverse habitats. There are a number of archaeological and historical features on this ancient estate centred on a celebrated Tudor manor house and its outbuildings in the Cotswold AONB. Small 1960s softwood plantations, and ash. Roe deer and badgers are prolific.

Popes Wood

(Mrs D D Walmsley) **F** 25ha

O.S.S. 162 - SO 875 126

Take lane off A46 behind "Royal William" public house, 2 miles NE of Painswick. There are no facilities, but good tracks. Please keep to these tracks with dogs under control.

Fine beech mixed natural regeneration. National Nature Reserve on Cotswold scarp.

*Queen's Wood: Southam

(Mr & Mrs P G Adlard) **A** 23ha

O.S.S. 163 - SO 974 254

01242 579334

Park in lay-by near de la Bere Hotel. Walk diagonally across field opposite to gate on gravelled track entering wood on the Western edge. There are no facilities nor public rights of way

within the wood but walkers with dogs under control are welcome with the owners' permission.

Queen's Wood is a semi-natural woodland of ash, oak and wych elm with 30 year old plantations of beech, larch and other conifers. Bluebells are spectacular in season. Public footpaths adjoining wood lead to a limestone grassland SSSI and Cleeve Common.

Stancombe Wood
(N D Barlow) **F** 30ha
O.S.S. 162 - ST 741 979

Park in parking lot on Stinchcombe golf course. The wood is always open, there are no facilities and no charge is made for access.

From the top of Stinchcombe Hill, there are spectacular views of the Severn Vale. The woods are made up of old established mixture of beech, larch and sycamore. Healthy growth of wild flowers.

Westonbirt Arboretum
(Forest Enterprise) **R** 240ha
O.S.S. 163 - ST 854 900
01666 880220

A433 3 miles S of Tetbury. Facilities include ample parking for cars and coaches, a visitor centre with gift shop, exhibition and video presentation, courtyard cafe and a plant centre specializing in trees and shrubs. There are 17 miles of waymarked trails and the grounds are open 365 days a year but the facilities are only fully open from Mar to Dec. Charges are £2.60 for adults, £1.70 for senior citizens and £1 for children. Educational visits by appointment. (See special feature on page 252).

Westonbirt is the largest arboretum in the country and one of the most important in Europe. It is particularly renowned for its autumn colours and spring flowers.

GREATER LONDON

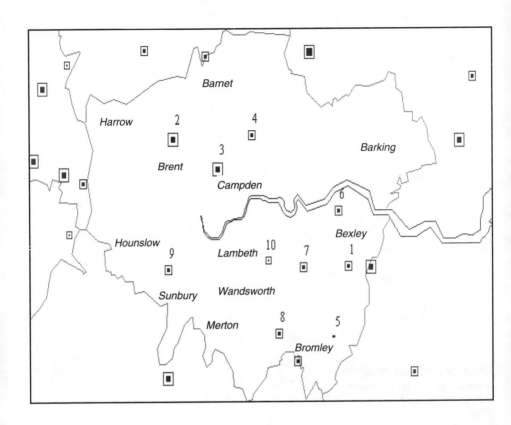

1. Chalk Wood
2. Fryent Country Park
3. Hampstead Heath
4. Highgate Wood
5. Hockendon Wood
6. Lesnes Abbey Woods
7. Petts Wood: Chislehurst
8. Rookery Estate Woods
9. Sheen Common
10. Sydenham Hill Wood

Chalk Wood
(London Borough of Bexley) **F** 26ha
O.S.S. 177 - TQ 494 708
0181 309 6638
🛉🙂 ● 🦌 ☂

Off A223 heading S turn L into Parsonage Lane. At top of lane, dirt track leads to Chalk Wood. Track is not suitable for domestic vehicles. The wood is open 24 hours daily. Permitted bridle path around perimeter of wood.

Ancient ash / maple wood converted to sweet chestnut coppice. Forty two ancient woodland indicator species including green hellebore and solomon's seal. Winter roost of long-eared bats. At least 265 species of invertebrates, only a small number of total probably present. Two acidic meadows, one having Melampyrum pratense (common cow-wheat), a rarity in the London area. Hazel coppice regime started in 93/94.

Hampstead Heath
(Corporation of London) **F** 272ha
O.S.S. 176 - TQ 260 850
0181 348 9908
🛉🙂 ● WC ♿ ⓘ ☂🅿️ ■ ♞

Underground to Golders Green or 210 bus Hampstead (British Rail). Gospel Oak area of heath has children's play areas plus cafe. Golders Hill Park has a children's zoo. There are WCs, including for the disabled. There is fully open access to the heath with rights of way on foot and horserides, not bridleways.

Undulating open space including a small area of ancient woodland at Kenwood. There is no real heath left but 29 ponds, including 2 at Kenwood, and some acid grassland remain. Wildlife ranges from grass snakes and slow worms to purple hairstreak and gatekeeper butterflies, plus nine species of dragonfly.

*Fryent Country Park
(Brent Council) **F** 100ha
O.S.S.176 - TQ 196 877
0181 900 5659
🛉🐕 ● ⓘ ☂

Accessible on foot from either side of Fryent Way and from roads adjacent to the Country Park. By car; as above, but a car park is situated on the W side of Fryent Way approximately in the centre of the Country Park (i.e. at the above grid reference). Kingsbury and Wembley Park underground stations are within walking distance. There are many footpaths. For leaflets and events programme telephone above number.

A deciduous community woodland. Managed by Brent Council and local volunteer groups. Woodland includes a Humphrey Repton woodland dating from 1793, 10 km of hedgerows, scrub, oak coppice, elm coppice and recently planted woodlands (circa 15,000 trees planted). Multi-purpose forestry is practised: much of the woodland is now being coppiced. The volunteers run a tree nursery, using local seed and providing several hundred trees a year. Wildlife of lowland farm woodlands. Wild fruits, meadows and over 20 ponds.

Highgate Wood
(Corporation of London) **F** 28ha
O.S.S. 176 - TQ 280 870
0181 444 6129
🛉 ● WC ♿ ⓘ ☂

Nearest station is Highgate underground station, main entrance off Muswell Hill. WCs, including disabled. Children's playground, vegetarian cafe, pathways suitable for disabled access. No cycling allowed. Network of easily accessible pathways open 7.30 am to 30 minutes after sunset, 365 days a year. Guided visits can be arranged, contact Parks and Gardens Department on 0181 472 3584, or Manager, Highgate Wood on 0181 444 6129. The site is patrolled by Corporation staff and there is an Information Centre.

Originally part of the old forest of Middlesex, Highgate Wood was dedicated as "an open space forever" in 1886 after being offered to the Corporation of London in 1885 by the Ecclesiastical Commission. Dominant tree species include oak, hornbeam and beech. There is also a diverse herbaceous understorey. A large variety of bird life has been recorded; 70 bird species, including nesting birds, which remain throughout the year and migratory birds which use the wood as a feeding station. Excavations of the site undertaken in

1962-74 led to discovery of kilns, pits and ditches and established that it had been used by potters at about the time of the Roman conquest in AD43.

picnic areas beside the formal gardens, and the ruins of a 12th century Augustinian abbey attract many visitors. The woods contain deposits of tertiary age fossils, and digging for fossil sharks teeth can be arranged by appointment.

Hockenden Wood

(Naturist Foundation) **A** 20ha
O.S.S.177
01689 871200

Write for appointment (weekdays in autumn and spring) and directions: Naturist HQ, Orpington, Kent, BR5 4ET.

50 acres of woodland/parkland including several acres of coppiced chestnut. Variety of specimen trees. Ancient woodland mentioned in Domesday Book. Extensive wild bird population. Wild flowers under woodland canopy. Fauna includes foxes, squirrels, voles, rabbits and badgers. Recreational facilities developed within the estate will not be in use at the time of visits, but the Foundation welcomes enquiries from those who wish to benefit and help their work.

Lesnes Abbey Woods

(London Borough of Bexley) **F** 88ha
O.S.S. 177 - TQ 478 787
01322 351150

By rail: Abbey Wood Station. By bus: London Transport routes 99 and 469 between Erith and Woolwich both pass the woods. By car or by foot: 600m E of the centre of Abbey Wood on the B213. Off-site parking available in Abbey Road (B213) and New Road. Toilets and information centre open 9.00 am until dusk, every day.

These ancient semi-natural woodlands are mainly stored coppice with oak standards but are very varied. The display of wild daffodils in early spring is famous throughout SE England. Bluebells and other flowers also abound. The woods contain a Victorian ornamental woodland pond and a remnant of the heathland which once covered Bexleyheath. There are

Petts Wood: Chislehurst

(National Trust) **F** 45ha
O.S.S. 177 - TQ 450 687
01892 890651

The 45 hectares of Petts Wood includes Edlmann Wood, and is preserved as a public open space.

Petts Wood is so called after the Pett family who were royal shipbuilders from the time of Henry VIII to Charles II. William Willett, the founder of British Summer Time, who was an active Chislehurst resident, is commemorated in Willett Wood. It is an ancient, semi-natural wood with predominantly oak and birch.

Rookery Estate Woods

(Rookery Estates Co.) **F** 56ha
O.S.S. 177 - TQ 410 664
01981 240367

The woods lie 1 - 2 miles S of Bromley High Street and are bounded by Hayes to the W, Bromley Common to the E and the Croydon Road to the S. Access is from any public road or path. Please keep dogs on a lead.

This is ancient woodland all managed as coppice with standards. It is ecologically diverse, containing about eight stand types with large areas of two rare categories, lowland sessile oakwood and plateau alder. The flora is superb including some 45 ancient woodland indicator species and 35 native trees and shrubs. There are woodbanks, old pollards and an intricate natural drainage pattern as well as three miles of old rides and a rich bird life.

Sheen Common

(London Borough of Richmond) **F** 21ha
O.S.S. 176 - TQ 197 745
0181 332 2184

 WC [i]

Main entrance is off Fife Road, East Sheen - or go in from Bog Gate in Richmond Park - clearly marked on the "A to Z". Interpretive boards explain management. Pond dipping equipment/ ranger service, nature trail. Open 24 hours. Toilets available during day and when pavilion is in use. To borrow a pond dipping pack, ring the ranger on 0181 876 2382 or pick up a nature trail leaflet at the pavilion.

Sheen Common has a fascinating history. Once a golf course and rifle range, it has now developed into a delightful woodland. Birch trees host nesting woodpeckers and a nature trail will lead you to the pond with its dipping platform. Watch out for conservation projects which you can join in with or book up to borrow the pond dipping/survey equipment to study the site. Don't miss the Woodland Open Day held in May each year.

Sydenham Hill Wood

(London Borough of Southwark) **F** 9ha
O.S.S. 177 - TQ 344 724
0171 278 6612/3

[i] ⚘ ʇ

The main entrance is in Crescent Wood Road, SE26, which is off Sydenham Hill - which can be reached from either the A212 to the S at Crystal Palace, at the South Circular (A205), to the N by the Horniman Gardens, Forest Hill, SE23. Bus route 63 (Crystal Palace to King's Cross) stops right by Crescent Wood Road. Sydenham Hill Station is 10 minutes walk. Limited car parking on Crescent Wood Road. Self-guided trail, information leaflet available, numerous events.

The wood is part of the largest surviving fragment of the historic Great North Wood - an economic resource for charcoal, timber and tanning - and today exhibits the results of varied recent history - old Victorian gardens and an old railway trackbed. Almost 200 species of flowering plants are present, together with a

multitude of fungi, birds and insects - notable species include all 3 woodpeckers, chiff-chaff, treecreeper, wild garlic and wood anemones under the dominant trees of oak, hornbeam, ash and yew. Declared a Local Nature Reserve in 1990.

GREATER MANCHESTER

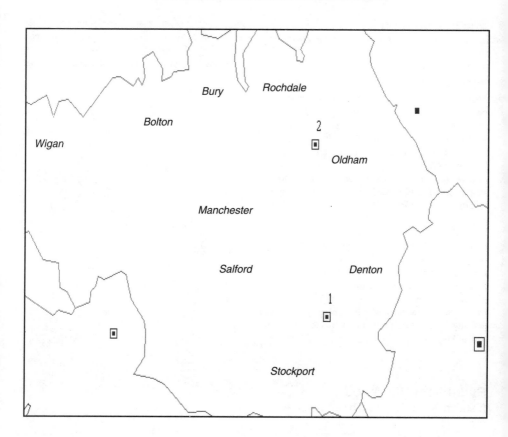

1. Hulmes Wood
2. Tandle Hill Park

Hulmes Wood

(Tameside Metropolitan Borough Council) **F**
10ha
O.S.S. 109 - SJ 923 937
(0161 342 3306

🚗🚌🚉🔔○🎈❋ⓘ🦅🔔🚩

From Denton, take A6017 signposted Stockport. After 1.5 miles there is a lay-by, opposite a sewage treatment plant. Entrance to wood is via the gate/stile at this lay-by. Bridlepaths, footpaths.

Part of Transpennine trail. A small piece of ancient woodland bordering the river Tame. The woodland was the site of Hulmes mine, and industrial archaeology from the mine is still visible. A small pond has been created on the site of one area of the mine, and this pond is a haven for wildlife.

Tandle Hill Park

(Oldham Leisure Services) **F** 22ha
O.S.S. 109 - SD 907 087
(0161 627 2608

🚗🔔🎈❋🧺🏕🔔🚽🚩

3 miles N of Oldham. Access is off A671 Oldham to Rochdale Road; turn into Tandle Hill Road. Country Park is signposted from the end of this road. The car park is at the end of Tandle Hill Road. Access is free. The Cafe is open at weekends 10.30 am to dusk during the winter, and 10.30 am to 4 pm in the summer, and week days 12 noon to 4 pm during the summer. Both summer and winter events leaflets are available. An orienteering course is in the park and maps for this are 90p from the Rangers office or the Cafe.

A magnificent beech woodland, planted historically in the early 19th century to prevent marching practice for the Peterloo Massacre, Manchester 1819. The Park was opened Sept 1919 and was a gift from Mr Norris Bradbury as a thanks offering for peace after the 1914-18 war. He wanted it to be used for people's enjoyment and freedom forever. The Rangers now look after the Park for both people and wildlife.

HAMPSHIRE & ISLE OF WIGHT

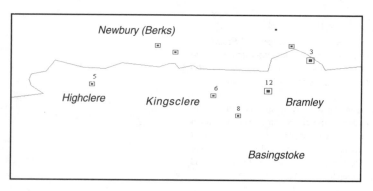

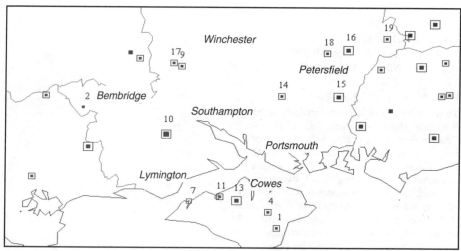

1. America Wood	11. Newtown Woods
2. *Ashridge	12. Pamber Forest
3. Benyons Inclosure	13. *Parkhurst*
4. Borthwood Copse	14. *Phrympth Wood
5. The Chase	15. *Queen Elizabeth Country Park*
6. The Holt	16. Selborne Common
7. Mill Copse	17. Spearywell Woods
8. Morgaston Wood	18. Stoney Brow
9. Mottisfont Woods	19. Waggoner's Wells
10. *The New Forest*	

America Wood: Isle of Wight

(Woodland Trust) **F** 11ha

O.S.S. 196 - SZ 568 819

01476 74297

America Wood is situated 1.5 miles W of Shanklin between the A3056 and the A3020 roads. There is at present no parking available immediately adjacent to the wood. This wood is unsuitable for wheelchairs. There are several public bridleways and footpaths leading to America Wood and it is best to park in nearby Shanklin or on one of the surrounding roads and walk to the wood.

America Wood is one of a few remnants of the deciduous woodland which once covered the Isle of Wight, and is a fine example of ancient oak and birch woodland. Bats inhabit some of the old hollow trees and America Cottages, next to the wood, have a resident population of pipistrelles. If you look up into the trees, you may catch sight of the red squirrels that live there. Hemlock water dropwort (known as "deadman's fingers") grows profusely in the damper areas of the wood and in the adjacent meadow amongst the goat willow. A special warning - hemlock water dropwort is poisonous so *please do not pick it!*

*Ashridge

(David J Dampney) **P** 30ha

O.S.S. 184 - SU 098 153

01725 518200

£1.80,£1.50,£0.50 WC

Take B3078 from Fordingbridge to Cranborne. Immediately W of Damerham, turn L 1/4 mile, turn R by telephone kiosk signposted. Coaches only by appointment. Open Sun and Bank Hol., Mon 9 Apr to 2Jul, also for National Gardens Scheme. A self guided nature trail of 2 miles, leaflet with map provided.

Through an arboretum to open country with 5 year old forestry spinney leading on to 30 acres of semi-ancient woodland. High forest of oak, ash with hazel coppice, some of which is still in rotation. There are ponds and clearings and a very varied fauna including green hellebores, helleborines, orchids and bluebells.

HAVEN WOODLANDS
Management of woodland, hedgerow & heathland habitats. Management plans & survey.
17 Archers Road, Eastleigh, Hants, SO509AQ.
Tel: 01703 496715

*Benyon's Inclosure

(R H R Benyon)**R** 180 ha

O.S.S. 175 - SU 625 640

01734 302504

From Mortimer going W towards Heath End, immediately after Mortimer West End. The wood is on the S side of the road. Roadside parking. Riding by permit only, details from above number. School and group visits welcome, by appointment.

A coniferous forest, principally of Scots pine with Douglas fir and scattered broadleaved species. There is mainly alder in the valleys and the wood is a County Heritage site.

Borthwood Copse: Isle of Wight

(National Trust) **F** 23ha

O.S.S. 196 - SZ 567 843

01983 526443

2m W of Sandown, 1 mile N of A3056. No facilities. For further information telephone above number.

Area of varied oak, ash and hazel semi-natural woodland with some very fine trees and some small plantations.

The Chase

(National Trust) **F** 56ha

O.S.S. 174 - SU 442 630

01256 881337

6 *3 miles SW of Newbury of W side of A343. Car park is off station road on the W side of the woods. No facilities. Telephone above number for further information.*

Mixed conifer and broadleaves. Open rides and young woods after 1990 storm. There is a lake.

The Holt

(Major R A Colvile) **F** 68ha
O.S.S. 174 - SU 557 617

On the B3051 N of Kingsclere.

The wood is mainly oak, fairly even aged. Worst areas were planted 1966-80 mainly with conifers, larch, Douglas fir, western hemlock and some poplar, red oak, cherry and nothofagus. Some natural regeneration of sallow, alder and ash. Ashford Hill Nature Reserve (English Nature) adjoins on N side. Apart from trees felled as part of thinning regime it will be many years before timber is obtainable. As most of the wood is on clay, gum boots or strong boots are usually advisable.

Mill Copse: Isle of Wight

(Wight Nature Fund) **R** 5ha
O.S.S. 196 - SZ 357 891

Park in local borough council car park off A3054 at Yarmouth. Walk along sea wall to old railway and then turn R then L onto footpath to wood. There are no facilities, nearest WC, Yarmouth, parking in council car park. A public footpath runs through the wood and there is no restriction on time of access. Please keep to obvious paths to prevent undue disturbance to wildlife.

An ancient woodland site with small area of hazel coppice, home to bluebells, orchids, dormice. Rest of wood is mixed conifer plantation including coastal redwood with clear felled areas being replanted with broadleaves. Paths allow views over Yar River and adjoining wet meadows. Management hopes to convert this plantation back to the splendour of a hazel coppice, typical of other West Wight woodlands.

Morgaston Wood - The Vyne

(National Trust) **F** 63ha
O.S.S. 175 - SU 625572
01372 453401

4 miles N of Basingstoke, midway between Bramley & Sherborne St John. Limited car parking adjacent to wood. Ample parking with shop and tea room, April-Oct at The Vyne house - woods signposted from garden.

Semi-natural oak woodland and mixed plantations. Close to The Vyne house and garden.

Mottisfont Woods

(National Trust) **F** 52ha
O.S.S. 185 - SU 316 276
01794 341257

N on B3084 from Awbridge to Broughton, cross level crossing at Dunbridge - 1.25 miles - Spearywell Wood and car park on left. Other woods on the estate also open to visitors. Tea shop in village. Close to Mottisfont house and garden.

A mixture of managed plantations and semi-natural woodland.

*The New Forest

(The Forestry Commission) **F** 26500ha
O.S.S.196/195 - SU 300 080
01703 283141

Guided walks available. Contact the education officer at the Queen's House, Lyndhurst. Educational Information Service available to groups, especially planning and advice before visits. A Permissions system exists for field studies (prior arrangements with the Forestry Commission - at least 4 weeks notice advisable). Ranger-led activities/field studies - charges available on request. New Forest Museum and Visitor Centre in car park at Lyndhurst (not

Forestry Commission) makes good starting point (Exhibitions, audio/visual programme)

The finest example of multi purpose forest management in the country, catering for such diverse interests as the growing of trees for timber, the pasturing of commoners' stock, the safeguarding of a biologically diverse ecosystem and the provision of facilities for recreation and education.

Newtown Woods: Isle of Wight
(National Trust) **F** 21ha
O.S.S. 196 - SZ 430 905
01983 526443

Midway between Newport and Yarmouth, 1 mile N of A3054. No facilities. Full and free access Telephone above number for further information.

Semi-natural hazel coppice with oak. Coppice is under active management. Look out for red squirrels.

Parkhurst: Isle of Wight
(Managed by Forest Enterprise) **F** 390ha
O.S.S. 196 - SZ 473 897
01420 23666

Parkhurst is signposted from the A3054 Newport to Yarmouth, about 2 miles from Newport. Facilities include car park, toilets, picnic area and educational facilities.

Parkhurst Forest is a mixed broadleaved and conifer woodland. The forest was mentioned in the Domesday Book in the 11th Century. The forest has diverse habitats including mature oak, plantation conifer, coppice, heathland and wetlands. An excellent education service has been established to promote understanding of woodland management, conservation and sustainability. This helps to meet the requirements of the national curriculum. in schools.

*Pamber Forest
(The Englefield Estate)**R** 180 ha

O.S.S. 175 - SU 625 605
01734 700155

Off A340 Basingstoke/Tadley road. About 1 mile S of Tadley turn E at Pamber Green. At Little London turn N towards Silchester. Forest Entrance is about 1200m on L. Riding by permit only, details from the above number. School and group visits welcome, by appintment.

Oak and coppice woodland, Pamber Forest is an SSSI run as a local nature reserve by Basingstoke and Dean Borough Council. The wood is renowned for its butterfly species including purpole emporors.

*Phrympth Wood
(Captain R F Phillimore RN (Ret'd)) **F** 22ha
O.S.S. 185 - SU 578 184
01730 265933

From Droxford on A32, at crossroads with B2150, take lane to Dundridge (2.5 miles). From Winchester, take the B3335 to Colden Common, B2177 to Bishops Waltham, thence N on the B3035, turn R into lane to Dundridge (1.5 miles). The Hampshire Bowman PH permits use of car park; access to the wood is via signed footpath 100 yards S, through farm. FP/BP runs full length of wood.

On a chalk slope of SW aspect with acidic cap erosion material in gullies and humus surface layers, this is an ancient woodland site with natural regeneration abundant and now part of management regime. Currently under 50% conifer cover from 1974 plantings, and a 1991 hardwood plantation replacing 1987 storm losses. Phrympth's special character is the great diversity of downland flora, including toothwort, broomrape, orchids including twayblades as well as many ancient woodland indicator species. Management practices used to maintain this diversity include biennial mowing of rides and removal of sycamore. Small shoot uses the wood as do local foxhounds; please respect these pursuits and keep clear of them. Unusual name, believed Saxon, appears in 16c tithe records as "Phrempth' (Bishop of Winchester's 12c Palace at Bishops Waltham is an English Heritage site).

*Queen Elizabeth Country Park

(Managed by Forest Enterprise in partnership with Hampshire County Council) **R** 600ha
O.S.S. 197 - SU 718 185
01420 23666

🏠 🚗 ⛺ WC ♿ ⛺ 🐕 🌳

The park is signposted from the A3 S of Petersfield. There is a car park for which there is a charge. Other facilities include a visitor centre and cafe, toilets, with all ability access, forest walks, ranger service. The forest centre is open 1000 - 1630 hrs.

The country park is located in the South Downs and is split between Butser Hill, an area on ancient downland, and War Down which is part of Buriton Woods. The woodland is predominantly beech, with a large range of flora and fauna. The park centre has education facilities and information, as well as a cafe and gift shop. The South Downs Way passes through the park as do a number of bridleways.

Selborne Common

(National Trust) **F** 108ha
O.S.S. 186 - SU 742 335
01428 683207

🚗 🐕 🌳

4 miles S of Alton between Selborne and Newton Valence W of B3006. Zig-zag path and woods are a short walk from car park in village. No other facilities. Telephone above number for further information.

Beech hanger woods on slopes around Selborne. Selborne Common is a large semi-natural wood of mainly oak, beech and hazel.

Spearywell Woods

(National Trust) **F** 52ha
O.S.S. 185 - SU 316 276
01794 341257

🚗15🐕

Travelling N on the B 3084 from Awbridge to

Broughton, cross level crossing at Dunbridge - 1.25 miles - Spearywell Wood and car park for 15 cars on L. There is a tea shop in village. Other woods on the estate also open to visitors. Full and free access with a choice of waymarked walks.

A mixture of managed plantations and semi-natural woodland.

Stoney Brow

(Sir James Scott) **F** 72ha
O.S.S. 186 - SU 688 304
01420 588207

🐕

1 1/2 miles S of East Tisted on the A32, turn R for Ropley, the wood is immediately either side of the public road. There is full access but no facilities. There are no public rights of way through the woodland.

Stony Brow is a semi-mature oak and beech, sweet chestnut coppice growing on a 30 year rotation. 10 year old mixed hardwoods and conifers, 20 year old pure Norway spruce and western hemlock, 25 year old Douglas fir, 40 year old mixed larch, oak and beech, 2 year old European larch in tree shelters. Area of natural scrubland with groups of natural regeneration of ash and birch; area of old mature broadleaves.

Waggoner's Wells

(National Trust) **F** 29ha
O.S.S. 186 - SU 863 344
01428 683207

🚗 🐕 🌳

1.5 miles W of Hindhead on S side of B3002. There is a car park but no other facilities. Telephone above number for further information.

Mature beech woodland and a series of picturesque lakes.

HEREFORD & WORCESTER

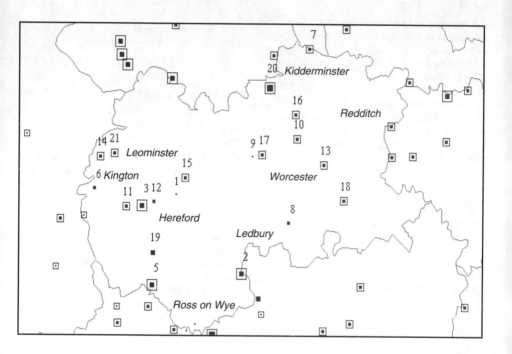

1. Coedgwen
2. *Dymock Wood*
3. *Garnons Hill Wood
4. The Hills Wood
5. Kentchurch Deer Park
6. * Kiln Ground Wood
7. Kingswood Country Park
8. *Langdale Wood & the Lills
9. Longfield Coppice
10. Monk Wood

11. *Monnington Wood
12. Nash Wood
13. Nunnery
14. Parkwood
15. *Queenswood Country Park
16. *Shrawley Wood*
17. *Tedstone Court
18. Tiddesley Wood
19. *Whitfield Woods
20. *Wyre Forest*
21. Yeld Wood

Coedgwen

(Jennie Guille) **P** 0.3ha
O.S.S.149 - SO 494 473
01432 - 830518

Off Hereford to Leominster road A49, turn L into Wellington; in 1/2 mile turn L for Auberrow/Burghill; in 1/2 mile turn L for Auberrow Common. There are no charges and no facilities. The wood is open 18 June to 8 July.

This new little wood - planted in 1987 mainly with ash and alder - leads to an ancient hay meadow enclosed with tall hedges, which is in the Countryside Commission Stewardship Scheme, and looks very colourful before it is cut for hay. The wood is enriched with Norway maple, hornbeam, lime, cherry, walnut, wild service and a few other interesting trees. It is managed for growing veneer quality or furniture timber for future generations, so any likely stems are pruned high. Others will be coppiced for firewood for use in the short term.

Dymock Wood

(Forest Enterprise) **F** 490ha
O.S.S. 149 - SO 679 285
01594 833057

From Gorsley on B4221, near Junction 3 on M50, follow minor road to Kempley village. There are car parks, forest walks, fishing and horse riding by permit from office.

The woodland is famous for the daffodils in spring.

*Garnons Hill Wood

(H R G Cotterell) **R** 110ha
O.S.S. 149 - SO 394 448
01981 22235

The only access is from village of Mansell Gamage. Turn off road by phone box. Small parking area at above OS reference but parking is entirely at own risk.. There are marked trails and no

charge is made for access. The wood is open from 1 Apr to 31 Oct during daylight hours. No dogs, bikes, or horses. Please keep to the waymarked routes. Do not touch squirrel hoppers. Forestry trails for the enthusiast.

Mixed woodland managed for production of quality timber. Beautiful views over Wye valley.

The Hills Wood

(The Penoyre Trust) **F** 6ha
O.S.S. 148 - SO 240 420

Take the B4347 from Hay on Wye towards Bredwardine. Approximately 3/4 mile outside the town limits a public footpath on the RH side of the road goes up into the wood on the far side of the hedge from a stone cottage.

The wood is on a steeply sloping bank, the upper slope being planted with mature oak, larch and a few Spanish chestnut, and the lower slope with spruce. If visitors walk above the conifers to the edge of the wood they will see in the adjoining field a stone obelisk built in 1830 as an unemployment project and a memorial to her father by Anna Maria Brodbelt-Stalland-Penoyre. The wood adjoins Mousecastle Wood, now owned by the Woodland Trust, which is also open to the public.

Kentchurch Deer Park

(J E S Lucas-Scudamore) **R** 100ha
O.S.S. 162 - SO 422 258
01981 500291

From Pontrilas A465 turn SE (B4347) to Kentchurch. Past church turn L up private drive to Kentchurch Court. There are no facilities. A charge of £1 will be made.

Kentchurch Deer Park is one of three fully enclosed deer parks left in the county, with a herd of upwards of 200 fallow. Within the park and surrounding it are woods of oak and conifers. Typical landscape with fine views.

*Kiln Ground Wood
(Lt Colonel E C Phillips) **A** 16ha
O.S.S. 148 - SO 267 488
01981 500282

Take A438 from Hereford. Turn R past Whitney Church signposted Brilley. Pass Whitney Church on R. Turn R on top of hill. Gate and stacking area 1/2 mile on L. By appointment only but there is no charge. There are rough rides.

Coppicing operation. Oak and cherry plantations '81/'86. Some larch and Norway spruce. Mid rotation oak and ash c.1971.

Kingsford Country Park
(Hereford & Worcester County Council)
F 81ha
O.S.S. 138 - SO 836 821
01562 710025

Follow signs from B4189 at Wolverly. Bus service 9/9A to Cookley Terminus (1 mile walk from park). Information and Educational material available from area office.

Between Kinver and Wolverly, Kingsford Country Park adjoins the National Trust land on Kinver Edge. The Park slopes gently covering 165 acres of cool pine forests, red sandstone outcrops, beautiful birch woods and open heathland. The commercial plantations are mainly Scots and European larch dissected by wide grassy rides. There are miles of footpaths including two self-guided trails (The Fox Trail - 40 mins, and The Deer Trail - 1.5 hours) and the sandy soil makes an ideal surface for the horse routes. This quiet and peaceful park almost guarantees an undisturbed walk or ride. The park overlooks some of the finest countryside in the area and is the starting point for the Worcestershire Way (50 miles), Staffordshire Way (92 miles) and the North Worcester Path (26 miles).

*Langdale Wood & The Lills
(Three Counties Agricultural Soc) **A** 25ha
O.S.S. 150 - SO 784 427
01684 892751

Follow Three Counties showground signs off motorway M5 and M50; B4208/4209 and road signs nr Malvern. Ample free parking. Open all year. All visits by appointment, notice only required for guided visits: Adults £2, Children £1, self guided visits: Adults £1, Children 50p. Leaflets available for each participant which explains various stops.

Planted in about 1890, Langdale Wood has a remarkably interesting and varied history. The wood was originally part of the Blackmore Estate and was probably planted to increase the shooting potential of the estate. During the last 80 years over 15 different timber species have been planted in blocks to increase the income from the wood. Good stands of oak, Douglas fir, western hemlock and western red cedar occur in the wood, although the storms of January 1990 inflicted much damage. Despite being only 100 years old, the wood has developed a remarkable variety of plants, birds and insects. Throughout the year some 38 different species of birds use the wood and in the summer 16 species of butterfly may be seen. These are largely dependent on the well developed layer of shrubs and bramble that occurs in the wood.

Longfield Coppice
(E W Evans) **A** 9ha
O.S.S. 150 - SO 705 564
01886 21431

Take gated road off A44 c.11 miles W of Worcester, 4 miles E of Bromyard. Call at first farm on R (Longlands). Longfield coppice is approx 1/2 mile from farm. As you come from Worcester on the A44, the turning onto the gated road is to the R, about 300 yards beyond the Whitborne turn at the Wheatsheaf Inn. As you come from Bromyard the turning L is very tight and it is safer to go past it to the Wheatsheaf, turn round in the car park and come back towards Bromyard in order to make the turn. Car parking is in wood (dry weather only).

Network of rides cut annually. Open all the year round by appointment, subject to timber operations. Please give as much notice as possible.

Longfield contains a great variety of woodland both in age and species. It grows exceptionally high quality oak, some of which has been harvested over the last 20 years. These felling areas, now restocked, illustrate different methods of establishing oak woodland. There are several stands of conifer, mature oak, ash, and many other species amongst the main crop trees. Longfield offers a picture of an evolving, uneven aged productive wood, with a wide range of wildlife habitats.

*Monk Wood
(Worcestershire Wildlife Trust) **F** 61ha
O.S.S. 150 - SO 804 606
01905 754919

2.5km W of A443 Holt Heath - Worcester road. Open dawn to dusk every day except Christmas Day.

Managed as coppice with standards until 1950. Until late 1980s used to grow and produce hardwoods for brush handles. Now managed as a combination of coppice with standards - mainly oak, some ash, silver birch, over hazel - and uneven aged high forest - many of the blocks are beech dominated planted by the previous owner. An expansive series of interconnecting rides and tracks meet at glades which are managed for the benefit of birds and butterflies. The rare wood white butterfly is found here. A medieval ditch crosses the wood. Many ancient woodland indicator species - wild service, small leaved lime, lily of the valley, orchids. The objectives of management are wildlife conservation, timber production and public recreation.

*Monnington Wood
(H R G Cotterell) **R** 30ha
O.S.S. 148/149 - S0 351 445
01981 22235

Turn off A438 (S0 357451) heading SW. Entrance to wood at above O.S. reference. Access and parking is entirely at own risk. Open from 1 Mar to 1 Aug during daylight hours. No dogs, bikes or horses. Please keep to the waymarked routes.

Mixed forestry. Lovely views over the River Wye from the Scar SSSI. Monnington walk and Wye Valley walk.

Nash Wood
(David Davenport) **P** 54ha
O.S.S 149 - SO 426 456
0198122 224

The rendezvous will be signposted from Mansel Lacy Church (O.S. Ref as above). Mansel Lacy is 7 miles W of Hereford on the A480. A guided walk lasting some 3 hours will be led personally by the owner starting at 2.30pm on Sunday, 2 July 1995. Plenty of hard standing for parking. No WCs. Dogs on lead only. Donations of £2 a person (children under 18 free) to the Forestry Trust.

Nash Wood is on the Foxley Estate which was landscaped some 200 years ago by Sir Uvedale Price. The landscape is listed Grade II. Mature groups or individual trees of oak, sweet chestnut, lime, Lebanon cedar, holm oak, beech, yew, acacia. Discussions will take place along the route on forestry, timber production, the landscape and flora and fauna.

*Nunnery Wood: Worcester Woods Country Park
(Hereford & Worcester County Council) **F** 20ha
O.S.S. 150 - S0 875 545
01905 766493

Approximately 3 miles from Junction 7 of M5 follow brown and whiite signs to Countryside Centre. Alternatively catch Citibus 28 and ask for Countryside Centre. Self-guided trails and map reading games available.

Over 20 hectares of ancient semi-natural woodland. Access at any time from nearby car park. Easy access trail for wheelchairs and pushchairs around 3 miles of woodland.

designated, the woodland supports a rich variety of woodland birds, whilst many of the glades in the arboretum have a spectacular display of spring flowers.

Parkwood
(R A Banks) **R** 16ha
O.S.S. 148 - SO 280 563
🏠 £1,£0.50 ⟵ ●

Kington is on A44 40 miles W of Worcester and 60 miles E of Aberystwyth (though by-passed). From Kington take Hergest road (signed Brilley etc), then first R Cutterbach Lane (very narrow) 1/4 mile to Haywood Common. Parking on common for 10 cars. Entrance Adults £1, children 50p. There are two public rights of way running through the wood, other paths through rhododendrons and ornamental trees open to paying visitors to Hergest Croft garden from Easter to end Oct and to others at all times, except weekends Oct - Jan - payment in box near cottage. All dogs mut be kept on lead, and please keep to paths and tracks.

About 7 hectares are planted with rhododendrons and exotic trees and shrubs which are exceptionally beautiful from Mar to Jun and again in autumn. The main wood consists of mixed age oak with understorey of beech and some conifers. It is a habitat for buzzards, ravens and badgers.

*Queenswood Country Park
(Hereford & Worcester County Council)
F 70ha
O.S.S. 137 - SO 506 515
01568 797052
🚗150🚌3↲🔄 ♦ ☀ ⚑ WC ♿ ℹ️ ⛉ 🎣
🥾 ⛺ 🚯 🎏 🏠

6 miles S of Leominster on A 49 Leominster to Hereford road at Dinmore Hill.. Open all year dawn to dusk.

Award winning arboretum (tree collection) with over 600 varieties of tree surround by the ancient woodland Local Nature Reserve of predominantly oak. SSSI

Shrawley Wood
(Managed by Forest Enterprise) **F** 85ha
O.S.S. 150 - SO 800 665
01584 874542
🚗 🛈

Entrance alongside post office 1 mile W of Shrawley on B4196. Park in New Inn car park. The landlady of the New Inn has kindly agreed to allow parking. Please patronise the pub. Informal walks only.

Shrawley Wood is a Site of Special Scientific Interest. Half the woodland area is an attractice matrix of small leaved lime.

*Tedstone Court
(R J Bellville) **R** 35ha
O.S.S. 149 - SO 710 570
01886 821304
🚗4↲🔄 ♦ ⚑ 🛈 🚯

From Worcester take A44 for 10 miles. Turn right at Wheatsheaf Inn. Follow signs to Tedstone Delamere. From Bromyard take B4203 to Stourport. After 4 miles take third turning right to Tedstone Delamere. Woodland open all year marked with 3 walks of different lengths. Some days of year woods will be closed. Notice at car park for information.

Wood was replanted wood in the 1960s with conifer and hardwoods and situated in a small beautiful valley with a trout stream at the bottom. Tree species include Norway spruce, larch, poplar, oak, ash, cherry and Douglas fir, and other native trees and shrubs. There are easy walking rides branching off a hard forest road. Wildlife includes brown trout, pheasants, buzzards and other birds. There are also dormice. There is also a deer farm which can be visited by appointment only.

Tiddesley Wood
(Worcestershire Wildlife Trust) **F** 75ha
O.S.S. 150 - SO 929 461
01905 754919
 FP

Take the A44 from Pershore towards Worcester - 1/2 mile out of Pershore take L towards Besford Bridge. Entrance to wood on L after 1.5 miles. Park on roadside. DO NOT BLOCK ENTRANCE GATES. Gated track leads into wood. Open dawn to dusk every day except Christmas.

Although some planting of conifers has taken place, much of the woodland retains its original broadleaf cover. Oak, ash, birch and others. Species such as wild service tree, midland hawthorn and herb Paris, restricted to ancient woodland, are present in good numbers. Spring flowering bluebells and primroses are an attractive feature. The wood is continuously worked. Management includes coppicing, thinning and the creation of warm glades and rides to encourage butterflies, birds and wild flowers. The objectives of management are wildlife conservation, timber production and public recreation. Keep clear of the fenced off rifle range: danger area when red warning flags are flying.

*Whitfield Woods
(G M Clive) **A** 400ha
O.S.S.149 - SO 423 335
01981 21375

Whitfield entrance is 8 miles from Hereford on A465. Turn R from Hereford. Meeting point 2 miles up drive. There are no facilities. The wood is open by appointment and charges are by arrangement. Educational parties are not usually charged.

Mixed woodlands surrounding parkland. Landscaped woodland walk, including pinetum with 1851 grove of Sequoia sempervirens (coast redwood). Old oak woodland, many 1960s onwards plantations, including oak, ash, softwoods. Many ornamental trees, including 1780 gingko, 1982 maple walk. Mixed plantations being converted to broadleaves. Native species such as wild service tree and small-leaved lime.

*Wyre Forest
(Managed by Forest Enterprise) **R** 1000ha
O.S.S. 138 - SO 753 740
01584 874542
(£0.80)

3 miles W of Bewdley on A456. Visitor centre, forest shop, refreshment bar, forest walks, car park - charge 80p. Visitor centre open 11.00 - 16.00 hrs. Forest events programme with 35 annual events available from district forest office. A forest classroom is available for parties. Please telephone for details.

Wyre is a very attractive ancient royal hunting forest which now has an exciting visitor centre and varied woodland walks, including an all ability trail. The visitor centre has a fascinating display on the history, wildlife and management of Wyre, including a living wood ants' nest. A leaflet illustrating the walks is available from the visitor centre, price 50p. The all ability trail is designed for families with pushchairs, and for people with walking difficulties or in a wheelchair.

Yeld Wood
(W L Banks) **R** 49ha
O.S.S. 148 - S0 284 568
01544 230160

Off A44 W of Kington, follow signs to Hergest Croft Gardens. Footpaths signposted. There are no facilities and there is no entrance fee. The wood is open daily all year round. A footpath runs the length of the wood - visitors may use the main rides only. Dogs on leads.

There is a fine stand of oak and beech about 200 years old at the E end of the wood. There are good stands of Douglas fir dating back to the 1860s and 1890s. Much of the wood was replanted following an ice storm in 1941. Wildlife includes buzzards, ravens and sparrowhawks and a good variety of smaller birds.

HERTFORDSHIRE

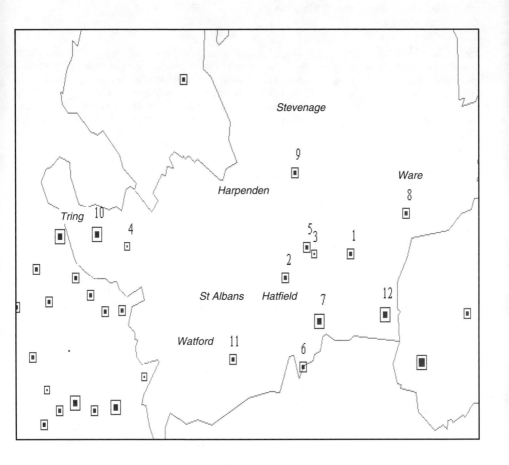

1. *Broxbourne & Bencroft Woods
2. *Bullens Wood
3. The Bushes
4. Hardings
5. Home Park
6. *Monken Hadley Common
7. Northaw Great Wood
8. Post Wood
9. Sherrardspark Woods
10. *Triing Park Estate
11. *Wall Hall Estate Woods
12. Wormley Wood

*Broxbourne and Bencroft Woods

(Hertfordshire County Council) **FE** 60ha
O.S.S. 166 - TL 328 069
01279 843067

⟶50⬜🏕 🏌 ⚲ ⬛

The woods are near the village of Brickendon, 3 miles S of Hertford. The location of small car parks in the wood is shown on the Ordnance Survey Landranger Map 166. Telephone the Countryside Management Service on above number if in doubt about how to drive to the woods. Alternatively, the woods are only a one mile walk away from Bayford railway station, to which there is a regular train service from London (Moorgate) and Stevenage. (Telephone 0171 278 2477 for timetable). There is parking for a total of approximately 50 cars in 4 separate car parks, where picnic tables are also provided. There are no other facilities in the woods, but refreshments and toilets are available in pubs in the nearby villages of Brickendon, Bayford and Wormley West End. There is a network of footpaths including public rights of way and other waymarked routes along which the public are permitted to walk. These and other County Council woods feature in the "Stepping Out" programme of guided walks which is organised by the Countryside Management Service. - telephone the above number for more information. Other guided visits for parties of 20 or more can be arranged with David Dench, Countryside Management Service Manager, Planning and Environment Dept, Herts County Council, County Hall, Hertford, SG13 8DN (Tel 01279 843067).

These ancient woodland sites are part of an extensive and spectacular tract of densely wooded countryside, Hertfordshire's distinctive "wild wood" scenery close to London. Broxbourne Wood comprises mixed broadleaf and conifer areas where work to protect and enhance wildlife habitats and the landscape is being successfully integrated with timber production. Bencroft Wood is a superb example of semi-natural oak, hornbeam and birch woodland which continues to be managed by traditional coppicing, perpetuating a varied woodland structure rich in wildlife.

*Bullens Green Wood

(Hertfordshire County Council) **F** 17ha
O.S.S. 166 - TL 214 065
01992 556230

Turn S off the A414 into the village of Colney Heath which is situated between St Albans and Hatfield. After 2/3 mile through the village, turn L at a roundabout on to Roestock Lane and drive 2/3 mile to the end of the lane. There is parking for cars and coaches along the roadside at the end of Roestock Lane. There are no facilities in the wood, but refreshments and toilets are available in nearby pubs in Colney Heath and Roestock. There is a network of footpaths including public rights of way and other waymarked routes along which the public are permitted to walk.

This is the first large new broadleaved woodland to have been created in Watling Chase Community Forest. The planting is already transforming a damaged urban fringe landscape next to the A1(M) motorway. A good place to see silvicultural practices used to establish trees and how new woods can be designed successfully to integrate environmental objectives with timber production.

The Bushes

(Marquis of Salisbury) **R** 4ha
O.S.S. 166 - TL 247 088
01707 264412

💷£2.60,£2.00🌳 🔦 🦌 wc ♿ ⅈ 📖🏕 🏌 ⚲🅿 ⬛🌳 🏠

Entrance directly opposite Hatfield railway station. 21 miles N of London, on Great North Road (A1000). Easy access from M1 and A1(M). 7 miles from M25. Open March - October every day, except Easter Monday and Good Friday, 10.30am - 8.00 pm daily (last entry 5pm to nature trails/play area).

Formerly ancient woodland containing many dead and dying trees which were felled and replanted in 1973 with a mixture of Japanese larch and hardwoods.

Hardings
(Richard Mabey) **R** 7ha
O.S.S. 165 - SP 946 095
10 Cedar Road, Berkhamsted, Herts HP4 2LA
🚗3🦌 ● ☀ 𝕐 ⓘ 💷

The wood is in Crawleys Lane, 1/2 mile NE of Wigginton. There are no facilities and visitors are welcome at all times. There are permissive footpaths only so please keep to them. No horses. Nature Trail and descriptive booklet available by post to owner's address, £1 p & p included.

A mixed deciduous ancient wood. Run as a community wood since 1981, with special attention to wildlife conservation. Very rich range of ancient woodland indicator plants and semi-natural stand - types unusual for the Chilterns.

Home Park
(Marquis of Salisbury) **R** 99ha
O.S.S. 166 - TL 245 095
01707 264412
💷£2.60,£2.00🚗🚌🚶👤𝕐 WC ♿ ⓘ
📖♿♿♿🖼💷🏕

Entrance directly opposite Hatfield railway station. 21 miles N of London, on Great North Road (A1000). Easy access from M1 and A1(M). 7 miles from M25. Open March - October every day, except Easter Monday and Good Friday, 10.30am - 8.00pm daily (last entry 5pm nature trails/play area).

Home Park is mainly ancient and semi-natural woodland which has been invaded by sycamore. There are some mixed conifer plantations of between 10 and 50 years old. Home Park has been under continuous tree cover dating back to the medieval period and beyond, when it was a wood pasture.There are still a few very ancient pollarded oaks which could well date from these early times.

*Monken Hadley Common
(The Trustees) **F** 74ha
O.S.S. 176 - TQ 275 972

Milnes & Milnes, Solicitor & Clerk to the Curators
23 Wood Street, Barnet.
🚗50🦌 ● ☀ 𝕐 ♿ 💷

Western approach: follow Barnet High Street N to Hadley Green. Cross Green to Monken Hadley Church. Pass through ancient gates. The Common and woods beyond now lie before you. Eastern approach is via Games Road, 1.5 miles NW of Cockfosters Station on the Piccadilly tube line. Apart from access at the W and E ends of its woodland, entry and exit are possible along its length at various points. The car park is at the foot of Bakers Hill off the metalled road which runs through part of the property.

Monken Hadley Common displays considerable variety in its relatively small area. A high open plain descends through mature deciduous woodland to a picnic area. The main BR route to the north bisects the woods beyond this point and is crossed by a bridge leading to a sunken lane flanked by thick woods leading to a further plain and thence to a large lake. Beyond woodland paths wend towards the eastern exit. Originally part of the Royal Chase of Enfield, the Common has been continuously owned by Trustees since an Act of 1771 made the land over from the Crown.

Northaw Great Wood
(Welwyn Hatfield Council) **F** 117ha
O.S.S. 166 - TL 284 043
01707 872213
🚗(£1)WC ⓘ ♿

Entrance off the Ridgeway at Cuffley on the B157. 2 miles from Cuffley Railway Station towards Hatfield. Car park closes 6.00pm in summer, 4.30pm in winter. Wood open 8am to sunset all year round. No vehicles allowed in wood. There is a warden on site, telephone number above.

Northaw Great Wood is a remnant of the extensive forest and woodland common that covered much of Essex and Hertfordshire before the Norman Conquest. Declared an SSSI in 1953 and obtained Country Park status in 1968. Sessile oak and hornbeam predominate throughout the area and provide cover for a range of interesting flora and fauna. Recent management work includes ride widening.

Post Wood
(East Herts District Council) **F** 22ha
O.S.S. 166 - TL 359 129
01279 655261 ext 485

Exit off A10 at Hertford A414 junction and take road off roundabout signposted to Gt Amwell. Take first exit off Gt Amwell road over A10 and first R down single track road. Car park 400m down track on L. The wood is across the playing field. There are no charges for entrance to the wood which is open daily all year round. The car park is also free, which is open from dawn till dusk. No WCs.

Oak/hornbeam ancient woodland on glacial gravels, dissected by three dry valleys. Good displays of bluebells in spring. The wood was cleared of sycamore in 1991 and restocked with oak, hornbeam and cherry. The eastern dry valley is managed and cut annually as a glade. It has a rich ground flora and a few very large specimens of wild cherry on the lower slopes. A good wood to see hawfinches.

Sherrardspark Woods
(Welwyn Hatfield Council) **F** 75ha
O.S.S. 166 - TL 228 138
01707 331212

Entrance in Rectory Road - car park next to Reservoir off Great North Road, B197, E of Ayot Green, or Campus West car park, access via old railway line footpath. Entry is free and the wood is open all year round. Pay on exit. Facilities include public footpaths, bridleways, display boards.

Sherrardspark Woods was designated an SSSI in 1986, because it is one of the larger remnants of ancient semi-natural sessile oak/hornbeam woodlands with associated flora in lowland England. Managed for recreation and conservation. Active woodland management taking place each year throughout Autumn and Winter, including coppicing and high forest management. Voluntary wardens patrol the wood daily.

*Tring Park Estate
(Lady Weiss) **F** 165ha
O.S.S. 165 - SU 942 089
0171 371 8500

Off A41 on minor road through Wigginton Bottom. There are no facilities but there is free and full access at all times by means of the many public footpaths that cross the property. For educational visits contact the agent on the above number.

A former Rothschild property, the woods contain some fine large beech, typical of the Chilterns and now being felled at the end of its rotation. Natural regeneration of beech, oak and birch is encouraged. Conifers, particularly larch, grow well, though they have been severely attacked by the edible doormouse, Glis Glis. Numerous nesting boxes have been installed by the Natural History Museum now housed in the former Rothschild mansion in Tring.

*Wall Hall Estate Woods
(Hertfordshire County Council) **F** 52ha
O.S.S. 166 - TQ 139 985
01992 556230

The woods can be reached easily via public footpaths from the nearby village of Aldenham, which is situated just off the B462 midway between Radlett and Watford. Alternatively, the Ver-Colne Valley walk leads out of Watford to the other side of the woods. Watford is easily accessible by train from London. There is roadside parking for cars in Aldenham, especially near the church and village green. There are no facilities in the woods, but refreshments and toilets are available in nearby pubs at Round Bush and Patchetts Green. There is a network of footpaths including public rights of way and other waymarked routes along which the public are permitted to walk. An interpretative woodland trail leaflet, produced in conjunction with Watling Chase and the Countryside Management Service, and the Ver Colne Valley walk leaflet can be obtained by telephoning 01707 050041.

These woods are some of the most varied and interesting woodlands in Watling Chase Community

Forest. The woods are partially ancient and semi-natural but are mostly mixed plantations, some of which are mature 'estate' planting dating from the 19th and 20th centuries. Many broadleaf and conifer species are present in these uneven aged woods where silviculture for high quality timber production is being successfully combined with wildlife and landscape conservation.

Wormley Wood
(Woodland Trust) **F** 138ha
O.S.S. 166 - TQ 330 060
01476 74297

From the A1(M) going S take the A414 road to Hertford and turn S towards Bayford before reaching the town, then follow signs to Wormley. There is a car park in the adjacent county council property of Bencroft Wood (the western car park) which via track No.1 gives access to Wormley Wood.

Wormley is a magnificent wood with a feeling of wildness and seclusion. The bird life of Wormley is one of its most notable features, with hawfinch, redstart and, if you are lucky, you might spot the green and great and lesser spotted woodpecker. Wormley Wood is almost entirely ancient woodland; both native oaks as well as hornbeam are present. You will see many different plants as you walk through the wood including sweet woodruff, bluebell and honeysuckle.

HUMBERSIDE

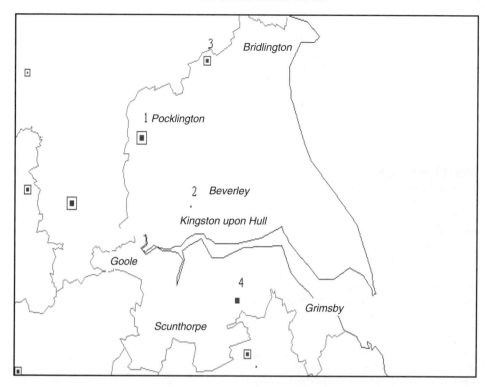

1. *Allerthorpe Wood*
2. The Arboretum
3. The Avenue
4. Elsham Hall Country & Wildlife Park

Allerthorpe Wood
(Forest Enterprise) **F** 150ha
O.S.S. 105/106 - SE 753 479
01751 72771

Turn SW off A 1079 0.5 mile W of Barmby Moor.

The Arboretum
(P W J Carver) **A** 0.5ha
O.S.S. 106 - SE 893 323
01430 422203

The Arboretum is situated in North Cave which is 1.5 miles from Junction 38 M62, 15 miles W of Hull. Entrance through oak handgate, east end of churchyard. Park on roadside. The Arboretum is strictly by appointment at any visiting time.

A small arboretum planted in 1990. Approximately 80 species in attractive setting adjacent to 12th century parish church. Mown paths meander round the planting which was laid out by David Garnett to replace early 19th century woodland. An encouragement to all who want to see "The glades be grown anew".

The Avenue
(Sir Tatton Sykes Bt) **R** 14ha
O.S.S. 101 - SE 938 647
01377 236221

Take the B1252 just SE of Sledmere village and follow Humberside County Council permissive footpath signs. There is no parking space on highway adjacent to wood. There is no entrance fee and facilities include toilets, cafe, exhibition at Sledmere House (in season only). Open when not closed by Humberside County Council "No Entry" signs - but mostly open throughout year except in shooting season. Dogs on lead only (HCC bye law) This is a permissive footpath only and not a bridleway.

The Avenue has mature hardwoods forming S boundary to Sledmere park - landscaped by Capability Brown circa 1780 - with recent replanting following gale damage with aim to restore landscape feature. Forest Condition Monitoring plot (Forest Authority) at eastern end. The outward route is through an avenue of beech circa 1750 and return through Sledmere deer park. This latter requires agility over ladder stiles to deer fence.

Elsham Hall Country and Wildlife Park
(Capt & Mrs J Elwes) **A** 150ha
O.S.S. 112 - TA 031 118
Elsham, Brigg, S Humberside, DN20 0QZ

M18 junction 5, follow signs to park.

Arboretum and gardens set in woodlands. Special trails, talks and good conference and catering facilities. Ideal for school visits or evening talks on forestry or gardening.

KENT

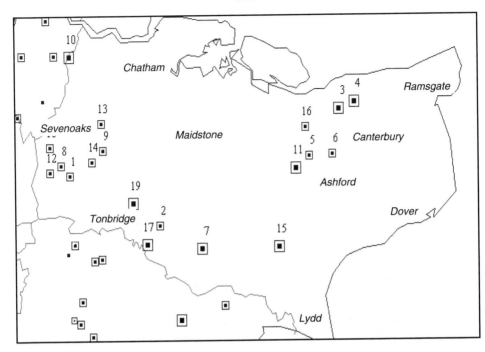

1. *Batfold, Bushy and Kilnhouse Woods
2. *Bedgebury Pinetum*
3. *Blean Woods Nature Reserve
4. Clowes Wood
5. Cutlers Wood
6. Denge & Pennypot Wood
7. *Hemsted Forest*
8. Ide Hill
9. Ightham Mote Woodlands
10. Joydens Wood

11. *Kings Wood*
12. Octavia Hill Woodlands
13. Oldbury Hill & Styants Wood
14. One Tree Hill
15. *Orlestone Forest*
16. Perry Wood
17. Scotney Estate
18. Toys Hill
19. *Tudeley Woods

*Batfold, Bushy & Kilnhouse Woods: Bore Place

(The Neil Wates Charitable Trust Commonwork) **F** 30ha
O.S.S. 188 - TQ 505 490
01732 463255

🚗20🚻2🔞🧎‍♂️🎈❄️🌳 wc ♿ ⓘ 📖 ⛺
♿FP 🚲🥾

Bore Place is SW of Sevenoaks, near Bough Beech reservoir. Take the B2027 which runs between Edenbridge and Tonbridge and follow the signposts to Bore Place. There is a free car park. Field Trail leaflet (30p). The woods are included in the Field Trail (total time needed at a leisurely pace: up to 2.5 hours).

Bushy Wood has been designated a Site of Nature Conservation Interests and with Batfold Wood is partly ancient woodland. Many examples of woodland flora and fauna including orchids, wild service trees, dormice, roe deer. The ancient practice of coppicing has been reintroduced and the woodlands are managed to provide a variety of economic uses as well as to maintain wildlife. Examples of environmental sculpture are also visible. The Field Trail also includes other copses and some interesting woodland ponds. Educational visits to Bushy Wood only can be arranged.

Bedgebury Pinetum

(Managed by Forest Enterprise) **F** 60ha
O.S.S. 188 - TQ 715 388
01580 211044

💷£1.80🚗🚻🔞🌲❄️wc⛺🥾♿🛍️

Take the A21 N from Flimwell and after about a mile turn R on the B2079 to Goudhurst. Entrance fees for 1995 season £1.80 for adults with concessions for children and senior citizens. Bedgbury Pinetum is the National Conifer Collection and contains over 4,000 specimens rpresenting 900 species and varieties of conifer; it is recognised as the best tree collection of its type in Europe.

The Pinetum is an attractive place to visit at all times of year. In spring there are rhododendrons and azaleas in bloom and in September and October there are varied autumn colours. National collection of coniferous trees. There is a great variety of fungi (protected) which are particularly abundant in autumn and uncommon birds such as hawfinch and crossbill are regular visitors.

*Blean Woods Nature Reserve

(RSPB) **F** 310ha
O.S.S. 179 - TR 122 594
01227 462491

🚗🥾🎈⛺

Take A290 Whitstable Road out of Canterbury, turn L after 1.5 miles into Rough Common, R after 500 yards, following stone track for 500 yards to car park where information leaflets are on sale. The car park is open from 7 am to one hour after sunset, but the reserve is open to walkers at all times. There is no entrance fee. If you must bring a dog, please keep it on a lead. 63 hectares of the reserve are leased from three local authorities. There are three waymarked trails - 1.0/1.75/ and 2.5 miles.

The reserve is one of the largest semi-natural, broadleaved woodland reserves in southern England, with extensive mature oakwood, plus managed coppice, rides, glades and heath. The wide range of breeding birds includes nightingale (about 30 pairs), redstart, wood warbler, tree pipit, kingfisher, and nightjar. One of the few remaining sites for the endangered heath fritillary butterfly. Management includes conversion of some of the sweet chestnut coppice (poor in wildlife) to mixed coppice or high forest; and limited felling of mature oaks to break up the uniform age structure. Production of quality timber is not a priority objective, but timber and coppice are harvested regularly in order to improve the reserve for wildlife. Reserve warden would be happy to show groups the extent to which these two aims are seen as being compatible at Blean Woods.

Clowes Wood

(Forest Enterprise) **F** 236ha
O.S.S. 179 - TR 137 629
01580 211044

🚗🧎‍♂️🌳

From the A2 roundabout in Chestfield take the minor road through Radfall towards Tyler Hill. The car park can be found on the R 50 yards after a sharp L hand bend. Horseriding is available via SE Toll Rides.

*Cutlers Wood

(T W Reed) **A** 56ha

O.S.S. 179/189 - TR 043 523

01227 730330

8 miles SW of Canterbury on A252, 2.5 miles from junction with A28. No charge for cars or coach. The first visit per family or group, with conducted tour, will be charged at £25, with 4 free visits within one year. Visits can be arranged at any time after sunrise until one hour before sunset all year round. These times can be extended for badger watching.

An ancient mixed woodland and undulating topography, with some planting but also long periods of neglect, have produced a wide range of trees, shrubs and ground flora. The mammals, which include dormice and badgers, are equally diverse. A ''no burning'' policy to increase the humus content of the soil has increased fungal and insect diversity. These in turn have encouraged insectivorous birds. Prime timber and care for the environment are the present objectives.

Denge and Pennypot Wood

(Woodland Trust) **F** 50ha

O.S.S. 179/189 - TR 105 525

01476 74297

Turn off the A28 Ashford to Canterbury road to Shalmsford Street and Chartham. Follow the road through the village and take the right hand turning towards Thruxted. After 3/4 mile turn left into Pennypot Lane towards Thruxted. Pennypot Wood is on the L of this lane after about 1 mile.

The structure of Denge Wood is varied, with a large area of sweet chestnut coppice. In other parts of the wood you will find a mixture of hazel and hornbeam coppice along with some fine yew and beech trees. Due to the mixture of habitats the wildflowers of Denge Wood, including bluebell, are a picture in spring and summer. The Warren, which is an area of shrubby grassland in the east of the wood, is one of the few places in Kent which supports a colony of Duke of Burgundy fritillary butterflies. Also around the area of the Warren you may hear the beautiful song of the nightingale.

*Hemsted Forest

(Forest Enterprise) **F** 404ha

O.S.S. 188 - TQ 813 344

01580 211044

From the cross roads at the W end of Benenden village turn N towards Sissinghurst. Take the next R turn opposite the entrance to Benenden School. The entrance to the car park is on the left after about 500 yards. Horse riding by permit.

Ide Hill

(National Trust) **R** 13ha

O.S.S. 188 - TQ 485 515

01892 896651

1 mile E of Toys Hill and 2.5 miles S of Brasted.

Wooded hillside overlooking the Weald.

Ightham Mote Woodlands

(National Trust) **F** 16ha

O.S.S. 188 - TQ 585 535

01892 890651

3 miles S of Ightham, 6 miles E of Sevenoaks, just W of A227. Entrance for visitors with disabilities to Scathes Wood, which has a trail for the disabled, is through a locked gate. The combination to the gate is available from the ticket office.

A broadleaved woodland, with disabled access via a circular walk, which was funded by Rotary International, District 112, Kent and East Sussex.

Joydens Wood
(Woodland Trust) **F** 137ha
O.S.S. 177 - TQ 500 720
01476 74297

Travelling N on the M25, leave at junction 3 and go through Swanley on the B2173. Turn into Birchwood Road on the NW side of Swanley. Then turn L into Summerhouse Drive. Park in Summerhouse Drive, with due regard to local residents. There is no fee for entrance to the wood and there are no facilities. The wood is accessible to pushchairs.

Joydens Wood contains a number of interesting archaeological features; perhaps the most significant is Faesten Dic (Dyke), which is referred to in a Saxon boundary survey of AD814. The ground is rich in flowers, over 300 species have been counted, and honeysuckle and wild clematis are found among the trees. Many native trees have survived and these support a varied population of woodland birds. Redpoll, jay and bullfinch are present in large numbers and turtle doves are summer visitors to the wood.

Kings Wood
(Forest Enterprise) **F** 514ha
O.S.S. 189 - TR 025 500
01580 211044

From the junction of the A251 and A252 in Challock village take the A251 towards Ashford. Take the next L (1/2 mile). The car park can be found on the L some 400 yards distant. The wood is permanently open and entrance is free. There are waymarked walks. Horse riding by permit.

Octavia Hill Woodlands: Toys Hill
(National Trust) **R** 42ha
O.S.S. 188 - TQ 465 512
01982 890651

Oldbury Hill and Styants Wood: Wrotham
(National Trust) **F** 61ha
O.S.S. 188 - TQ 582 561
01892 890651

On N side of A25, 3 miles SW of Wrotham.

The south half of an Iron Age hill fort of about 100BC.

One Tree Hill: Sevenoaks
(National Trust) **R** 14ha
O.S.S. 188 - TQ 560 532
01892 890651

2 miles SE of Sevenoaks on E side of Knole Park, between Underriver and Bitchet Common.

Site of supposed Roman burials. Wonderful views to the South.

Orlestone Forest
(Forest Enterprise) **F** 451ha
O.S.S. 189 - TQ 986 348
01580 211044

From Ham Street village take the A2070 towards Ashford. At the next crossroads (1 1/2 miles) turn L and then L again. The car park is on the R 50 yards beyond this junction. The wood is permanently open and entrance is free. There is a waymarked walk.

Perry Wood

(Swale Borough Council) **F** 59ha
O.S.S. 179 - TQ 045 558
01795 424341
←40○ **⊤ ▲**

From the A2 passing Faversham, turn towards Selling at the Macknade Garden Centre. Follow the road past the Sondes Arms. Take the 3rd L turn. Perry Wood is signposted. The wood is open 24 hours a day all the year. Perry Wood provides only for informal recreation - walking and horseriding. No other activities are permitted.

Perry Wood consists of several blocks of varied trees separated by bridle and footpaths. The largest blocks are sweet chestnut coppice stands felled on a 15 year cycle. Other areas include plantations of Scots pine, European larch and mixed native hardwoods. Following the 1987 storm large areas of very young native trees have now grown, particularly on the higher ground. The wood provides some very attractive walks detailed on the car park information board. There is also an excellent viewpoint looking over the canopy of the wood to the adjoining hop fields and orchards.

Scotney Estate

(National Trust) **R** 317ha
O.S.S. 188 - TQ 688 353
01892 890651

1.5 miles S of Lamberhurst on E of A21, 8 miles SE of Tunbridge Wells.

Woodland surrounding Scotney Castle Garden, a famous landscape garden (admission fee for entrance to garden). Many defined public footpaths.

Toys Hill

(National Trust) **F** 81ha
O.S.S. 188 - TQ 465 517
01892 890651
← ᕃ

2.5 miles S of Brasted, 1 mile W of Ide Hill. Free car park with information board. Many marked

footpaths including a disabled route. (Part being left alone as research area to follow regeneration after 1987 and 1990 storms).

Much of this woodland is recognised as Grade 1 site of national importance for nature conservation .

*Tudeley Woods

(RSPB under management agreement with the Trustees of the Goldsmid Estate)
RE 708ha
O.S.S. 188 - TQ 616 433
Crown House, Petteridge Lane, Mayfield,
Tonbridge, Kent TN12 7LT
← ✕ **⊤ ●** [i] 𝍠

Lying beside the A21 Tonbridge to Hastings road and entered off the minor road to Capel, 2 miles S of Tonbridge. There is a car park but no other facilities. Entrance is free and the wood is open at all times. No dogs are allowed on the Reserve. Please keep to waymarked trails.

Deciduous woodland on Tunbridge Wells sand and Wealden clay comprising mature oaks with sweet chestnut and mixed coppice; also some grazing pasture. Green, greater-spotted and lesser-spotted woodpeckers are common and nuthatches are abundant. Blackcap, garden warbler, willow warbler and whitethroat inhabit the coppice. Tree pipit and hawfinch occur annually while hobby, nightjar, crossbill, siskin and long eared owl may breed occasionally. In springtime carpets of bluebell and primrose can be impressive. Seven species of orchid including greater butterfly, bird's nest and violet helleborine are found in the woodland. For educational visits write to the RSPB warden, Martin Allison at the above address.

LANCASHIRE

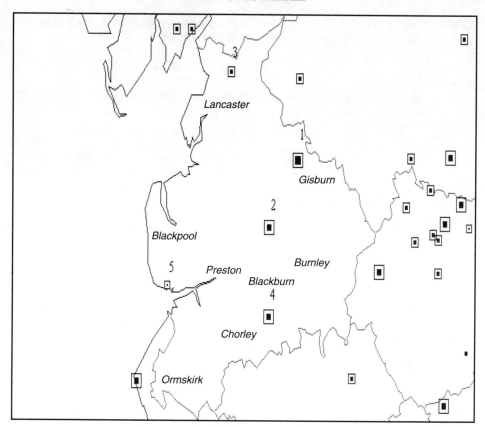

1. *Gisburn Forest*
2. Longridge Fell
3. *Lords Lot*
4. Roddlesworth & Tockholes Woodlands
5. Witchwood

Gisburn Forest
(Forest Enterprise) **F** 1200ha
O.S.S. 103 - SD 746 551
01200 448256

🚗🚌🛇🚶❋💺🛈🔭🛗

N of the B6478 midway between Slaidburn and Long Preston, the Cocklet Hill car park and picnic area is signposted at Stephen Moor crossroads.

This, the largest area of woodland in Lancashire, was first planted immediately following the second World War. It has recently undergone extensive clearfelling and is being replanted to cater for the multi-purpose needs of the 21st century. The forest now ably demonstrates the way in which Forest Enterprise manages a second rotation forest, by creating in open space, planting broadleaves and providing opportunities for public access and wildlife conservation.

Longridge Fell
(Tilhill Economic Forestry) **F** 322ha
O.S.S. 102/103 - SD 663 396/687 406
01524 272249

🚗5🛇🚶❋💺

Take the Longridge to Clitheroe "Fell Road" ie NOT the B6243. Two miles E of the New Drop Inn on the L is main entrance. The other entrance is at Kemple End one mile W of Hodder Bridge Inn.

From the top of the wood there are impressive views out towards the Trough of Bowland to the N and Pendle Hill to the S. Scattered groups of Scots pine and larch up to 200 years old have been retained amongst the commercial conifer crops planted 25 years ago. Both Sika and roe deer are present in the forest.

Lords Lot
(Forest Enterprise) **F** 71ha
O.S.S. 97 - SD 549 706
01229 860373

🚗20🛇🚶❋💺

Roddlesworth and Tockholes Woodlands
(North West Water) **F** 162ha
O.S.S. 103 - SD 664 215
01254 830293

🚗100🚌2🛇🚶❋💺🛈🔭🔭💺FP🚶🛗

N from Bolton on A675, through Belmont village, turn R after 1 mile. Signpost for Tockholes. Woodland on left of Tockholes road. Visitor centre and permanent orienteering course - maps available at visitor centre.

One of largest predominantly broadleaved areas of woodland in Lancs. Protects the catchment area for Upper and Lower Roddlesworth and Rake Brook Reservoirs. From viewpoint an impressive view north over 90% of woodland. Predominantly mature woodland, main planting carried out in early part of century. Broadleaved species include beech, sessile oak, ash, alder, sycamore, rowan, gean, birch. Conifer species include Scots and Corsican pine.

Witchwood
(Lytham St Annes Civic Society) **F** 4ha
O.S.S. 102 - SD 365 274
01253 736397

🚗10🚌1🛇🔭🛗

Train to Lytham, entrance W side of of railway bridge, or A584 to Lytham along Beach Road to main car park on the green, S side of road. Turn N 400 yards to railway bridge as above.

A pleasant walk is to go one mile through the wood, turn S over the railway and return along the promenade to Lytham with views over estuary and sea. Witchwood is a mixed broadleaf woodland, mainly sycamore, beech, oak, willow, and chestnut. Wildlife includes tree creeper, wren, blue tit, woodpecker and grey squirrel. In the middle of the wood there is a gravestone which states ''The Witch 1888'. Grave of favourite horse of Squire Clifton who formerly owned all the land. Leaflet available from Information Centre.

LEICESTERSHIRE

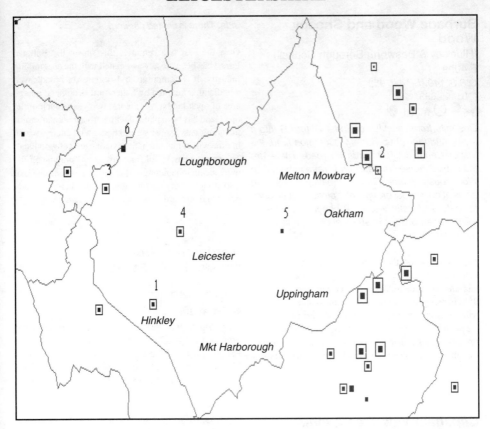

Loughborough

Melton Mowbray

Oakham

Leicester

Uppingham

Hinkley

Mkt Harborough

1. Burbage Wood & Sheepy Wood
2. *Clipsham Yew Tree Avenue*
3. Land at Willesley
4. Martinshaw Wood
5. Red Lodge Wood
6. *Staunton Harold Estate Woodlands

Burbage Wood and Sheepy Wood

(Hinckley & Bosworth Borough Council)
F 40ha
O.S.S. 140 - SP 445 953
(01455 633712
🍴● ∪ WC *i* ●

One mile from Hinckley on the A47 turn R into a lay-by and then R up Burbage Common road, the Visitor Centre is 100 yards up road. There are footpaths, horse routes, and refreshments at Woodhouse Farm. Group bookings; rates on application; school groups, etc. please get in touch for details of activities, work sheets, etc. Visitor Centre open 6 days in summer, 4 days in winter (ring for details).

This is some of the richest coppice woodland in Leicestershire. Known for its spring flowers and birds, this area of ancient woodland is part designated an SSSI in recognition of its conservation value. Although wildlife is the priority for the site, the area is open to the public at all times with a network of paths covering several miles. The woodlands adjoin Burbage Common, 50 hectares of unspoiled meadows. Leaflets available.

Clipsham Yew Tree Avenue

(Managed by Forest Enterprise)**R** 1ha
O.S.S. 130 - SK981 169
(01780 83394
🚗15🍴 ♿ WC *i* 🏕 ▮

Land at Willesley

(Woodland Trust) **F** 40ha
O.S.S. 128 - SK 335 142
(01476 74297
🚗🍴●

Access is from the A42, S of Ashby de la Zouch. Take the turning signed B5006 and follow the signs to Willesley. On approaching Ashby, turn sharp L on the bend after the golf course, continue for 1 mile to the first crossroads. Turn L onto Willesley Wood side and the site is 150 yards on the RH

side. There is limited parking.

Over the past two centuries this site in the National Forest has been closely associated with the coal mining industry. It is composed of 4 hectares of broadleaved woodland, a lake fed by Saltersford Brook and a large area of open land. Over the last two years much of the open land has been planted with native trees and shrubs including oak, ash, silver birch and wild cherry, which in time will complement the existing area of woodland. The sparrowhawk, vole and tawny owl are among the more recent inhabitants of this new woodland. The lake also attracts many visitors including the heron, Canada goose and pochard.

Martinshaw Wood

(Woodland Trust) **F** 99ha
O.S.S. 140 - SK 511068
(01476 74297
🚗🍴♿ 🏕

From the N and Leicester take the main A50 road and turn off at Groby, then follow signs towards Ratby. From S, leave the A47 towards Kirby Muxloe and then Desford along the B5380. Turn off R to Ratby and continue through the village in the direction of Groby. Limited parking space is available in both Groby and Ratby. Stout footwear is advisable due to the wood's heavy clay soil.

Martinshaw Wood is a haven for wildlife. Despite coniferisation, patches of original woodland survive. Oak and hazel can still be found along with aspen, holly and the unusual eared willow. The Toothills area supports a rich variety of flora, with broadleaved helleborine, primrose and wood sanicle of special interest. Also interesting botanically, is a boggy area near Well Finish Crossroads where bogmoss, which is uncommon in Leicestershire, and two rare willow herbs are found.

Red Lodge Wood

(Mr D N Duxbury) **A** 12ha
O. S. S. 141 - SK 753 073
(01162 605533

Take the B6047 to Tilton on the Hill, then Marefield Lane to Red Lodge Lane. There are no facilities. By appointment only.

This is an opportunity to see a wood in the making and may well appeal to those who could be tempted to create a wood of their own. First planting took place in 1988 and for the subsequent four years, and consists of 12 hectares of broadleaf hardwoods grown on a commercial basis on former arable land in accordance with the requirements of the Forestry Commission's woodland grant scheme.

*Staunton Harold Estate Woodlands
(John Blunt) A 110ha
O.S.S. 128 - SK 378 210
(01332 863337
🗎2🚗🔫🏕️ 🌲 WC ♿ FP 🍴 🔨

Meeting point is the courtyard of the Ferrers Centre behind Staunton Harold Hall (Ryder Mission) amd 3 miles from Melbourne, Derbyshire on B587. There is ample parking, a large craft centre with tearooms, toilets (facilities for the disabled). Charges for children £1. Visitors will go by car to the woods which are within 1.5 miles of meeting point.

These mixed woodlands, the largest private ownership within the new National Forest, are managed for timber production with conservation as a natural concomitant. Species include oak, ash, sycamore, larch and Scots pine. Much of the conifer is in mid-rotation but overall there is a constant programme from planting, brashing and thinning through to final felling. The estate is unusual in that it processes much of its produce through to end user. Interested parties can inspect the saw mill, drying sheds and sales outlets; even some of the furniture made from home-grown hardwoods can be admired.

LINCOLNSHIRE

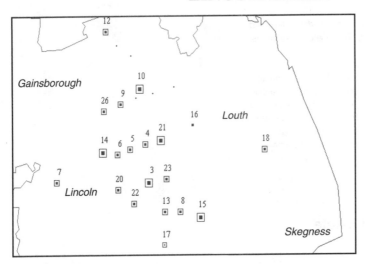

1. *Bourne Wood
2. Callans Lane Wood
3. *Chambers Farm Wood
4. College Wood
Dog Kennel Woods (see Mkt Rasen Wds)
5. Great West Wood
6. Hardy Gang Wood
7. Hartsholme Country Park
8. Kirkby Moor
Legsby Woods (see Mkt Rasen Wds)
9. Linwood
10. Market Rasen Woods
11. Morkery
12. Nettleton Woods
13. New Park Wood
14. Newball Wood
Osgodby Wood (see Mkt Rasen Wds)
15. Ostlers Plantation
16. *Park Gate Plantation
17. The Pinewoods
18. Rigsby
19. Ropsley Rise Wood
20. Scotgrove Wood

21. Sotby Wood
22. Southrey Wood
23. Stixwould & Horsington
24. Temple Wood
25. Twyford
Wallesby Woods (see Mkt Rasen Wds)
26. Wickenby Wood
Willingham Woods (see Mkt Rasen Wds)

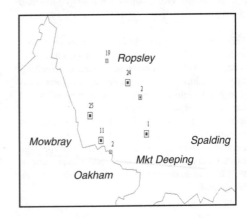

*Bourne Wood

(Forest Enterprise) **F** 217ha
O.S.S. 130 - TF 079 204
01778 422649
⊞70(£1)🚌5(£1)🏕 🛇 ⵏ WC 🚻 [i] ⛺
🏞 🛝 🛂 🥾

Access to car park is off the A151 Bourne to Colsterworth road, approximately 1 mile west of Bourne. Easy access trail, interpretation panels, sculpture trail. Open all year but car park closed 2200 - 0800hrs. Bourne Wood is a working wood: pleasecomply with any warning notices on display.

Working coppice plot and Bourne wood ponds. Keep an eye out for fallow and muntjac deer. Spring time displays of bluebell and wood anemone. Summer populations of white admiral and white letter hairstreak butterflies.

Callans Lane Wood

(Forest Enterprise) **F** 59ha
O.S.S. 130 - TF 061 271
01778 422649
⊞5🏕 🛇 ⵏ 🛝

Chambers Farm Wood

(Forest Enterprise) **F** 350ha
O.S.S. 121 - TF 148 739
01623 822447
⊞50🚌2🏕 🛇 ⵏ WC [i] 🛏⛺🥾 🛝 🍴

Clearly signposted from Wragby, Chambers is located 3 miles south, just off the B1202 Bardney road. Seasonal refreshments and information, 3 waymarked walks.

This is the largest, most varied and important habitat in the area with extensive areas of semi-natural woodland interspersed with broadleaved and conifer plantations on old farmland. Butterflies, fungi and other flora and fauna abound. 3 waymarked walks of 1, 2 and 3 miles depart from the car park. Seasonally staffed centre sells refreshments and various environmental literature, adjacent butterfly garden with path enables wheelchair access.

College Wood

(Forest Enterprise) **F** 64ha
O.S.S. 121 - TF 119 754
01623 822447
⊞5🏕 🛇

Dog Kennel Woods

See also Market Rasen Woods
(Forest Enterprise)
01623 822447

Great West Wood

(Forest Enterprise) **F** 70ha
O.S.S. 121 - TF114 764
01623 822447
⊞5🦌 🛇

Hardy Gang Wood

(Forest Enterprise) **F** 36ha
O.S.S. 121 - TF 095 753
01623 822447
⊞5🏕 🛇

Hartsholme Country Park

(Lincoln City Council) **F** 40ha
O.S.S. 121 - SK 945 698
01522 686264
⊞60🚌1🏕 🛇 WC 🚻 [i] 🛏⛺🏞🥾 🛝
🍴🍽 🛂 ⛺🚐🛂

Signposted from A46 Lincoln bypass, 2 miles SW from centre of Lincoln. Free access all year round. Visitor centre, cafe, and camp site (for which there are charges) open Easter to end of October. Country Park open all the time, ranger service.

Mixed woodland areas, remnants of formal landscaping scheme planted in 1860s. Good specimens of sweet chestnut, cedar of Lebanon, redwood, Wellingtonia and swamp cypress. Fine areas of oak/birch woodland. Demonstration coppice areas. Variety of birds, plants and fungi.

Kirkby Moor
(Forest Enterprise) **F** 33ha
O.S.S. 122 - TF 213 639
01623 822447
🚗5🐂 🔺

Legsby Woods
See also Market Rasen Woods
(Forestry Enterprise)
01623 822447

Linwood
(Forest Enterprise) **F** 41ha
O.S.S. 112 - TF 088 002
01623 822447
🚗5🔺 🔺

Market Rasen Woods
(Forest Enterprise) F 761ha
O.S.S. 113/112/121 - TF 138 884
01623 822447
🚗150🚌5🐂 ○ 🔺 WC 👤 ⛱ ⚱ ⚱ ⦿
On A631 2 miles E of Market Rasen.

Mixed woodland, predominantly pine. Comprises the individual woods of Dog Kennel, Legsby, Osgodby, Wallesby and Willingham.

Morkery
(Forest Enterprise) **F** 157ha
O.S.S. 130 - SK 955 193
01778 422649
🚗10🔺 🔺 🦌 🔺

Nettleton Woods
(Forest Enterprise) **F** 79ha
O.S.S. 112 - TF 088 995
01623 822447
🚗5🐂 🔺 .

New Park Wood
(Forest Enterprise) **F** 33ha
O.S.S. 122 - TF 213 639
01623 822447
🚗5🐂 🔺 .

Newball Wood
(Forest Enterprise) **F** 103ha
O.S.S. 121 - TF 083 758
01623 822447
🚗5🐂 🔺 .

Osgodby Wood
See also Market Rasen Woods
(Forest Enterprise)
01623 822447

Ostlers Plantation
(Forest Enterprise) F 101ha
O.S.S. 122 - TF 215 629
01623 822447
🚗30🚌1🐂 🔺 ⛱ 🔺

*Park Gate Plantation
(Mr Peter Dennis) **AC** 10ha
O.S.S. 122- TF 258 811
01507 343225
🚗10🚌2🔺 🔺 WC 👤 📖 📯

Meet at Moses Farm Yard, Stenigot - 1 mile S of Donington-on-Bain which is 7 miles SW of Louth. Pub lunches can be had in nearby Donington-

---

on-Bain and Goulceby. No charges but donations welcomed and shared by the Forestry Trust and St Nicholas Church, Stenigot. Visits by groups of 4 or more, and by schools and societies, between 1 Apr and 1 Jul, and by appointment only. Write 3 weeks in advance to: The Manager, Estate Office, Stenigot, Nr Louth, LN11 9SL, or phone as above.

Three woods total approximately 25 acres, consisting of mixed hard and soft woods with oak as the final crop. They were planted between 1958 and 1978 to provide timber for estate use and for sale. Sport and all forms of wildlife are given consideration and encouragement. Tree species are labelled and visitors will be guided whenever possible.

The wood lies at the foot of the Wolds some 1.75 miles W of Alford. Turn N towards South Thoresby at the crossroads on the A1104 road halfway between Ulceby Cross and Alford. Entrance 1.25 miles along road on R. There is no charge but a donation by post to the Trust would be appreciated. There are no facilities. There are waymarked footpaths which we would ask visitors to keep to. The wood is open only in daylight hours.

Rigsby is an ancient wood, managed by a traditional coppice system. It is mainly oak, ash and hazel with bluebells, wood anemone, etc. Birds include blackcap, tawny owl, and in winter redpoll and woodcock.

The Pinewoods
(Woodland Trust) **F** 8ha
O.S.S. 122 - TF 193 633
01476 74297

From Lincoln, to the NW, it is a 20 minute drive along B1188 and the B1191, which runs through Woodhall Spa to Horncastle. From Sleaford, take the A153 towards Horncastle and turn L in Tattershall on to the B1192 to Woodhall Spa.

The Pinewoods were once an almost pure pine plantation; now they have a much greater variety of species. Many native trees grow in the wood, especially birch, oak, ash and willow in the wetter spots, with rows of elegant limes along the wood's borders. Bracken and bramble are common in the wood. Brambles also attract many birds and animals. Gatekeeper butterflies, in particular, seek out the nectar from the bramble flowers. There is a wealth of fungi in the pinewoods, with numerous interesting species such as sulphur tuft and shaggy inkcap.

Rigsby
(Lincolnshire Trust for Nature Conservation) **F** 15ha
O.S.S. 122 - TF 421 762
01507 526667

Ropsley Rise Wood
(Managed Forest Enterprise) **R** 0.8ha
O.S.S. 130 - SK 972 337
01778 422649

Scotgrove Wood
(Forest Enterprise) **F** 45ha
O.S.S. 121 - TF 126 703
01623 822447

Sotby Wood
(Forest Enterprise) **F** 115ha
O.S.S. 122 - TF 185 782
01623 822447

Southrey Wood
(Forest Enterprise) **F** 83ha
O.S.S. 121 - TF 133 686
01623 822447

Stixwould and Horsington
(Forest Enterprise) **F** 95ha
O.S.S. 122 - TF 186 665
01778 422649

Temple Wood
(Forest Enterprise) **F** 242ha
O.S.S. 130 - TF 058 299
01778 422649

Twyford
(Managed by Forest Enterprise) **R** 195ha
O.S.S. 130 - SK 946 238
01780 83394

Wallesby Woods
(Forest Enterprise)
See also Market Rasen Woods
01623 822417

Wickenby Wood
(Forest Enterprise) **F** 46ha
O.S.S. 121 - TF 084 828
01623 822417

Willingham Woods
(Forest Enterprise)
See also Market Rasen Woods
01623 822417

MERSEYSIDE

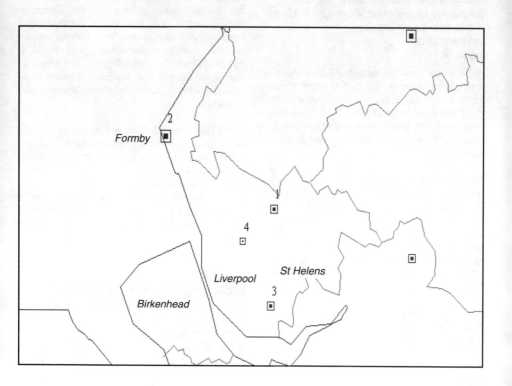

1. Acornfield Plantation
2. Formby
3. Halwood Triangle Country Park
4. Littlewood Community Wood

Acornfield Plantation

(Knowsley Metropolitan Borough) **F** 10ha

O.S.S. 108 - SJ 437 976

0151 443 3682

At SE end of Knowsley Industrial Estate (N). From East Lancs Road (A580) turn N along Coopers Lane, R into Molly's Lane, L into Perimeter Road and L into Spinney Road where there is a small car park on your R. Leaflet and programme of events available from Ranger Service. No charge for access.

Acornfield is one of the few original Kirkby woods remaining, and has been restored since 1983 when the closure of a chemical works removed a chronic pollution problem. A remarkable transformation now sees 70species of birds and all the common small mammals. At the centre of the site is a sphagnum bog hidden by rhododendron. A pond is much used by local schools and anglers. Part of the Mersey Community Forest.

Formby

(National Trust) **F** 209ha

O.S.S. 108 - SD 275 082

01704 878591

15 miles N of Liverpool, 2 miles W of Formby, 2 miles off the A565.

209 hectares of dune, foreshore and pinewood between the sea and the town of Formby. The woodlands are dominated by large areas of Corsican and Scots pine with some areas of maritime and lodgepole pine. Red squirrels can frequently be seen in the pine trees and the shoreline attracts waders such as oystercatchers and sanderlings. Wheelchair access along hard surface paths to the red squirrel reserve and Cornerstone Walk.

Halewood Triangle Country Park

(Knowsley Metropolitan Borough) **F** 28ha

O.S.S. 108 - SJ 442 859

0151 443 2277

Very easy to reach from Halewood station which has a half-hourly service on the Liverpool-Warrington line. Walk from station. 0.5 mile along cycle way to visitor centre. From M57/62 junction follow signs to Halewood village, past church, L into Okell Drive. Car park 0.5 mile on L. There is no charge for access and the park is open at all reasonable times. A leaflet and events programme is available.

Once a busy railway junction and sidings, the Triangle has returned to nature with oak and birch woodland covering about half of the park. Newts and dragonflies can be found in ponds. Wildflowers including orchids, centaury and ox-eye daisy, provide an attractive summer spectacle. The Trans-Pennine trail passes through the park which also caters for BMX/Mountain biking, fishing and orienteering. Part of the Mersey Forest.

Littlewood Community Wood

(Knowsley Metropolitan Borough) **F** 8ha

O.S.S. 108 - SJ 428 943

0151 443 3682

M57 Junction 2, N along Knowsley Lane, L into Stockbridge Lane, across roundabout to Waterpark Drive, across two further roundabouts and turn L into Hollow Croft. Path adjacent to wood, or in Ninetrees School (need to ask permission). There is a leaflet and occasional events. There is no charge for access, and the wood is open at all reasonable times. Evening/ night visits are not advised. Special care is needed to secure your car and belongings to avoid damage or theft.

One of the best woods is Knowsley, with oaks and sweet chestnuts, planted by Napoleonic prisoners of war in the early 1800s. There are several ditches, streams and ponds together with a rich woodland flora. A coach road links the wood to Croxteth Country Park with numerous attractions. The wood has been restored by the local community in partnership with the council to form part of the Mersey Community Forest.

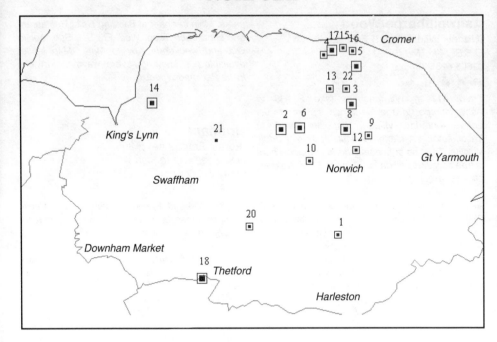

1. Ashwellthorpe Wood
2. Bintree
3. Blickling Park Woods
4. Bodham
5. Felbrigg Park & Great Wood
6. Foxley Wood
7. Gayton Thorpe Wood
8. Haveringland
9. Hevingham Park
10. Hockering
11. Honeypot Wood

12. Horsford Wood
13. Mannington Wood
14. *Sandringham Country Park
15. Sheringham Gathering Grounds
16. Sheringham Old Wood
17. Sheringham Park
18. *Thetford Forest Park
19. *Warren
20. Wayland Wood
21. *Weasingham Azalea Wood
22. Wolterton

Ashwellthorpe Wood

(Norfolk WildlifeTrust) **F** 37ha
O.S.S. 144 - TM 140 980
01603 625540

From A11 in Wymondham take B1135 to Ashwellthorpe Village, entrance to wood just before entering village, opposite road to Tacolneston. A leaflet is available from Norfolk Wildlife. Trust on above telephone number. There is free access on all days, 10 am to 5 pm. No dogs allowed, except guide dogs.

Alder, ash, oak, hazel and hornbeam coppice, with field maple, holly, elm, hawthorn and blackthorn. Guelder rose and spindle, with their attractive winter berries, and dogwood are also present. Ramsons, bluebells, dog's mercury, wood spurge, and early purple orchids in spring, followed by hairy St John's wort and herb paris. Butterflies abundant including white admiral.

Bintree

(Forest Enterprise) **F** 122ha
O.S.S. 133 - TG 004 227
01842 81027

Difficult to find. A 1067 Norwich to Fakenham road then Bintree to High Cross and Field Barn Buildings to N end of wood. Tracks lead down to the River Wensum on the western boundary, a road used as public footpath enters the wood on its southern boundary.

Mainly a pine woodland with some open views across the River Wensum valley. There is a northern beech and oak belt and large poplars beside the river. Recently replanted at the N end of the wood. Riding by permit only.

Blickling Park Woods

(National Trust) **F** 245ha
O.S.S. 133 - TG 176 286
01263 733084

Aylsham 1.5 miles. Free access. Four free car

parks. Main car park at Blickling Hall. Restaurant and shop open Tues, Wed, Fri, Sat, Sun, Apr to Oct and weekends Nov to Mar. Map leaflet available (£1) showing several waymarked walks in the Park and Woods.

Bodham

(Forest Enterprise) **F** 39ha
O.S.S. 133 - TG 107 400
01842 810271

Off the A148 at E end of High Kelling. Public footpath across the N edge of the wood suitable for walking only, no vehicles catered for.

Mostly pine with some Douglas fir, red cedar, Lawsons cypress, grand fir, and a beech strip along the northern boundary.

Felbrigg Great Wood

(National Trust) **F** 165ha
O.S.S. 133 - TG 190 400
01263 734924

The estate is 1 1/2 miles due S of Cromer on the B1436. There are 3 car parks and a picnic area. The main car park in front of the house. Paths are extensive with some waymarked. There is a family woodland guide and trail. Facilities open every weekend all year round and on advertised open days Apr-Oct. Most of this wood is an SSSI and adjoins an historic Park which also has SSSI status. Teachers' book available.

The woods are approximately 70% hardwood. The conifer areas were planted after World War 2. There is a Bronze Age burial mound in the woods and an 18th century ice house. The woods are particularly noted for the large number of lichens and fungi (160 species) and the ancient beech pollards.

Foxley Wood
(Norfolk Wildlife Trust) **F** 120ha
O.S.S. 133 - TG 049 229
01362 88l706

From Norwich take the A1067, Fakenham road. Foxley Wood is situated about 1/2 mile beyond Foxley village. From A1067 follow brown tourist signs. Access is free Fri to Wed, 10 am to 5pm (closed Thurs) - open all year. Guide dogs allowed.

Traditionally coppice with oak standards so there is a large diversity of ground flora - herb paris, bluebells, primroses and violets. Ride flora includes bog stitchwort, bugle, water avens, and tufted hair grass. Coppice was largely hazel although small-leaved lime, midland hawthorn and wild service tree are also present.

Gayton Thorpe Wood
(Julian Marsham) **A** 4 ha
O.S.S. 132 - TF 736 188
01553 636292

Take B1153 N from A47. 50 m N of crossroads signpost Gayton Thorpe to R turn into field entrance on L 200 m on R. There are no charges and no facilities. The wood is open by appointment - please telephone estate office on the above number.

Main wood mature ash, over hazel coppice, brought into production over last 10 years. Ponds and ornamental planting. Small hardwood stand planted in 1986. Primrose carpet in spring. Inte

Haveringland (Part)
(Forest Enterprise) **F** 113ha
O.S.S. 133 - TG 162 226
01842 810271

Off the B1149 Norwich to Holt road. No car park available. For walking only. In the N end of the wood on freehold area. Leasehold area to the S

not open to the public. Haveringland Lake is NOT Forest Enterprise land.

A purely conifer woodland with a public footpath at the N end. Pine woodland with some larch, grand fir and a few broadleaves.

Hevingham Park
(Forest Enterprise) **F** 92ha
O.S.S. 133 - TG 196 210
01842 810271

Off the A140 Norwich to Cromer road at Hevingham or at forest barrier. The area is open to the public to walk only.

Formerly a semi natural woodland site still having considerable conservation value despite being largely conifer plantation. The old woodland relics and the pools have interesting flora and insects. Mostly pine with some larch, oak and poplar. A public footpath from Hevingham bisects the area N to S providing an interesting woodland walk.

Hockering Wood
(Matthew Hutton) **P** 90ha
O.S.S. 133 - TG 072 150

7 km east of Dereham. Take A47 to Hockering. Turn north in village, then left after 2km. Main gate on l after 1.5km. Guided visits twice yearly with the Norfolk Wildlife Trust - 7a Cathedral Close Norwich, NR1 4DF.

An ancient semi-matural wood notified as an SSSI with a good ground flora and a large amount of small leaved lime, most of which is about 70 years old. Some 40% of the wood was replanted with broadleaf /conifer mixturesin the sixties. The wood is managed to produce an uneven aged group selection high forest, using natural regeneration where possible. Wildlife is being encouraged by widening rides and establishing coppice.

Honeypot Wood

(Norfolk Wildlife Trust) **F** 9ha
O.S.S. 132 - TF 934 143
01603 625540

🚗✖●ⓘ

From A47, through Wendling Village, head towards Hall Green. Concrete rides may be suitable for some disabled visitors. There are no charges and the wood is open every day from 10am to 5pm. Guide dogs allowed.

Coppicing has allowed a wide diversity of ground flora to develop - wood anemone, twayblade, bluebells, herb paris and marsh helleborine. Also supports an abundance of fungi including candle-snuff fungus, coral spot fungus and jew's ear.

Horsford Heath

(Forest Enterprise) **R** 82ha
O.S.S. 133 - TG 185 175
01842 810271

🚗6✖🔺Y🌳Ꞓ

Off the B1149 just N of Horsford. On Norwich to Holt road. For walking only on waymarked trails due to adjoining Forest Enterprise land being privately owned leasehold land.

A pure pine area with some surprises for the keen botanist and entomologist. Archaeologically an interesting wood.

Mannington Woods

(Lord Walpole) **RE** 80ha
O.S.S. 133 - TG 142 321
01263 874175

🚗(£1)✖🔺WC ᒻ ⓘ 🏠🌳🅱Ꞓ ᴬ

1.5 miles from Saxthorpe. (Brown signs from Saxthorpe). B1149 Norwich - Holt road and B1354 Fakenham - Aylsham road. The woods are open all year round 9am to 5pm or dusk if earlier. Information Centre/Board, waymarked walks and trails - leaflet available. Boardwalk for wheelchairs. Guided visits for schools and societies are arranged. Education materials to illustrate all

aspects of wildlife will be provided, for which a charge will be made. Preliminary visit recommended. Always consult notice board at Information Centre to see if any restrictions apply.

Walks take you round a series of woods with their own individual characters on gently undulating ground to the N of the upper reaches of the River Bure and along one of its tributaries. At least three are ancient woodlands, most woods had been established by 1742. The woods have recently obtained a Forestry Award of Excellence for access, wildlife habitats and environmentally friendly timber production and in 1994 the Phil Drabble Award for Commitment to Youth.

*Sandringham Country Park

(Her Majesty the Queen) **F** 270ha
O.S.S. 132 - TF 690 290
01553 772675

🚗500🚻60✖🔺Y ⓘ 🏠🌳 ᴬ 🅿🚽🎁
🚉🏕🛍

From the Knights Hill roundabout on the eastern side of Kings Lynn, take the A149 to Dersingham and Hunstanton. Take the fifth turning on the R signposted Sandringham Country Park: you are now in the country park. However, if you follow this road for approximately three quarters of a mile you will find car parks, a cafeteria, shops and toilets on your left. Tractor and trailer tours. Facilities open Easter Sunday until beginning of October. There are 2 caravan sites.

Management of the park started in 1862 when the Estate was purchased by Prince Albert for Edward, Prince of Wales. Prior to this it was an area of open heathland with few trees. The woods are managed commercially to produce timber, as well as for public recreation and conservation. They contain a wide variety of conifer and broadleaf trees which provide a habitat for many acid loving plants and fungi. The woods are also home to many birds, small mammals and a few deer. A natural history guide and other books are available from the Rangers Room.

Norfolk

Sheringham Gathering Grounds Wood

(Anglian Water Services Ltd) **F** 11ha
O.S.S. 133 TG 155 417
01223-372612
�car20🔄 ♀ 👤

Follow A148 into Cromer and take a L onto A1082, there is parking on R.

Sheringham Gathering Grounds are part of Pretty Corner Woods, owned and managed by North Norfolk District Council. The wood falls within the Norfolk Coastal Area of Outstanding Natural Beauty. The present trees date from around 1900 and are a mixture of broadleaved/coniferous species such as oak, sweet chestnut, beech, European silver fir and Scots pine. Birch, rowan, sycamore and ash have regenerated in naturally created clearings. There is good access to the wood by footpaths. The primary aim of the management plan for this site is to preserve and enhance the wildlife habitats within the wood. As the name 'Gathering Grounds' implies, the site has many natural springs. Anglian Water has created ponds by excavating at these. Amphibians thrive in the damp habitats created.

Sheringham Old Wood

(Forest Enterprise) **F** 23ha
O.S.S. 133 - TG 158 410
01842 810271
🔄 👤

Beside the A148 Holt to Cromer road S of Sheringham near the North Norfolk coast. A low key site for walking only, adjoining North Norfolk District Council woodlands where car parking is available.

A varied wood containing both conifers and broadleaved trees. Mainly Corsican pine with Scots pine, Douglas fir, larch, grand fir, western hemlock, plus beech, sweet chestnut and other broadleaved trees. Bisected N to S by a public footpath from Sheringham.

Sheringham Park

(National Trust) **F** 126ha
O.S.S. 133 - TG 139 412
01263 823778
🚗(£2.30)🔄 WC ♿ ⓘ 📷 🏔

Sherngham 2 miles. Car park signposted off A148. Open daily dawn to dusk . Map guide (£1) available showing waymarked walk. Towers give superb coastal views and are an excellent way to see the rhododendrons.

The park was laid out by Humphrey Repton - his favourite work.

*Thetford Forest Park

(Forest Enterprise) **FE** 20,000ha
O.S.S. 144 - TL 811 852
01842 810271
🚗200(£1.50)🚐5(£15)🔄 ⛺ 🏔
WC ♿ ⓘ 📖 ⛺ 📷 🚴 🏔 🚩 🍴 🚂 🏠 📷

High Lodge Visitor Centre is the focal point, off B1107 between Brandon and Thetford, 1 mile up Forest Drive to the car park. Thetford is on the A11 trunk road from London to Norwich. Visitor Centre opens on Easter weekend: closes in early October except at weekends. Special Xmas opening with seasonal programme of events. For other opening times please phone the District Office on the above number.

4000ha with freedom to roam for walkers based on High Lodge Visitor Centre. Conifers include Corsican pine, Scots pine, Douglas fir, larches and a few spruce. Broadleaves include oak, beech, birch, sycamore, poplars and ash and cover 12% of the total area. Lynford Arboretum near Munford boasts in excess of 200 species with scenic lake and woodland walks nearby. The forest park provides 15 car parks, 1 arboretum, 1 Class B caravan site, 7 bridle trails for horse riding by permit, orienteering and much more. There are two specialist bird trails.

Warren

(R W Meynell) **A** 7ha
O.S.S. 130 - TG 095 115
01603 880215

10 miles W of Norwich - directions given when making appointment to visit. There are no charges, and no facilities. Visitors will be taken round the wood by the owner - appointments can be made at any time except during March, September and December.

Uneven aged mixed woodland managed for the production of high quality timber, wildlife and aesthetic aspects, demonstrating that these objectives are complementary.

Wayland Wood

(Norfolk Wildlife Trust) **F** 34ha
O.S.S. 144 - TL 924 995
01603 625540

Between Watton and Thetford on the A1075. Access is free and the wood is open every day from 10 am to 5pm. No dogs allowed (except guide dogs).

Said to be the setting for the Babes in the Wood tale, Wayland is still managed on a rotational basis, as coppice with standards. Bird cherry, field maple and hazel are all cut allowing large diversity of ground flora. In spring, swathes of bluebells and dog's mercury carpet the floor along with wood anemone, yellow star of Bethlehem growing here in its only Norfolk locality. Coppicing also benefits birds, including woodcock and the exotic golden pheasants which breed on the woodland floor.

SARACENS HEAD
Adjacent to Wolterton Hall. Delightful en suite accomodation. Individualistic cooking (G.P.G. Norfolk Dining Out Pub 1994 and 1995), Egon Ronay, EATB. Courtyard, gardens, log fires. Addictive atmosphere. Wolterton, near Erpingham. Tel: 01263 768909.

---

*Weasenham Azalea Wood

(Major R L Coke) **P** 22ha
O.S.S. 132 - TF 847 199
01328 838288

Midway between Swaffham and Fakenham on the A1065. Free car parking on side of minor public road. No other facilities. Entrance charges and programme of events Adults £2, Children under 12 years 50p. Open from 2pm to 5pm on 28 May, 29 May, 4 Jun for general public. Parties at other times by arrangement. Dogs allowed only if kept on leads. People expected to keep to paths. Flowers not to be picked. No smoking inside wood.

A wood situated on old heathland and managed since 1907 on an uneven aged system with no clear felling, with the combined objectives of high quality timber production, amenity and conservation. It is mainly mixed conifers with some hardwoods. The tallest trees up to 140 feet. It also contains flowering shrubs e.g. rhododendrons (not ponticum), azaleas, magnolias etc. and also specimens of some of the rarer trees.

Wolterton

(Lord Walpole) **RE** 60ha
O.S.S.133 - TG 163 320
01263 584175

A140 Norwich to Cromer road. 2 miles N of Aylsham turn L for Erpingham. Follow brown signs. Always consult notice board at car park to see if any restrictions apply. Open all year round, 9 am to 5pm, or dusk if earlier.

18th and 19th century parkland, woods varying from near arboretum type stands to alder carr. The woods have recently obtained a Forestry Award of Excellence for access, wildlife habitats and environmentally friendly timber production. Phil Drabble Award for Commitment to Youth, 1994.

NORTHAMPTONSHIRE

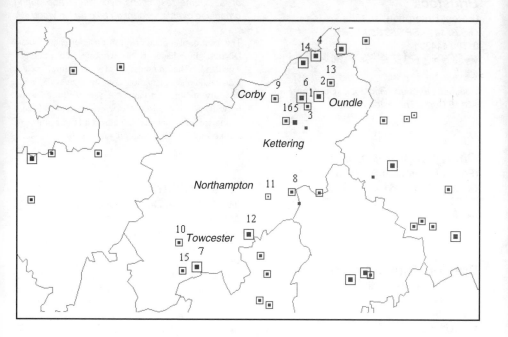

1. *Brigstock*
2. *Cherry Lap/Mounterley*
3. Drayton Estate Woodlands
4. **Fineshade Wood*
5. * Grafton Park
6. *Harry's Park*
7. *Hazelborough*
8. *Irchester Country Park
9. King's Wood
10. *Plumpton*
11. Rotary Wildlife Corridor
12. **Salcey Forest*
13. Short Wood
14. *Wakerley Great Wood*
15. *Whistley Wood*
16. The Wilderness, Boughton Park

Brigstock
(Forest Enterprise) **F** 35ha
O.S.S. 141 - SP 953 850
01780 444394
🚗30🚃2🔤🙂🗡☀🗡 WC ♿ ⓘ 📖 ⛺
🔥 🗡 ⚒

Reached through Brigstock Country Park off A6116 Corby-Thrapston road.

Cherry Lap/Mounterley
(Forest Enterprise) **F** 124ha
O.S.S. 141 - SP 965 859
01780 444394
🦌 🗡 🗡

Drayton Estate Woodlands
(L G Stopford Sackville Esq) **L** 40ha
O.S.S. 141 - SP 950 794
01832 732405
🚗30🚃2🗡 ● 🗡 🗡 FP

A14 (M1/A1 Link) to Islip, near Kettering, then proceed to village of Slipton. There is limited parking at the Slipton Grange chip store. Please contact Edwin de Lisle on above number.

The Biomass trial plots at Slipton, on the Drayton Estate, were established in the mid 1980s for cuttings to fuel the large (1 million BTU) wood boiler in Drayton House. To fuel the boiler, the Estate is restarting the ancient practice of harvesting coppice with standards in some of the semi-natural ancient woodlands. There will be two guided visits to look both at the woods and at the Biomass wood chip store and boiler.

*Fineshade Wood
(Forest Enterprise) **F** 475ha
O.S.S. 141 - SP 978 985
01780 444394
🚗20🚃1🔤🙂🗡☀🗡 ⓘ 🗡 🍴 ⚒

From A47/A43 Junction go S on A43 towards Corby. About 2 miles Top Lodge is signposted

on L. Some restrictions over winter and during organised events. Mountain bike trail in wood.

The centre of operations for the Northants Forest District, Fineshade is a working multi-purpose woodland. The combination of semi natural ancient woodland and plantation forestry gives a wide diversity of flora and fauna. A very well used wood by walkers and cyclists. Other events such as Husky racing are held annually and attract a large number of people - well worth a visit all year round.

*Grafton Park
(His Grace the Duke of Buccleuch)
A 110ha
O.S.S. 141 - SP 935 814
01536 515731
🚗10🦌 🗡 🗡 🔥 ⚒

1 mile N of Grafton Underwood on the Cranford to Brigstock road, on RH side of road. There is car parking for 10 cars. Other facilities include a picnic area and permitted ways on foot through the wood. The wood is open from 1 Jan to 31 Dec, 0830 to 1800 hours or sunset if earlier. All visits by appointment only, in case the wood is being used for forestry or sporting operations. All group visits require 7 days notice, please contact Mr. G Fitzpatrick, The Living Landscape Trust, Boughton House, Geddington, Northants on the above telephone number.

A commercially managed woodland, with diverse broadleaved and coniferous tree species, incorporating a previous American Air Force Base dating from World War 2. Typical woodland fauna and flora are in evidence.

Harry's Park
(Forest Enterprise) **F** 186ha
O.S.S. 141 - SP 948 865
01780 444394
🦌 🗡 🙂 🗡

Hazelborough
(Forest Enterprise) **F** 407ha
O.S.S. 152 - SP 655 428
01604 696239
🚗6🚶 🦌 ♈WC

*Irchester Country Park
(Northamptonshire County Council)
FE 81ha
O.S.S. 152 - SP 910 660
01933 276866
🚗🚌🐕🚶♈WC ♿ 🛈 ⃞🍴🖼️ ⃓ FP ⛰️
🚻🏪⃟🏠

The park is off the B570 Irchester to Lt Irchester Road 1/3 mile from the Junction with A509. Facilities include a visitor centre, railway museum, ranger service, and ample parking. The park is open from 8.30am to 5pm in winter, and 8.30am to 6.00pm in summer. The park facilities are closed on Xmas Day and New Years Day, although out of hours parking is available and the Park itself is open to the public. Playschemes, walks, talks by Rangers by appointment. Full Education programme and school visits. Video available to teachers.

Irchester Country Park has been developed on the site of a former ironstone quarry the remains of which can be seen in the hill and dale landscape upon which the trees were planted. The 81 hectares offer plenty of opportunity for quiet strolls and nature watching.

King's Wood (Local Nature Reserve)
(Corby Borough Council) F 31ha
O.S.S. 141 - SP 865 871
01604 405285
🦌● 🛈

Within the built up area of Corby. From the A6003 follow the sign for Danesholme. The wood is to the north of this road. Please do not park in the entrances to the wood as these are often in use.

King's Wood is a remnant of Rockingham Forest. Old standard trees of oak and ash are plentiful together with

mature trees of field maple, crab apple and recent ash regeneration. Common and midland hawthorn, dogwood and guelder rose occur amongst the hazel, maple and ash underwood. There are also notable thickets of blackthorn and rose. Parts of the wood retain evidence of 19th century planting of exotic species. About a third of the wood is managed as coppice with standards. Open areas of grassland are maintained to support ragged robin and ladies bedstraw. A section near the boundary is being converted to wood pasture by pollarding standards.

Plumpton
(Forest Enterprise) **F** 54ha
O.S.S. 152 - SP 605 490
01604 696239
🦌●

Rotary Wildlife Corridor
(The Marquess of Northampton) **F** 4ha
O.S.S. 152 - SP 849 610
01604 696839
🚗🦌 🛡 🛈 ⃓ ⛰️

From A45 trunk dual carriageway between Northampton and Wellingborough turn southwards opposite Earls Barton, signed to Grendon and Castle Ashby. Proceed southwards for about 1 mile along Station Road. At Cogenhoe to Grendon Road junction turn W towards Cogenhoe to car park about 1 mile opposite to Whiston. There are no facilities other than a free car park. Free access to the central public footpath linked to the Nene Way etc. Walkers are asked to keep all dogs on leads to protect wildlife.

A belt of roadside trees over 1 mile long planted, Sunday, 29 Nov 1992 by Rotary International; Lord Northampton; and some 400 members of the public with support from Northamptonshire County Council, Nene valley project and South Northamptonshire Council. Species: all native to Nene valley, 600 ash, 280 field maple, 250 oak, 175 birch, crab apple, hazel, alder, cherry and 3,000 quickthorn as roadside hedge and many shrubs to encourage wildlife. Successful growth 1993-94, main interest to watch these young trees growing. Badger sett established 1994.

Salcey Forest
(Forest Enterprise) **F** 500ha
O.S.S. 152 - SP 795 515
01604 696239
⚗200🚌2↰∪ ⚓ 🌾 wc ᕀ ⓘ 📖 🛏 🐎
🏕 🅿 🦌

Leave M1 at junction 15 for Quinton. The forest is 2 miles from Quinton on the Hanslope road. Visits for schools can be arranged.

Mixed woodland which takes in an area of oak planted in 1847. Wildlife includes fallow and muntjac deer, great spotted woodpecker, sparrowhawk and nightingales which can be heard singing in early summer. Salcey is also home to 30 species of butterfly including the wood white and rare black hairstreak. The bird tables in the picnic site are visited by over 20 different species over winter months.

Short Wood
(The Wildlife Trust for Northamptonshire)
F 25ha
O.S.S. 141 - TF 015 914
01604-405285
⚗8↰ ⚓ ⓘ 🅿

Follow the road N from Oundle to Southwick. Near the top of hill, before Southwick, park in the lay-by on L. Go through the bridle-gate and across 2 fields. Please do not obstruct the gate.

Short Wood is a fragment of the ancient Rockingham Forest. It consists mostly of mixed coppice of ash, hazel and field maple with oak and ash standards. A number of interesting shrubs are found, including dogwood. spindle, wayfaring and wild service tree and guelder rose. There is an active coppice rotation in the wood and electric fencing is used to protect the regrowth. This management encourages a good display of spring flowers, particularly bluebells. Nightingales have returned since coppicing commenced. Elm in the wood is also being coppiced; the new elm growth is not susceptible to Dutch elm disease and by cutting on a short rotation the elm should remain healthy.

Wakerley Great Wood
(Forest Enterprise & Marquis of Exeter)
F 361ha
O.S.S. 141 - 962 987
01780 444394
⚗50🚌2↰∪ ⚓ 🌾 wc ᕀ ⓘ ⛺ 🛏 🏕
🅿

From A47/A43 roundabout go south on A43 towards Corby. Wakerley Woods is signposted about 2 miles on right. . Over winter there may be restrictions due to shooting activities. Dogs must be kept off the picnic sites. Riding is by permit only. Organised events must be booked in advance and further information is available across A43 at Top Lodge, Fineshade.

Wakerley Woods is a true multi-purpose woodland. The combination of ancient woodland and plantation forestry gives this wood a wide variety of environment which consequently encourage a wide variety of flora and fauna. It is well known and used for public recreation.

Whistley Wood
(Forest Enterprise) **F** 64ha
O.S.S. 152 - SP 615 415
01604 696239
⚗4↰ ⚓ 🌾

The Wilderness, Boughton Park
(His Grace the Duke of Buccleuch) **R** 11ha
01536 515731
🅱(£1)⚗🚌↰ ⚓ wc ᕀ ⓘ 📖 ⛺ 🏕 🦌

Follow directions to 'Boughton House' off A43 at Geddington. Entrance to park about 1 mile east of Geddington on RHS of road to Grafton Underwood. Visitors to report to the ticket booth or reception at Boughton House stables (The Living Landscape Trust). Park open 1 Apr-1 Oct, 12.00-5.00, or other times by appointment only.

Set as a backdrop to Boughton House, The Wilderness is a diverse block of mixed woodland, part of which is laid out to avenues forming an integral element of the larger Boughton Park (Grade I listed), and with some mature specimen trees.

NORTHUMBERLAND

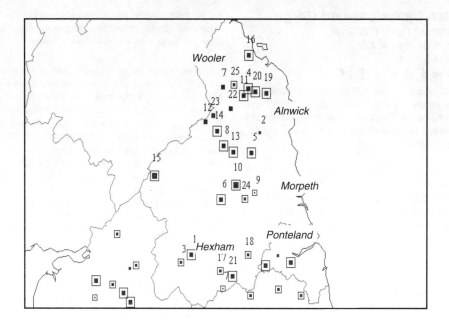

1. Allen Banks/Staward Gorge
2. *Birsley Wood*
3. Briarwood Banks
4. *Chillingham Woods
5. *Cragside*
6. *Fourlaws*
7. *Fredden Hill*
8. *Harbottle*
9. Hartburn Glebe Woods
10. *Harwood*
11. *Hepburn*
12. *Hepden Burn*
13. *Holystone*

14. *Kidland*
15. *Kielder Forest*
16. *Kyloe
17. Letah Wood
18. Priestclose Wood
19. *Quarry House*
20. *Ros Hill*
21. *Slaley*
22. *Threestoneburn*
23. *Uswayford*
24. Wallington, East & West Woods
25. *Wooler Common*

Allen Banks/Staward Gorge

(National Trust) **F** 200ha
O.S.S. 87 - NY 799 630
01434 344218

🚗🐕 🏕 ☀ WC ⛺ 🦌 ⚿

Access is from the A69 approaching Bardon Mill. Car parking provision at Allen Banks only. There is no charge but there is a donation box. Coaches not allowed. The woodland is open to the public all year round.

The woodland covers the valley sides of the River Allen and stretches from Allen Banks picnic site to Cupola Bridge at its southernmost point. The valley sides are very steep and, as a result, provide some breathtaking views, particularly during the autumn. At the southern end of the valley are the remains of Staward Pele. There are several footpaths leading from the Allen Banks car park, along the riverside and across a suspension bridge. There is a tarn to visit, and for the more energetic, footpaths lead from one end of this woodland to the other.

Birsley Wood

(Forest Enterprise) **A** 36ha
O.S.S. 81 - NU 111 094
01669 620569

🦌 🏕

Briarwood Banks

(Northumberland Wildlife Trust) **F** 12ha
O.S.S. 87 - NY 791 620
01912 846884

🚗20(.30)🚽1(£1)🔙 🏕 Y ⓘ ⛺ 🦌 ⚿

Turn L off the A69 W of Haydon Bridge towards Ridley Hall, go under the railway bridge, taking the L fork and park at the National Trust car park (30p) at Allen Banks (WCs available). Follow the public footpath beside the River Allen until you come to Briarwood Banks. Alternatively go past the NT car park and continue on minor roads to Plankey Mill, where parking is available. In summer the farmer makes a small charge. Cross the suspension bridge, turn R up the steps and follow the path until

the footbridge takes you across Kingswood Burn. Briarwood Banks is reached by the footpath on your L. Access is full and free all year round.

Briarwood Banks nature reserve is part of the once extensive area of ancient woodland growing along the Allen river and the Kingswood burn. It is an SSSI and was bought by Northumberland Wildlife Trust in 1988. The most common trees are ash and wych elm, sessile oak and birch. The shrub layer is made up of holly, bird cherry, blackthorn, honeysuckle, guelder rose and a few clumps of old hazel coppice. Spring is the best time to enjoy the wild flowers: wild garlic, sweet woodruff, giant bellflower, wood sorrel, wood sanicle and toothwort. Roe deer and red squirrel are both found here. Pied flycatcher and wood warbler, treecreeper, great spotted woodpecker are found as well as a number of common species.

*Chillingham Woods

(College Valley Estates Ltd) **R** 250ha
O.S.S. 75 - NU 063 260
01668 281611

🚗7🚶U 🏕 ☀ Y ⓘ ⛺ ⚿

Follow the B6346 NW from Alnwick for 8 miles, then carry straight on to the road for Old Bewick towards Chillingham for 4 miles. Go past the Castle entrance and take the next road off to the right, cross the old ford. Parking is by the Church. Opening times: May-Oct, 8am-7pm. Nov-Apr, 9am-4pm. The waymarked route is for walkers and horseback riders. Some areas may be subject to temporary diversions to accommodate necessary forestry operations.

The James Knott Charitable Trust purchased Chillingham Wild Cattle Park and the surrounding woodlands in 1982. As well as commercial forestry operations the estate has been undertaking a replanting programme to recreate the original parkland trees and copses. These are mainly broadleaved which were established in the 18th and 19th centuries, felled between the two wars and never replanted. There are approx. 4.25 miles of paths covering a variety of terrain. Picnic tables are located along the way at places offering extensive views of the surrounding areas.

*Cragside

(National Trust) **R** 350ha
O.S.S.81 - NU 073 022
01669 620333

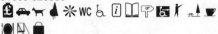

Cragside is situated on the B6341 Rothbury - Alnwick road, just N of Rothbury itself. There are several car parks at the main visitor centre and around the particularly scenic areas of the estate. The Armstrong energy centre and other facilities are situated at the visitor centre and there is fishing available. Cragside is open from 1 Apr to end of Oct. There are several footpaths along the Debdon Valley and around the lake shores and through the pinetum where many of the specimen trees are labelled for easy identification. Teachers' book available.

The woodland within Cragside Estate was planted between 1860 and 1880 by the first Lord Armstrong to transform the bare Northumbrian moorland. There is an arboretum immediately around and below the House, containing many specimen trees.

Fourlaws

(Forest Enterprise) **A** 352ha
O.S.S. 80 - NY 934 844
01669 620569

Fredden Hill

(Forest Enterprise) **A** 230ha
O.S.S. 75 - NT 955 270
01669 620569

Harbottle

(Forest Enterprise) **F** 599ha
O.S.S. 80 - NT 927 048
01669 620569

CLENNEL HALL

A 16th century building set in the grounds of a caravan site. Relax in the warm atmosphere of the historic surroundings; enjoy a drink and a meal in the fully licensed premises. An excellent base for forest and hill walking, fishing, pony treking, etc. Tel: 01669 650341. Clennel Hall, Clennel, Alwinton, Morpeth.

Hartburn Glebe Woods

(Woodland Trust) **F** 3ha
O.S.S. 81 - NZ 088 864
01476 74297

Hartburn is situated on the B6343 road running from Morpeth to Cambo. Roadside parking adjacent to the wood is possible but please park carefully since traffic can be travelling fast along the lane. There are no facilities and free and full access is available. Some paths are muddy at times and stout footwear is advisable.

Hartburn Glebe contains a number of features of considerable historic interest, including Roman earthworks and some very unusual 19th century architecture. A very striking plant in this wood is wild garlic, or ramsons. Also numbers of great woodrush and yellow pimpernel can be found. There is a rich variety of wildlife; red squirrel and roe deer are just some of the species you will see. Wildlife in Hartburn Glebe is enhanced by the adjacent stream, where pied and grey wagtails and dippers can be seen. Red-breasted mergansers have also been known to nest here.

*Harwood

(Forest Enterprise) **F** 2954ha
O.S.S. 81 - NZ 003 898
016696 620569

Hepburn

(Forest Enterprise) **F** 102ha
O.S.S. 75 - NU 073 248
01669 620569

From A697 at Wooperton turn east onto B6346, after about 2 miles turn L for Chatton. After further 2.5 miles turn R for Hepburn. Forest walks, picnic site. Woodland walks in thinned semi-mature conifers and some broadleaves. From high ground there are excellent views on a clear day.

Hepden Burn
(Forest Enterprise) **A** 101ha
O.S.S. 80 - NT 874 139
01669 620569
🚗2🄿🛏🛈🏕

Holystone
(Forest Enterprise) **F** 209ha
O.S.S. 80/81 - NT 950 024
01669 620569
🚗30🛏🄿🏕🌲🍴🚻🪵🚽

From Rothbury head W towards Otterburn on B6341. Ater 4 miles turn R for Harbottle and Alwinton. Follow through Sharperton over the bridge and turn L for Holystone. The picnic site is signposted in the village. Open all year round. Forest nature reserve, forest walks, picnic place.

Holystone Burn, oak woodland and mixed conifers.

Kidland
(Forest Enterprise) **F** 1113ha
O.S.S. 80 - NT 917 105
01669 620569
🚗10🚲🐎🄿🏕🌲🍺🚽

*Kielder Forest
(Forest Enterprise) **FE** 60000ha
O.S.S. 80 - NY 633 935
01434 220242
🚗(£1)🛏🏕🌲🍴

Recommend starting at Kielder Castle Visitor Centre (open Easter - end October and winter weekends), which is in Kielder village, off C200. 17

miles W of Bellingham and 3 miles S of Scottish border. Numerous walks, cycle trails, forest drive, raptor viewpoint. Car park at visitor centre, otherwise free. Cyclists are asked to keep to waymarked cycle routes. Kielder is a working forest so please obey all signing.

Kielder is Britains largest manmade forest, surrounding Kielder Water. Forest Drive (12 miles) crosses some of Englands most isolated moorlands between Kielder Castle and A68. Numerous easy access waymarked trails plus 3 long distance ''strenuous'' walks. Wide range of cycle routes for all abilities. Raptor viewpoint at Bakethin provides opportunity to see goshawks and other birds of prey. Exhibitions and forest recreation information in Kielder Castle, which also features a restaurant. Guided walks programme. The Archercleugh area of Kielder Forest recently received a Centre of Excellence Award for forest design.

*Kyloe
(Robin Fleming) **A** 391ha
O.S.S. 75 - NU 062 392
01295 688100
🚗15🚲1🄿🏕

From Berwick on Tweed take the A1 S for 9 miles. Turn R on to the B 6353 into Fenwick. Turn L at the telephone and drive up the hill for 1000 yards. The entrance to the wood is at the end of the road. Follow signs for the gate to the car park and meeting point. All visits should be arranged by appointment by contacting Peter Hale on the above telephone number.

The forest was established by C J Leyland of Haggerston Castle in about 1880 as a repository for his collection of exotic species. The wood gives a rare opportunity to view stands of fully mature large conifers. The forest is broken up into valleys by outcrops of rock forming crags. There are red squirrel, roe deer and badgers. Fulmars nest on Kyloe Crag which is about 120 feet tall. Adders are frequently seen.

Letah Wood

(Woodland Trust) **F** 13ha
O.S.S. 87 - NY 940 607
01476 74297

Take B6306 S of Hexham, turn first R after about 300 yards signposted to Slaley and Blanchland, and first L signposted to Ordley, Dye House and Whitley Chapel. Drive past small crossroads and downhill to Newbiggin. Turn R here towards Newbiggin Hill and park on the roadside. There are no facilities. Free and full access. Some of the paths within the woods can be muddy and they take you across the stream in Letah Wood. Stout shoes or wellingtons are advised.

The wild daffodils make this a very special place to visit in early springtime. It is a quiet, sheltered haven for wildlife and is particularly rich in bird life, including pied flycatcher, blackcap and garden warbler. At the crossroads, oak trees dominate. The ground flora changes here both above and below the path, from a carpet of great woodrush, bracken and honeysuckle, to a mixture of flowers which include sweet woodruff, wood sanicle and dog's mercury. North of the burn, on the S facing sunny slopes, the wild daffodils are abundant in April.

Priestclose Wood

(Northumberland Wildlife Trust) **F** 15ha
O.S.S. 88 - NZ 107 627
01912 846884

There is a pond-dipping platform suitable for children.

Little of the ancient woodland character remains unchanged at Priestclose. In the 1930s, a large part of it was destroyed by fire, after which more trees were felled to supply a nearby sawmill. Dominant among the trees now is the native oak. Birch and rowan are common. Ash, sycamore, Norway maple and beech also occur and a large black poplar grows close to the pond. Holly and elder are found throughout the wood. Bird cherry is found at the northern edge of the wood. Patches of wood anemone and celandine appear in spring followed by greater and wood stitchwort, wood

sorrel and bluebells and in a few places the greater woodrush. Brambles, honeysuckle and bracken provide abundant ground cover together with male fern. A good variety of birds is found in the reserve throughout the year. Roe deer occasionally visit the wood though they are seldom seen, also foxes and badgers. A leaflet is available from the above telephone number.

Quarry House

(Forest Enterprise) **F** 150ha
O.S.S. 75 - NU 110 247
01669 620569

Ros Hill

(Forest Enterprise) **F** 163ha
O.S.S. 75 - NU 091 254
01669 620569

Slaley

(Forest Enterprise) **F** 511ha
O.S.S. 87 - NY 979 548
01669 620569

Threestoneburn

(Forest Enterprise) **A** 711ha
O.S.S. 75/81 - NT 980 198
01669 620569

Uswayford

(Forest Enterprise) **A** 761ha
O.S.S. 80 - NT 880 143
01669 620569

Wallington, East and West Woods
(National Trust) **F** 15ha
O.S.S. 81 - NZ 030 843
01670 74283

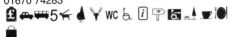

Wallington is situated 12 miles W of Morpeth (B6343), 6 miles NW of Belsay (A696) - take B 6342 towards Cambo. Facilities available during opening times, from 1 Apr to end of Oct. Reduced opening hours for the shop and restaurant from 1 Nov to 19 Dec. Free access to the woodland all year round. Most of the woodland walks are accessible to wheelchair users. Wheelchairs and electric scooter available by prior arrangement with the Administrator.

Amenity woodland situated around Wallington mansion and along the banks of River Wansbeck. Planted mainly over 200 years ago the woods are predominantly beech, but considerable felling and replanting has taken place in the last 20 years. There are extensive linked footpaths in both the East and West woods and along the River Wansbeck.

Wooler Common
(Forest Enterprise) **F** 81ha
O.S.S. 75 - NT 980 277
01669 620569

Access to Wooler Common is via Ramsay Lane which is found at the SE end of the main street in Wooler.

NOTTINGHAMSHIRE

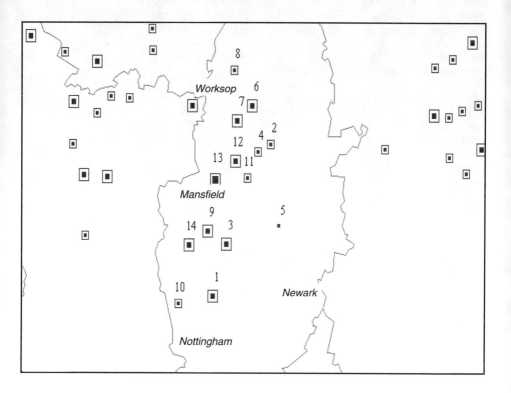

1. Bestwood Country Park
2. *Bevercotes Park*
3. *Boughton Brake*
4. *Blidworth Woods Complex*
5. Chevral Wood
6. *Clumber (part)*
7. Clumber Park
8. Forest Plantation
9. *Harlow Wood*
10. Oldmoor Wood
11. Rufford Country Park & Abbey
12. Sherwood Forest Country Park
13. **Sherwood Pines Forest Park*
14. *Thieves Wood*

Bestwood Country Park

(Nottinghamshire County Council
and Gedling Borough Council) **F** 164ha
O.S.S. 129 - SK 573 463
0115 9670042
🚗125🚌🚲🖐️∪● WC ♿ ⓘ 🏪🍵 🍴 ⛺🍺🏧🐾

Approximately 5 miles N of Nottingham, take the A60 out of the City, L into the B6004, first R into Queen's Bower Road and first R again into Bestwood Lodge Drive. Car park approximately 3/4 mile on the R. The country park is free for all to enjoy throughout the year with an adventure playground, picnic sites and countryside rangers on hand to advise and assist visitors. A year round programme of public events is organised, all with a natural history theme. You are welcome to join any of the public events, or if you would like to have a special event organised for you and a group of friends, please do not hesitate to contact the above number.

Bevercotes Park

(Managed by Forest Enterprise) **F** 92ha
O.S.S. 120 - SK 696 705
01623 822447
🍴🍺❄️

Blidworth Woods Complex

(Forest Enterprise) **F** 488ha
O.S.S.120 - SK 592 524
01623 822447
🚗200🚌10🖐️∪🍺❄️WC ⓘ 🍵🍺🏧
Along Longdale Lane situated between A60 and A614.

This complex includes Sansom and Haywood Oaks as well as Blidworth. Sansom and Blidworth comprise mainly of conifer with areas of broadleaves. Haywood Oaks contains some ancient oak trees which are the remnants of the ancient Sherwood Forest. A number of waymarked walks weave through all the woods, affording interesting views and providing a pleasant walk.

Boughton Brake

(Forest Enterprise) **F** 47ha
O.S.S. 120 - SK 669 692
01623 822447
🚗20🚌2🍴🍺

Chevral Wood

(Mr and Mrs D C Herbert) **A** 32ha
O.S.S. 120 - SK 715 565
01636 812335
🏧(£2)🍴●WC 🍴🏧

4 miles SE of Worksip, 6 miles SW of Retford. Signposted off A1. Drive to Hockerton, 2 miles N of Southwell and park in car park of Spread Eagle public house in Hockerton (O.S. Ref above) - from there by convoy. There are no facilities and the wood is only open by ringing or writing for an appointment. Please book two weeks in advance. Adults £2 and Children 50p..

Chevral Wood is an ancient woodland situated 1 mile N of the Nottinghamshire cathedral town of Southwell. When Southwell was granted its Royal Charter in 780 AD Chevral Wood was described in great detail as forming the northern boundary of Southwell. It is a broadleaved wood being mainly oak and ash. The ash has been coppiced for hundreds of years and many of the ash stools are very old. There are plenty of other trees such as "midland" hawthorn, hazel, willow, sycamore and horse chestnut. There is a duck flight pond and a large release pen for pheasant, 1500 pheasants being released yearly. It is also a source of many edible fungi - morels, chanterelles, blue stalks and parasol mushrooms. It is rich in bird life.

Clumber (part)

(Managed by Forest Enterprise) **F** 539ha
O.S.S. 120 - SK 645 773
01623 822447
🍴🍺

Clumber Park
(National Trust) **R** 400ha
O.S.S. 120 - SK 645 774
01909 476653
50 wc

4 miles SE of Worksop, 6 miles SW of Retford. Signposted off A1. Study Centre, Nature Trail, 3000 acres of parkland with doublelime avenue.

Forest Plantation: Hodsock Priory Estate
(Sir Andrew Buchanan) **F** 15ha
O.S.S. 120 - SK 616 834
01909 591204

1.75 miles from Blyth on B6045 to Worksop. Sign by entrance says Hodsock Farms. Wood is adjacent to road and cars can be parked at side of track. There are no facilities and free access is available at all times.

This irregularly shaped wood on well drained sandland, has a wide variety of species and ages of timber. There are some very fine beech, chestnut and oak planted about 100 years ago. The present owner is attempting to combine commercial forestry with amenity and insists on having wide rides. He replanted a two hectare block in 1970 and is currently restocking, with a mixture of replanting in tree shelters and natural regeneration.

Harlow Wood
(Managed by Forest Enterprise) **F** 147ha
O.S.S. 120 - SK 552 567
01623 822447
50 **2** wc

Oldmoor Wood
(Woodland Trust) **F** 15ha
O.S.S. 129 - SK 497 428
01476 7497

Leave the M1 at Exit 26 and take the A610 towards Nottingham. After 1 mile turn R onto the B6004, signposted to Stapleford and Bilborough. Continue on the B6004 for approximately 2 miles until Strelley is signposted to the R. Park in Strelley village, on the roadside to the S of the church. Full and free access. Stout footwear is advisable on the wood's heavy clay soils.

Oldmoor Wood has an attractive combination of high forest and open glades, with dense scrub along the SW boundary. There are many large mature trees in the wood, which can provide roosts for wren, tree-creeper and other small birds. Although ground flora in many parts of the wood is sparse there are abundant bluebells in spring, along with lesser celandine and common hemp-nettle. In more open areas bracken and bramble predominate.

Rufford Country Park and Abbey
(Nottinghamshire County Council Leisure Services) **F** 69ha
O.S.S. 120 - SK 645 647
01623 824153
600 wc

Situated on the A614, 17 miles N of Nottingham and 2 miles S of Ollerton, Rufford Country Park comprises a 25 acre lake, woodland walks and delightful formal gardens, including sculpture and herb gardens. In the heart of the park stands the impressive remains of a 12th century Cistercian abbey with exhibitions on life as a Cistercian monk and Rufford as a country house during the time of the Savile family. The facilities include a craft centre, restaurants, and Nottinghamshire heritage exhibition. The rangers run a programme of special events and activities details of which are available from Rufford Country Park, Ollerton, Notts NG22 9DF or telephone the above number. The country park is

157

open all year from dawn to dusk and admission is free although there may be a charge for some events and there is a car parking charge at weekends and Bank Hols from Apr to Oct and throughout the month of August. Abbey, craft centre and heritage centre open 10am to 5pm Apr to Oct, 10am to 4pm Nov to Mar.

Sherwood Forest Country Park

(Nottinghamshire County Council Leisure Services) **F** 182ha
O.S.S. 120 - SK 626 678
01623 823202

Situated on the B6034 N of the village of Edwinstowe, between A6075 and A616, 20 miles N of Nottingham. Sherwood is one of the most famous oak woodlands in the world. The name Sherwood means "wood of the Shire" and in the days of the Norman kings, Sherwood was a royal hunting forest covering one fifth of Nottinghamshire. Today you can follow the woodland paths through 450 acres of old Sherwood Forest to the mighty Major Oak, reputed to have been Robin Hood's favourite hideout. Situated on the edge of Sherwood Forest Country Park is a visitor centre with a range of facilities, including a Tourist Information Centre, site information and ranger's office, gift shop and colourful exhibition and Forest Table which serves snacks and refreshments. Leaflets detailing twice yearly events can be obtained from Ranger's Office, Sherwood Forest Visitor Centre, Edwinstowe, Mansfield, Notts NG21 9HN or telephone the above number. Open all year dawn to dusk. Visitor Centre - 10.30am to 5.00pm Apr to Oct: 10.30am to 4.30pm Nov to Mar. Free admission, although there may be a charge for some events, and there is a car parking charge at weekends and Bank Hols from Apr to Oct and throughout the month of August.

Sherwood is forever linked to the legend of Robin Hood but it is also a rare woodland habitat famed for its wealth of ancient oaks and insect fauna. The importance of this unique environment has been recognised with the area being designated an SSSI.

Sherwood Pines Forest Park

(Forest Enterprise) **F** 1000ha
O.S.S. 120 - SK 612 646
01623 822447

Access from B6030 Mansfield to Ollerton road east of Old Clipstone. Childrens play equipment, bike hire (weekends). Pony trekking is available in the forest. A 6 mile cycle trail includes an off-road mountain biking area.

Sherwood Pines Forest Park is the largest forest open to the public in the east Midlands. Its size and variety make it attractive to many forms of wildlife, including fallow deer.

Thieves Wood

(Managed by Forest Enterprise) **F** 194ha
O.S.S. 120 - SK 541 558
01623 822447

OXFORDSHIRE

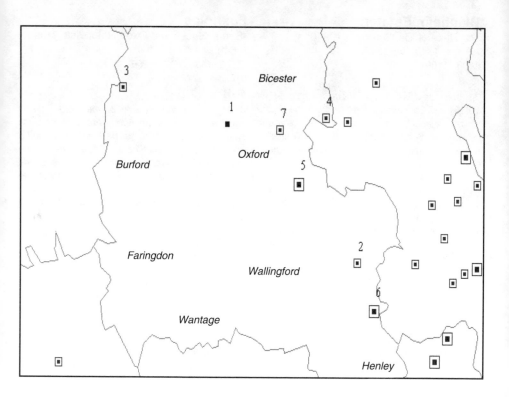

1. *Blenheim Estates
2. *Cowleaze Wood*
3. Foxholes
4. Piddington Wood
5. *Shabbington Wood*
6. Warburg Reserve
7. Whitecross Green Wood

*Blenheim Estates
(The Duke of Marlborough) **A** 840ha
O.S.S. 164 - SP 448 154
01993 811091

The main gate is on A44 about 1/4 mile SE of Woodstock. Educational tours around the estate can take place by prior arrangement all through the year via Schools Liaison Officer in writing or by telephoning above number. There is a guide for children.

Variety of woodland in varying stages of maturity looking at management problems, species, choice. Establishment, maintenance right through crop rotation. End uses of timber to be seen at the Estate Sawmill which is an important feature of educational visits, linking the growing tree with the produce we so often take for granted.

Cowleaze Wood
(Managed by Forestry Enterprise) **F** 29ha
O.S.S. 165 - SU 728 950
01296 625825

🚗50🚻2🕿 ⬥ ❋ i ⛺ ♿

From A40 between Stokenchurch and Postcombe, take road heading SW to Christmas Common and Nettlebed. Facilities include sculpture trail, signed by brown tourist signs from A40. There is free and full access to the wood at all times.

This small wood was planted with a mixture of conifers and broadleaves between 1957 and 1966. Management is aimed at producing a final crop of oak, with conifers removed during the rotation. In conjunction with the Oxfordshire sculpture project a "Sculpture Trail" has been set up. The number of sculptures will increase over time and, on occasions, the artists can be seen working on the site.

Foxholes
(Berks, Bucks and Oxon Naturalists Trust)
F 64ha
O.S.S. 163 - SP 254 206
01296 433222

🚗8🕿 ● i

A424 from Burford to Stow-on-the-Wold. Take R and just before Bruern Abbey turn L along track past Cocksmoor Wood car park on R after half a mile. A leaflet describing a wildlife walk around the reserve is available from the above phone number. No charge is made for access and the reserve is open all year. A BBONT nature reserve and an SSSI: Adjoining woods are private: please keep to rights of way.

Mainly a remnant of the ancient Wychwood Forest, soils and past management have created various habitats; wet ash - maple woodland, planted beech, hornbeam, larch, and mixed deciduous woodland, and open rides. In the ash - maple, early purple orchid and goldilocks buttercup appear in spring, with herb paris and common twayblade in summer. The rides support uncommon mosses and the heath spotted orchid. The wood is also good for fungi.

<table>
<tr><td>HAVEN WOODLANDS
Management of woodland, hedgerow &
heathland habitats. Management plans &
survey
17 Archers Road, Eastleigh, Hants, SO50 9AQ
Tel: 01703 496715</td></tr>
</table>

Piddington Wood
(Woodland Trust) **F** 10ha
O.S.S. 165 - SP 628 163
01476 74297

From Bicester take the A41 towards Aylesbury. Turn R onto the B4011 towards Oakley. After 3 miles Piddington Wood may be seen on the R and you may park along the verge. There is full and free access to the wood. Early maps show that Piddington is likely to have once been just outside the historic boundary of Bernwood

there is little doubt that it would have been managed as coppice woodland.

Classic oak and ash standards are the main tree species with blackthorn as the dominant shrub. The wood is rich in ground flora such as primrose and yellow archangel. A variety of wildlife inhabits the wood, including muntjac and fallow deer, badger, woodcock and elusive black and brown hairstreak butterflies.

Shabbington Wood
(Managed by Forest Enterprise) **F** 287ha
O.S.S. 165 - SP 611 117
0296 625825

🚗 🏕 ♨🔺

The wood is situated on minor road running from B4011 at Oakley, and B4027 at Stanton St John. Facilities include car parking, picnic area and Bernwood butterfly trail..

Shabbington Wood is a forest nature reserve and an SSSI.

Warburg Reserve
(Berks, Bucks and Oxon Naturalists Trust)
F 103ha
O.S.S. 175 - SU 720 880
01296 433222

🚗10🔙 ♨ WC ⓘ 𝄞

Leave Henley NW on the A423 and fork R at the end of the Fair Mile onto the B480. Turn L just N of Middle Assendon and follow the twisty lane for two miles. Shortly after the lane becomes a track you reach the reserve and car park. There is a reserve centre and nature trail. No charge is made for access and the reserve is open all year. A BBONT nature reserve and an SSSI.

A complex of woodland and grassland lying on chalk slopes in a winding valley. Over 450 species of higher plants have been recorded, as well as 850 species of fungi, 37 species of butterflies, 250 species of moths and 75 species of birds. Among the higher plants are 15 species of wild orchids and 50 plants usually only found in ancient woodland in the south of England.

Management includes coppicing some of the woodland and grazing of chalk grassland.

Whitecross Green Wood
(Berks, Bucks and Oxon Naturalists Trust)
F 62ha
O.S.S. 164 - SP 603 145
01296 433222

🚗 ♨ ⓘ

A43 north from Oxford. Turn right to Islip. In Islip turn L to Merton then first R. 1 mile after Murcott turn R onto track into the reserve. Go through two gates into car park. A leaflet describing a wildlife walk around the reserve is available from the above phone number. No charge is made for access and the reserve is open all year. A BBONT nature reserve and a Site of Special Scientific Interest (SSSI).

This is an ancient woodland harbouring about 200 plant species. Half the wood was felled in the sixties by the Forestry Commission and replanted with conifers. This area is now being returned to native woodland. The remainder is blackthorn - hawthorn thicket and overgrown hazel coppice with oak and ash standards. Some coppicing is done to encourage wildflowers such as bluebells, ramsons, and yellow archangel which are seen between April and June. The nightingale nests here, with many butterflies including black hairstreak and purple emperor.

SHROPSHIRE

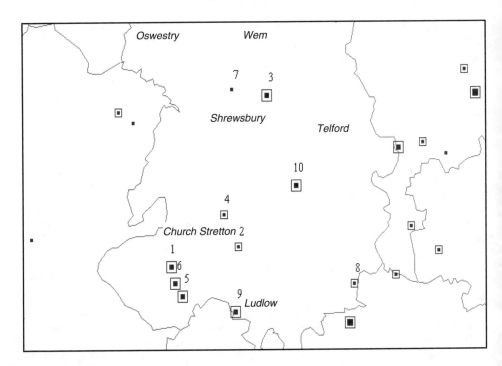

1. Bury Ditches
2. *Edge Wood
3. Haughmond Hill
4. Helmeth Wood
5. Hopton Forest
6. Hurst Woodlands
7. *Leaton Knolls
8. Longdon & Withybed
9. *Mortimer Forest*
10. Wenlock Edge

Bury Ditches
(Managed by Forest Enterprise) **F** 276ha
O.S.S. 137 - SO 334 839
(01584 874542
🚗20🐾 👤 ☀ 🌳 🥾 🚴

From Clunton, on the Craven Arms/Clunton road (B4368), take lane towards Brockton for 2½ miles (a brown tourist sign is sited on this junction). Car park on L. 3 waymarked walks passing through the magnificent Bury Ditches. Iron Age Hill Fort. Also cycle tracks. Contact Forest District Office on the above telephone number for brochure. Open all year dawn to dusk.

*Edge Wood
(Anne Dyer) **F** 28ha
O.S.S. 137 - SO 479 876
(01584 861293
Westhope College, Westhope, Craven Arms, Shropshire, SY7 9JL
🚗10🚌1🐾◡👤 ☀ 🌳 🥾

From Craven Arms take Much Wenlock road for 3½ miles. At the bottom of the second dip turn L for Westhope and Ticklerton. Continue on this road for two miles finally rising up hill to picnic area and car park. Room for 10 cars in car park and one coach on verge. Guided walks may be arranged by contacting Anne Dyer at the above address, giving at least one week's notice. Leaflets describing the trees, wildflowers and wildlife may be obtained from Westhope College.

The paths through the wood are kept clear of bramble. This is an SSSI planted about 1880 on scrubland. It is part of the 20 mile long Wenlock Edge escarpment. Many of the less frequently seen animals may be found here including badgers, polecats and dormice, and also a wide variety of birds, buzzard, owls, long tailed tits to name but a few. The woodland itself is mostly 100 year old oak and ash standards with a rich understorey of regularly coppiced hazel and other native species such as spindle, dogwood, guelder rose etc. The wood also has some rare plants.

Haughmond Hill
(Managed by Forest Enterprise) **F** 132 ha
O.S.S. 126 - SJ 546 148
(01584 874542
🚗50🐾 👤 ☀ 🌳 WC ♿ 🌳🔲 🥾

3 miles out of Shrewsbury on B5062, turn R at top of bank after Haughmond Abbey, car park on R. 2 waymarked walks and all ability trail. No charge. Open all year dawn to dusk. Fine view of Shrewsbury and Stretton Hills.

Helmeth Wood: Church Stretton
(Woodland Trust) **F** 24 ha
O.S.S. 137 - SO 468 938
(01476 74297
🚗🐾 🍴

From the A49 take the B4371 signposted to Much Wenlock. Immediately turn L along the Watling Street North for about 300 yards and park in the vicinity of Helmeth Road. Open at all times of the year. The paths to the wood, and within the wood, are usually muddy. Wellington boots or stout shoes are advised.

Helmeth Wood is an ancient sessile oak woodland, which has been traditionally coppiced. You will see some very impressive stools, or stumps, some as much as nine feet across. In springtime, the woodland ground cover is especially colourful with bluebell, primrose and dog's mercury. In summer, the woodland is alive with the song of summer visitors such as willow warbler and chiffchaff as well as resident birds, which include wren and great tit. Buzzards have also been known to nest here.

Hopton Forest
(Managed by Forest Enterprise) **F** 338 ha
O.S.S. 137 - SO 355 783
(01584 874542
🚗30🐾 👤 ☀ 🌳 WC ♿

8 miles SW of Craven Arms off B4367 at Hoptonheath, through Hopton Castle, turn L up forest road. Mountain bike trail - an innovative and exhilarating mountain bike course. Waterproof map showing numbered stations and contours is available from district office (£1.25). Walkers beware - specialist mountain bike area. Fantastic panoramic view from top of hill.

Hurst Woodlands
(Mr D Sainsbury) **F** 218ha
O.S.S. 137 - SO 338 807
(01588 673314
🚗12🚶🏇♨🌲🏕

Take the B4368 from Craven Arms towards Clun. After 6 miles turn left in the village of Clunton just before the Crown inn. Follow the small lane uphill and the wood entrance and car park can be found after 0.5 mile on the R. Walkers are asked not to approach or interfere with the bird nesting boxes set up in the north west part of the woodland.

The Hurst Woodlands form a single block of 218 hectares which faces north and rises from about 240 m to 440 m. The wood contains mixed species, with oak being the predominant broadleaf and Sitka spruce the predominant conifer. Along the northern edge and in two deep gullies within the wood stand some magnificent Douglas fir planted after the First World War and measuring up to 130 feet high. Walkers are asked to follow and remain on the numerous rides that run through the woodland.

*Leaton Knolls
(Charles Bridgeman) **P** 30ha
O.S.S. 126 - SJ 468 178
(01939 290384
🔋£2🚗30🚌1🚶🏇♨WC ℹ 📖 🏇

From Shrewsbury A528 North for 1/4 mile from town centre. L on to B5067 Baschurch. Approx 3.5 miles, soon after Church with spire on R, sharp L following "Leaton Forest" signs. Follow track for 0.5 mile and park adjacent to wooden buildings. Forest Fayre with self guided walks, country games, crafts and teas, Sunday June 11th 1.00 - 5.30pm. Other times, parties (min. 15) strictly by prior appointment with owner, 1st April - 1st October.

Mixed woodland on steep bank running down to River Severn. Largely replanted since 1950 with a wide variety of species. Tour includes The Dingle which contains a number of fine Redwoods, and there is a fine stand of beech. Specialities include Christmas trees and cricket bat willows. Managed for timber production, the wood contains varied wildlife, particularly along the river bank. Buzzards are often seen.

Longdon and Withybed
(E P Cadbury) **F** 80ha
O.S.S. 138 - SO 761 774 (Car Park) SO 752 780 (Button Oak Inn)
(01691 653400
🚶🅿🏇♨FP 🐾

B4194 2 miles from Bewdley town centre (hard right at church top of Loud Street) or Whittles Bus to Bulton Oak Inn. Park in Forest Enterprise car park, Hawkbatch. Cross B4194 with care, stile and gap in hedge.

Old coppice being converted to high oak forest by underplanting with conifers, Norway spruce, Scots pine, tsuga, abies grandis, and Douglas fir. Paths run on into National Nature Reserve where oak regeneration is being encouraged. This area let to English Nature, to whom enquiries should be referred. Fallow deer. Some wild service trees. Norman E. Hickin's "Natural History of an English Forest" gives further information.

Mortimer Forest
(Managed by Forest Enterprise) **F** 950ha
O.S.S. 138 - SO 474 732
(01584 874542
🚗40🚶🏇♨🌲ℹ 🍽📷🏇🥾

High Vinnalls car park is 4 miles W. of Ludlow on Wigmore road. The Forest District Office is two miles from Ludlow along this same road. During office hours please call in for details. 4 waymarked walks, 1.5 to 10 miles long, all ability trail, geological trail and educational trail. Open all year round dawn to dusk. Forest events programme with 35 annual events available from Forest District Office.

This beautiful mixed woodland has four waymarked walks, one of which has a superb panoramic view of the surrounding countryside), an all ability trail which passes two attractive ponds, a geological trail which explores the Ludlovian rocks in the Silurian system, 24 page booklet available from district forest office and a self-guiding educational trail. An attractive and comprehensive information pack detailing woodland walks within 20 separate Forest Enterprise woods available from District Forest Office for £2.25 plus p&p.

Wenlock Edge
(National Trust) **F** 225ha
O.S.S. 137 - SO 613 996, SO 584 976
(01694 723068

Access to northern section of Wenlock Edge (Harley Bank) from N.T. car park situated 0.5 mile S of Much Wenlock on the B4371 - alternative car park at Blakeway Coppice 3 miles SW of Much Wenlock adjoining the B4371.

This mixed woodland limestone escarpment, which lies within an AONB, runs from Ironbridge to Craven Arms and provides fine views over the surrounding countryside. It is famous for its geology, in particular its coral reef exposures. A rich limestone flora includes the wild service tree and several species of orchid.

SOMERSET

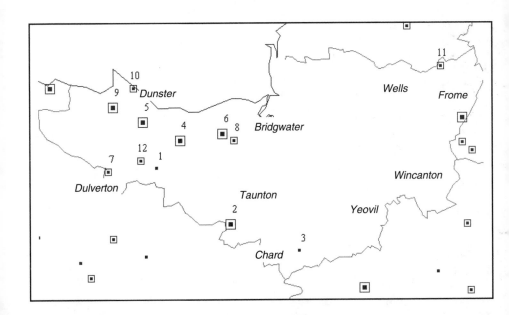

1. *Bittiscombe
2. *Blackdowns*
3. *Chard Wood
4. *Combe Sydenham
5. *Dunster Wood
6. *Great Wood*
7. *Hadborough Plantation
8. Hawkridge
9. Horner, Luccombe and Selworthy
10. *Moor Wood
11. Nap Wood, Amberdown
12. Wimbleball Lake Woods

*Bittiscombe

(B H Malyon) **A** 89ha
O.S.S. 181 - ST 011 293
01364 3316
🚗10 ⛴ ❄ 🍴 🥾

From Bampton 7 miles N of Tiverton, proceed N on B3190 for approximately 5 miles to Upton, then after one mile turn R at "The Lowtrow Inn". After 200 yards Lowtrow Lodge on R.   All visits by appointment only. Please give 21 days notice for each visit and contact Alistair Sandels 01364 3316 for details and bookings. Guided visits can be arranged at certain times of the year, preferably in the months of Feb, Apr, Jul and Oct. Donations made to Forestry Trust.

Bittiscombe Woods offer the opportunity to view and walk around a very fine example of a multi purpose forestry estate, with four trout lakes and ancient semi-natural woodland. The conifers were established between 1954 and 1971. Planted with a mixture of Douglas fir and larch which are highly productive. Small areas of western hemlock, red cedar, spruce, grand fir and redwood can be found. Also beech, poplar and ancient semi-natural oak woodland. Deer, wildfowl and birds of prey can be regularly seen.

Blackdowns

(Managed by Forest Enterprise) **F** 400ha
O.S.S. 181/193 - ST 174 158
01392 832262

Exit M5 at junction 26. Head S at top of hill approx. 3 miles turn L. Facilities identified on N side heading E at regular intervals. 3 car parks, picnic areas, viewpoint, forest walks.

*Chard Wood

(Dr J D Jackson) **P** 17ha
O.S.S. 193 - ST 345 092
01258 453262
🚗20 🥾 ⛴ 🍴

The wood is 1½ miles E of Chard on Avishayes Lane which runs parallel to and N of A30. Car parking on verge in lane. The owner will conduct a

Woodland Walk on June 11th at 2.30pm. Contributions to Forestry Trust.

These two small woods were planted by the Lord of the Manor following the enclosure of Chard Common in 1819. The earthen boundary embankments made at the time can still be seen together with a few original oaks. After extensive felling in both World Wars, most of the wood has been replanted more than once and now contains some useful Scots pine, Douglas fir and some beech and oak. The shallow and poor soil causes the trees to be subject to wind-throw. A stream runs through Tudbeer towards Chard Reservoir.

*Combe Sydenham Country Park

(Theed Estates) **RE** 200ha
O.S.S. 181 - ST 074 364
01984 656284
♿£4🚗🚌🥾⛴❄🦌 WC ℹ️ 📖 ☂ FP 🚶
🚻🍴🛍🏕🛍

From Taunton take the Minehead road A358 to Bishops Lydeard, L onto B3224 (under railway bridge), follow brown signs to Combe Sydenham Country Park turning R at crossroads in 5 miles. Entrance in valley 1 mile on L. There is parking for 10 coaches and 350 cars. There are WCs on the site. Attractions include fly-fishing for beginners, working watermill and bakery, fish farming, ancient trail of trees, Alice trail, tearoom serving lunches, restored Court Room, deer park, deserted hamlet and ornamental tree nursery. Combe Sydenham, the family home of Sir Francis Drake's second wife, has an extensive schools' programme. There are forest trails with different themes and information leaflets contribute to the enjoyment and understanding of the woodlands which are open from Easter to end Oct, Sun to Fri, 10am to 5pm and all Sundays in Nov. No booking is necessary for individual visits, 7 days notice is required for all group visits. Car parking is free. Visits are £4.00 for adults and £1.50 for children 5-16 years, children under 5 free.

The woods are set in a deep valley rising from 300 to 1000 feet with viewing points over the Bristol Channel and taking in the whole of the Quantocks.

The coniferous plantations have been planted over the last thirty years and are interspersed with ancient and amenity woodlands. The woods produce fine timber and are exceptional to walk in, recently recognized by a Forestry Authority Centre of Excellence Award and a Sandford Award for contributions to Heritage Education.

*Dunster Wood

(Crown Estate) **RE** 400ha
O.S.S. 181 - SS 978 424
01643 821309

🚗🐎🔨 ⊙ ❋ 𝖄 ⓘ ☂ 🏕🏚

Head S from Dunster, taking a LH turn off the A396 towards Luxborough. After 0.5 mile bear R at fork and the car park is situated approximately 0.5 mile along the L-hand side and is signposted "Nutcombe Bottom". Facilities here include car parking, picnic areas and a children's play area. Special parking and picnic facilities are available for disabled visitors.

Along the trails are various stops which have on-site interpretations - these refer to forest operations and archaeological evidence such as hill forts and enclosures. The tallest tree in England is also to be found. Awarded Centre of Excellence Award in 1995.

Great Wood: Quantocks

(Managed by Forest Enterprise) **F** 600 ha
O.S.S. 181 - ST 175 375
01392 832262

🚗🍴 WC ♿ ☂

From Taunton follow signs to Kingston St. Mary, pass through Kingston St. Mary, follow signs to Nether Stowey. 1 mile S of Nether Stowey turn L (sign Over Stowey), take next turning L. Toilets (with disabled access), car parks, forest walks.

Hadborough Plantation

(Somerset County Council/Exmoor National Park) **F** 18ha
O.S.S. 181 - SS 868 284
01398 23665

🚗🍴🌲 WC 𝖄 ⓘ 🏚

B3180 from Bampton following signs to Wimbleball Water Park. Follow for about 4 miles. At top of climb road turns sharply R, Haddon Hill car park signed.

A circular walk is possible through the mixed plantation, turning right and back on oneself to return via the higher moorland track. Sitka spruce, western hemlock, Scots pine, Japanese larch and beech. Spectacular views across Exmoor moorland landscape as well as Wimbleball Dam and Lake. Red and roe deer frequent the plantation as well as foxes, badgers, and several species of butterfly.

Hawkridge: Quantocks

(Stephen Penny) **F** 11ha
O.S.S. 181/182 - ST 202 358
01823 480651

🚗2🦌🔨❋𝖄

From Bridgwater (Junctions 23 and 24, M5) follow signs for Durleigh, then keep straight on past four forks to Hawkridge reservoir (about 5 miles). About 50m after the end of the car park is a gateway with stile. From Taunton (Junction 25, M5) follow signs to Kingston St. Mary. Follow main road through village and up Buncombe Hill (2 miles). At top of hill go straight (slightly L) over at five cross roads. Keep straight on through Lower Aisholt until the west end of Hawkridge reservoir is reached. Turn R and the gateway with stile is 100m on R. For this gateway park at reservoir car park. There is another gateway with stile on the Aisholt road with parking for one or two cars outside the gate. (NG ST 201357) No access when forestry operations in progress.

This attractive woodland is situated on the edge of the Quantock Hills, which is an area much frequented by the public. Hawkridge has a nice balance of semi-mature broadleaves and conifers, which were planted between 1963 and 1968. It is very rich in both flora and fauna, containing some rare plant species and also both red and roe deer are present. Within the woodland is an interesting old lime kiln, which is in reasonable condition, together with a number of quarries. These are fenced on the top edge but please take care.

Horner, Luccombe and Selworthy (Holnicote Estate)
(National Trust) **F** 480 ha
O.S.S. 181 - SS 903 440
01643 862452
🚗50🚽3🚶 🅿 ✳ Y WC ♿ ⓘ 📖⛺ ☕
🚩 💷

2 miles S of Porlock in Exmoor National Park. Parking at Horner, Webber's Post and Selworthy. Pile's Mill Study Centre

Horner Wood consists mainly of oak and is designated an SSSI, with walks that lead you through medieval village sites and past charcoal pits, a wood not to be missed. Luccombe and Selworthy by contrast are mixed with conifers and broadleaves. Well worth a look is the cathedral-like Douglas fir in Luccombe, planted in the 1920s, or perhaps a walk on one of the 20 miles or so of footpaths in Selworthy Woods, finishing in Selworthy village with its thatched cottages, National Trust shop and a well earned visit to the tea rooms.

*Moor Wood
(Somerset County Council/Exmoor National Park) **F** 22ha
O.S.S. 181 - SS 953 475
01398 23665
🚗🚶 🅿 📖⛺🚶

Turn off Minehead High Street into Blenheim Road. Turn L just past "Plume of Feathers" pub (signed to North Hill). Follow road for 2 miles around tight bends. past church and uphill. The wood is located above a small campsite. Car park, picnic tables, woodland trail (available from Information Centres).

The wood contains a great variety of tree species, both conifer and broadleaf, due to its past as an amenity estate woodland. It was severely damaged in the gales of January 1990, but has now been restocked with European larch, Scots pine and beech. This was for visual attractiveness and an early return from the conifers. A longer term crop is represented by the beech. Various establishment systems have been used to experiment and demonstrate restocking techniques.

These include 2m deer fencing, 1m rabbit fencing, multi sized tree shelters and plastic mesh guards. The pros and cons of these techniques are demonstrated. Both roe and red deer frequent these woods and many woodland birds species are also well represented. Close proximity to the sea and large areas of coastal heath and farmland make this wood a varied and complex site.

Nap Wood, Ammerdown Park
(Lord Hylton) **F** 20ha
O.S.S. 183 - ST 715 535
01761 437382
🚗🚶 🅿

Take A362 (Frome) road SE. from Radstock junction with A367 for 2½ miles. At junction A362/A366 (Terry Hill) enter wood through iron gate on S side of crossroads. Nature trail marked. Open at all times in daylight. Visitors to keep strictly to marked paths. No vehicles. Parking by entrance gate. No horses.

Conifer and broad leaved woodlands at all stages of development from young plantations to mature stands. Full spectrum of indigenous flora.

Wimbleball Lake Woods
(South West Water Services Limited) **F** 39ha
O.S.S. 181 - SS 970 310
🚗🚶 🅿 WC

Follow signs from A396 to Wimbleball Lake. Car parking and WCs available on site. There is a charge for car parking in the main Cowlings car park, other smaller areas free. Open all year round.

West Hill Wood consists of ancient oak coppice, full of wild flowers in the spring. Other woods are more modern but being converted to mainly broadleaf. Many wonderful views over Wimbleball Lake.

STAFFORDSHIRE

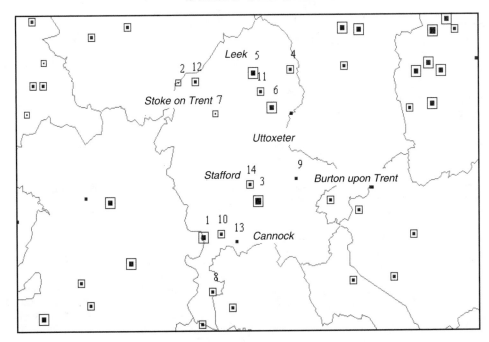

1. Big Wood
2. Black Firs
3. *Cannock Forest
4. Castern Wood
5. Combe Valley
6. *Dimmings Dale*
7. Hem Heath Wood
8. Himley Plantation
9. *Jacksons Bank
10. The Lower Avenue
11. *Moseymoor Wood*
12. Parrot's Drumble
13. Somerford
14. Stafford Plantation

Big Wood

(Peter Giffard) **R** 100ha
O.S.S. 127 - SJ 864 068
01902 850768

£2.50 🚗🚐👤☀🍴

From the N, M6 to Junction 12. From the S, M6 to Junction 10A and M54 to Junction 2. Take A449 (Wolverhampton to Stafford road). Turn off at double roundabout, through Coven to Brewood and follow signs to Chillington. Free parking in front of the house. This is not suitable for coaches. Coaches must always make a prior appointment. The charge for the house and grounds, which includes the woodlands, is £2.50 per person. The charge for the grounds only is £1.25 per person. Children are half price. The grounds, which include the woodlands, are open on all days when Chillington Hall is open to the public. In 1995 the opening days are Thursdays from Jun to Sept 14, Easter Sunday and Sundays prior to May Day and Spring Bank Holidays and all Sundays in Aug, 2.30 to 5.30 pm. Parties of at least 15 can come at other times by prior arrangement; applications should be made in writing at least 4 weeks ahead. Visitors should park in front of the house and call at the house to obtain a pass.

Big Wood forms part of Chillington Park which was enlarged and improved by 'Capability' Brown. Much of the woodlands is a site of Ancient Semi-Natural Woodland. All is comprised within the Chillington conservation area. The woods are managed commercially but with a view to enhancing Brown's Park and Brown's Great Lake of 85 acres. There is a signed walk around the lake for 4 miles which passes through the woods for most of its way. There are young trees as well as mature trees and an observant visitor may be able to spot 30 different species of trees.

Black Firs

(Staffordshire Wildlife Trust) **F** 3ha
O.S.S. 127 - SJ 746 500
01889 508534

Off A531 Crewe-Newcastle road, at Balterley Heath. Park at Post Office Lane. Paths and interpretative signs. Open at all times. Black Firs is

a designated SSSI.

A wood which has developed on an old wetland site as a result of planting and natural regeneration. Still shows character of wetland habitat.

*Cannock Forest

(Managed by Forest Enterprise) **F** 2600ha
O.S.S. 127/128 - SK 019 171
01889 586593

🚗🐴👤☂ℹ🍴🎣

Take the A51 through Rugeley. Turn into Hagley Road at the traffic lights between the two roundabouts signposted to Cannock Chase visitor centre. Follow road out of the town, in approximately 1 mile turn L into forest centre. Signposted. Car parking, deer museum, caravan site, orienteering, permit fishing, permit horse riding, education facilities, wildlife hide, forest walks. Mountain bikers are requested to follow the mountain bike code and give way to pedestrians.

Castern Wood SSSI

(Staffordshire Wildlife Trust) **F** 21ha
O.S.S. 119 - SK 119 537
01889 508534

🚗🐴🚶ℹ🍴

Approach via the unclassified road running due SE from Wetton. This continues almost straight for 1.5 miles over a small crossroads. At the end of the lane, turn R by a tall public footpath sign, through a gate and into a field. Follow the track to a small parking area at its end. Interpretative signs. Open at all times.

Deciduous woodland, scrub and grassland in a steep-sided valley sloping down to the R Manifold. Excellent views of the Manifold Valley and Beeston Tor. Woodland is a mix of ash, wych elm and sycamore with a few field maple and lime. Shrub layer includes hazel, blackthorn, hawthorn and dogwood. Dogs mercury carpets much of the woodland floor and several different ferns grow. In many of the shady spots both wood avens and water avens are found. Mammals include the stoat, weasel, bank vole, wood mouse and fox, while birds such as redstart, all three woodpeckers, blackcap, nuthatch and treecreeper are present. There are also records of sparrowhawk, tawny owl and woodcock.

Combe Valley
(RSPB) **R** 104ha
O.S.S. 119 - SK 005 530
01538 384017

Take the A523 from Leek to Ashbourne. After 3 miles turn right up the minor road to Apesford as signposted. The reserve is on the left after 1 mile. Reserve nature trails are open every day from 9.00am until 9.00pm, or sunset when earlier. Visitor centre open most days from May to August inclusive, and weekends only from September to April.

The reserve comprises a steep-sided valley with a rocky stream. The slopes are covered largely by oak, but with a range of other species such as ash, birch, holly, rowan, bird cherry and hazel. The wood supports a breeding bird community typical of more western oakwoods, including pied flycatcher, redstart, wood warbler, tree pipit. Sparrowhawks, tawny owls and three species of woodpecker occur here, whilst dippers, grey wagtails and kingfishers frequent the streams. Badgers are numerous with several setts, and the woods harbour an outstanding invertebrate fauna.

Dimmings Dale
(Managed by Forest Enterprise) **F** 260ha
O.S.S. 119/128 - SK 063 432
01889 586593

From Cheadle take the B5417 to Oakamoor village, turn R at the bottom of steep hill, before the bridge in the village. Take first L and follow narrow lane towards Alton. In 1½ miles car park is on L by the Ramblers Retreat Café. Forest walks, car park, café, all ability access along valley floor from car park. Please, no mountain bikes on the forest walk.

Dimmings Dale in the Churnet valley has a rich industrial heritage with ore smelting and quarrying. In the 1800s the Earl of Shrewsbury laid out magnificent carriage drives leading from his country seat at what is now Alton Towers. The forest walk winds through ancient woodland, and crosses the Ranger SSSI, one of the last remaining ancient hill pastures in the area. Water flows quietly down the valley through a series of large fish ponds.

Hem Heath Wood
(Managed by Staffordshire Wildlife Trust)
F 8ha
O.S.S. 118 - SJ 885 412
01889 508534

On S side of A5035 between Trentham and Longton. This is on the southern fringe of Stoke-on-Trent. Nature trail, access for disabled, interpretive signs on site. Open at all times.

This wood was planted about 150 years ago and includes 34 species of tree. Plants include moschatel, yellow pimpernel, common twayblade, broadleaved helleborine, marsh marigold and marsh cinquefoil. A wide variety of woodland birds use the wood, including sparrowhawks. There is a large pond which is being restored.

Himley Plantation
(Woodland Trust) **F** 24ha
O.S.S. 139 - SO 870 914
01476 74297

Approaching from the E, leave the A449 Wolverhampton to Kidderminster road on to the B4176 to Bridgnorth. From the W, the B4176 signposted to Dudley off the A454. Continue along the B4176 Bridgnorth road to Himley and turn off into Himley Lane, signposted to Halfpenny Green and Swindon. Immediately after passing under the railway bridge, turn R into the country park car park. Please note that the car park is closed overnight; the closing time is displayed at the entrance to the parking area. You will find the main access point to Himley Plantation is at the far end of the car park. The wood is open at all times of the year. Some paths may be muddy so stout footwear is advisable particularly in the winter months.

MEYNELL INGRAM ARMS, HOAR CROSS
A fine old country inn serving fresh home cooked food lunch times and evenings. Good real ales and quality wine list. Log fires in all bars: walkers welcome. Tel 01283 575202.

The main body of Himley Plantation is mixed high forest with oak and common lime as the main tree species. There is a variety of birds present in the wood such as tawny owl, barn owl and three species of woodpecker. Other birds in the wood are more difficult to observe, including hawfinch and bullfinch. There are some fine, tall alder trees in the wood and areas of thick willow scrub which remain wild, and largely undisturbed. Under these conditions sphagnum, the 'bog-moss', and many species of sedge can be found.

*Jacksons Bank

(Duchy of Lancaster) **A** 35ha
O.S.S. 128 - SK 139 233
01283 512244

 30 ☂ ☉ ☼ ⛺ ⛰ 🏕

The wood lies to the W of the A515 Lichfield to Ashbourne road, approximately 4 miles N of Yoxall. Turn L at Newchurch. The wood is approximately 1/2 mile on the RH side. There is parking for 30 cars. There is a picnic area with hard path access, woodland trails and a horse trail. All group visits by appointment only. There are self-guided trails in the wood. For further details/appointments please contact C P Meynell, Messrs John German, 1 Lichfield Street, Burton on Trent, Staffordshire, DE14 3QZ or telephone above number.

Jacksons Bank forms part of the ancient forest of Needwood and is within the National Forest boundary. Felled during the second World War, the wood was replanted between 1949-53 with a mixture of conifers and broadleaf and has further developed with natural regeneration, providing a changing character and colour throughout the year. There is a wide variety of ground flora, some of which is rare and particular to the Needwood Forest area in Staffordshire.

The Lower Avenue

(Peter Giffard) **F** 11 ha
O.S.S. 127 - SJ 898 076 or SJ 882 075
01902 850768

Take the A449 Wolverhampton to Stafford road. Turn off at double roundabout (O.S. 913063) and proceed towards Brewood. A small car park (not suitable for coaches) is available in Park Lane. Open all the year. A broadleaved wood in the making. The Lower Avenue is over a mile in length and runs from Brewood to Coven road (O.S. sheet 127 - 898076) to Park Lane (O.S. 882075).

Originally a beech avenue which was part of the private approach to Chillington Hall. Most beeches have been removed and the whole Avenue has been planted (1955-1975) as an oak wood with some elm, sweet chestnut, beech and hornbeam. The driveway down the centre has been dedicated as a public right of way on foot. The Lower Avenue forms part of a designated Conservation Area. It crosses the Shropshire Union Canal by a fine ornamental bridge by Telford.

Moseymoor Wood

(Managed by Forest Enterprise) **F** 23 ha
O.S.S. 128/119 - SK 025 476
01889 586593

The wood can be entered on foot by the footpath from Froghall wharf, signposted from the A52 at Froghall between Ashbourne and Stoke-on-Trent.

Parrot's Drumble

(Managed by Staffordshire Wildlife Trust)
F 12ha
O.S.S. 118 - SJ 817 523
01889 508534
Between A500 and Janage Industrial Estate. Access is by public footpath from lay-by on

eastbound carriageway of A500 between Alsager and Newcastle-under Lyme turn-offs. Path. Open at all times.

A rich deciduous valley woodland and stream, dominated by oak, birch, alder and hazel. Around the edge are a number of mature beech and occasional turkey oaks. Along the stream are several hybrid poplars, thought to have been planted in the early 1800s and a sizeable patch of alder. Good for bluebells.

Viscount Anson, later created Earl of Lichfield. The woodland is managed on continuous cover principles. The Shugborough estate, which is the seat of the Earls of Lichfield, comprises 400 ha of parkland, woodland and formal garden. The mansion house, county museum and working farm museum are open to the public. Details from the property.

Somerford

(AS Monckton) **A** 40ha
O.S.S. 127 - SJ 911 080
Stretton Hall, Stafford, ST19 9LQ

Take A449 north from M54. After 3 miles pass Harrows Inn. Enter transport cafe on left after 250 metres. Tour with owner, by appointment only.

Private wood with large variety of hardwoods. Easy walking. Tour 1 hour approx.

Stafford Plantation, Shugborough Park

(National Trust - managed by Staffordshire County Council) **F** 50ha
O.S.S. 127 - SJ 991 216
01889 881388

4.5 miles E of Stafford, on the A513 Stafford/ Lichfield road. The meeting point is the farm car park which may be approached via the main entrance (well signposted) or, if this is closed, via the exit to the park, one mile to the E. Guided walks available by prior arrangement. Schools and coach parties welcome. Charges - variable for guided walks. Open throughout the year. It may be necessary to restrict access to parts of the woodland during forestry operations, which take place in the winter.

An attractive mixed woodland of oak, beech, sweet chestnut and Scots pine, with specimen trees, most of which were planted between 1820 and 1833 by

SUFFOLK

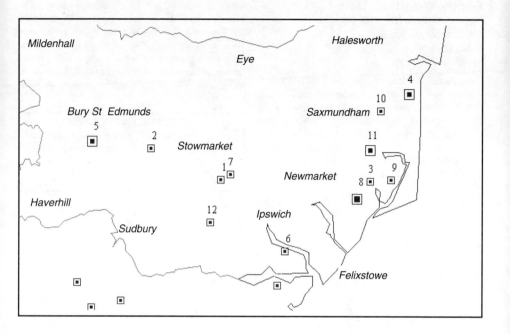

1. Bonny Wood
2. *Bradfield Woods
3. *Chillesford Wood*
4. *Dunwich Forest*
5. Ickworth Park
6. Pinmill
7. Priestley Wood
8. *Rendlesham Forest*
9. *Sudbourne*
10. *Theberton Woods*
11. *Tunstall Forest*
12. Wolves Wood

Bonny Wood
(Suffolk Wildlife Trust) **F** 20ha
O.S.S. 155 - TM 076 520
01449 737996

From Needham Market take the B1078 south to Barking Tye. Park at the village hall opposite the pub. Walk south along the roadside verge, past the garage and take the footpath past the water tower down toward the wood. Follow the path and cross the narrow arable field into the wood. Do not enter the woodland to the left of the entrance as this is private. Wellies usually needed.

A marvellous ancient wood with spectacular spring flowers including anemone, orchids, herb paris and violets. Wide range of native trees. Coppicing has been reintroduced. Spring birds including nightingale abundant.

> ## THE SIX BELLS
> Home cooked food, good beer,
> non smoking restaurant.
> Church Road, Felsham
> 01449 736268

*Bradfield Woods National Nature Reserve
(Suffolk Wildlife Trust) **R** 68ha
O.S.S. 155 - TL 935 581
01449 737996

Take the A134 Sudbury road S from Bury St. Edmunds. At Sicklesmere, just past the Rushbrooke Arms, turn L for Lt. Whelnetham and Bradfield St. George. Go through both villages towards Felsham. The woods are on the R. There is a small car park. Open at all times. Access restricted to rides and paths. No dogs except on leads. Leaflets available at all times. Visitor centre open Sundays and Bank Holidays Easter to end September, 1300 - 1700 only.

One of England's finest ancient woodlands. Foremost example of actively coppiced woodland unbroken since at least 1252. Many ancient stools, masses of

spring flowers, oxlip, wood anemone, herb paris. Migratory birds, invertebrates, fungi, small mammals. NB The fences are for deer exclusion! Educational visits welcome at all levels. Contact Asst. Warden. Occasional green wood work courses. Groups may arrange guided walks - £1.30 per head, £16 minimum. More detailed information sheets available on some subjects.

> ## THE FOX AND HOUNDS
> Home cooked food and snacks are on the
> menu at tne Fox and Hounds, washed down
> by Greene King IPA and Abbot Ale.
> Felsham Road, Bradfield St. George.

Chillesford Wood
(Forest Enterprise) **F** 62ha
O.S.S. 156 - TM 377 519
01394 450164

1 mile from Butle village going east on B1084 between Woodbridge and Orford.

Small conifer woodland with some broadleaf areas.

*Dunwich Forest
(Forest Enterprise) **F** 484ha
O.S.S. 156 - TM 461 712
01394 450164

2.5 miles south of Blythburgh off B1125 and surrounding Dunwich village. Car park is situated 1 mile west of Dunwich village on road to Blytyburgh. (Forest Trail leaflets 80p from the Westleton Post Office or National Trust, Dunwich Heath). Additionally there is a permit horse trail and an off road cycle trail (details from the Forest Office, Tangham, Woodbridge, IP12 3NF). Donations to Forestry Trust.

Medium sized coniferous woodland block that was extensively damaged by the Great Gale of 1987. Now replanted the forest has a mixture of heathland and wetland sites that may be visited at random or by following the Dunwich Forest Trail.

Ickworth Park
(National Trust) **F** 241ha
O.S.S. 155 - TL 815 616
01284 735270

 WC *i* 🍴 🚻

Take the A143 SW from Bury St. Edmunds for approximately 3 miles to the village of Horringer. Ickworth Park and car park is clearly signposted in the village. There is a large car park in the middle of the park offering an info-point map service which shows several waymarked routes of varying lengths including the 8 mile Grand Tour. Toilets and restaurant are available when the house is open. Refreshments in car park during summer. There is a deer enclosure near the main car park. The woodlands are open year round to the public. There is a charge of £1.50 adult, 50p children Apr to Nov. No charge for walkers.

These woods form a visual perimeter around the park and are predominantly hardwood. Some of the woods are ancient semi-natural woodlands. Large areas - Lownde Wood - are oak standards with hazel coppice. In the associated park there are over 200 ancient oak pollards (2 oaks being over 700 years old). There is a wide range of fauna and flora associated with these woods.

Pinmill
(National Trust) **F** 26ha
O.S.S. 169 - TM 206 379
01263 733471

🚗

Coastal wood near Chelmondiston on River Orwell. Free parking.

Priestley Wood
(Woodland Trust) **F** 23 ha
O.S.S. 155 - TM 080 530
01476 74297

From Stowmarket follow the B1113 S to Needham Market. Turn R on to the B1078 to Barking. Priestley Wood is to the R of this road, just before

the village of Barking.

Priestley Wood is considered to be one of the finest woods in Suffolk for plant life. Ash and maple coppice poles spring from stools - occasionally gigantic and ancient - in a mixture with other species. Small-leaved lime, hornbeam and wild pear, considered the rarest of all native trees, are present in the wood. Nightingales frequent areas of dense coppice regrowth, while the secretive woodcock and many roe deer are also present in the wood.

*Rendlesham Forest
(Forest Enterprise) **F** 1443ha
O.S.S. 169 - TM 353 484
01394 450164

🚗50🚻2🐕 ∪ ♠ Y WC & *i* 🍴 🛒
🏕 🔥🍴 🏪 🚂

Take A12 from Ipswich towards Lowestoft. After bypassing Woodbridge take A1152 through Melton and over a level crossing, then take B1084 to Orford. After 3 miles turn right at sign for Forest District Office and facilities. Phoenix Trail car park is 1 mile on. Car park, toilets, disabled facilities, picnic areas, 2 waymarked trails with interpretation (of which 1 is surfaced for wheelchairs), cycle trail, privately run campsite. No charge but walks leaflet 50p and cycle leaflet 80p.

Rendlesham Forest suffered catastrophic damage during the 1987 gale although attractive areas of mature forest remain and damaged areas have been replanted. The Phoenix Trail passes through areas of mature and young forest and information is available on how Forest Enterprise took the storm damage as an opportunity to create a more diverse forest than before with special management for woodlark and nightjar populations as well as the encouragement of other local heathland species on ride edges and in scallops. Also of significance is the conservation of the Tang Valley wetland area which has a series of large ponds with bridge and boardwalk access where necessary.

Sudbourne
(Forest Enterprise) **F** 78ha
O.S.S. 156 - TM 420 520
01394 450164
🚌1 ↦◯ ⚐ ⵏ
On B1084 from Woodbridge to Orford 1 mile from Butley village.

Small mainly coniferous productive wood with some broadleaves..

Theberton Woods
(Forest Enterprise) **F** 32ha
O.S.S. 156 - TM 422 655
01394 450164
🚌3 ↤ ⚑ ⵏ ⵏ

Off B1122 Leiston to Yoxford road, 1 mile west of Theberton village. Take turning opposite the church.

Small clay based wood probably of ancient woodland origin undergoing conversion from mixed wood to broadleaved wood.

Tunstall Forest
(Forest Enterprise) **F** 950ha
O.S.S. 156 - TM 381 560
01394 450164
🚗30 ↦◯ ⚐ ⵏ ⬛ⵏ ⵏ ⵏ ⵏ
Sandgall car park lies 1 mile from the B1069 Tunstall to Snape road on the east/west road to Iken.

Large coniferous production forest with an intensive road and ride structure ideal for the adventurous walker. Much of the forest has been replanted since the 1987 Great Storm and this restructuring is allowing the area to be replanned for open spaces, wide rides and greater conservation and recreation appeal.

Wolves Wood
(Royal Society for the Protection of Birds)
F 37ha
O.S.S. 155 - TM 055 436
01255 886043
🚗10 ⵏ ● ⵏ ⓘ ⬛ⵏ ⵏ
The Reserve entrance is 1½ miles E of Hadleigh on the A1071 Ipswich to Hadleigh road. Bold entrance sign. Marked visitor path. Seasonal information centre. No charges for car park but donations appreciated. Reserve leaflet available from Warden (50p). Occasional guided walks - details from Warden. Lecture service.

A very wet wood - wellies often advisable. Not suitable for wheelchair users at any time. An extensive area of mixed species coppice characterised by the large number of ponds (46). A diverse flora includes herb paris, several species of orchids and a wide range of tree and shrub species. Nightingales abound in spring along with willow warblers, blackcaps, ly hawfinches, and woodcock can be seen occasionally at dusk and dawn. The ponds attract a range of dragonfly species including the ruddy darter, and grass snakes are common.

SURREY

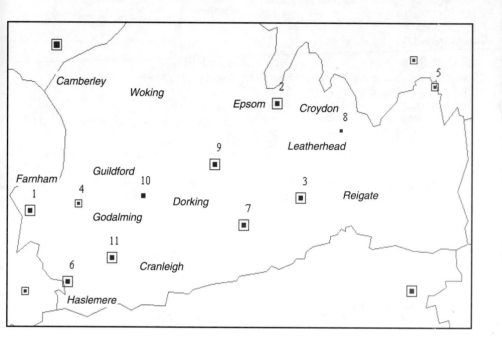

1. *Alice Holt Woodland Park
2. Ashtead Common
3. Box Hill
4. Britty Wood
5. Crabwood / Cold Blow Shaw
6. Hindhead
7. Leith Hill
8. *Nower Wood
9. Ranmore
10. *Winterfold Forest
11. Witley Common

Alice Holt Woodland Park
(Managed by Forest Enterprise) **F** 925ha
O.S.S. 186 - SU 810 416
01420 23666

★200🚻10🔥∪👤🦌Υ WC ♿ ⓘ 📖 ☂
📷 🔥 🗑 🖼 🛍

Forest Centre is signposted from Bucks Horn Oak village, SW of Farnham (Not Alice Holt Lodge). Forest Centre, situated in a fine woodland setting, has a gift shop and information point. Walking trails, family cycling routes and an all ability trail available. Car parking, toilets, and facilities for the disabled, light refreshments. Fishing lake by permit. Cycle hire. Events venue, education service by Ranger staff. Up to date information about "what's on" always available from Forest Centre, open Wed - Sun 1000 - 1600hrs.

An ancient area of forest with over 200 years of history.

Ashtead Common
(Corporation of London) **F** 200ha
O.S.S. 187 - TQ 175 580
01372 279083

🔥∪👤🌸Υ🦌🍺

Approaching Ashtead from the A24, turn L down Woodfield Lane opposite the Leg of Mutton and Cauliflower pub. Continue down the lane for 800m, straight on at the mini roundabout, then over the level crossing and Ashtead Common lies in front of you. There are no facilities. There is fully open access to the woodland with an extensive network of public footpaths, bridleways and concessionary horse rides. Guided visits can be arranged by appointment, please contact the Community Woodlands Officer, on the above number.

First recorded history dates back to 1st century AD, the earliest evidence of human habitation being the remains of a Roman villa. Contains six major types of habitat: ancient pasture woodland, closed canopy woodland, bracken dominated areas, scrubland, grassland, and several ponds. Designated as an SSSI in 1955. Pollarded oaks, birch, and aspen. The various habitats support many species of invertebrates together with a rich community of breeding birds, roe deer

thriving in the woodland areas. Purple emperors and purple hairstreaks are amongst the numerous species of butterflies and moths.

Box Hill
(National Trust) **FE** 217ha
O.S.S. 1847- TQ 171 519
01306 742809

🅿£1★🚻🔥∪👤🌸Υ WC ♿ ⓘ 📖 ☂
📷 👤 🔥 🗑 🛍

Coaches to approach from E side of hill B2032 or B2033. 1 mile N of Dorking, 2.5 miles S of Leatherhead on A24. Bus: Epsom Buses 551 Dorking - Box Hill (passing BR Betchworth) (tel. 01372 272201). Station Boxhill/West Humble 0.5 mile.

The woodland is semi-natural beech, yew and box with some areas of open downland.

Britty Wood
(R E Thornton) **R** 62ha
O.S.S. 186 - SU 900 454
01483 810208

★🦌👤🌸Υ ⓘ ☂ 🔥

Situated between Guildford and Farnham near Cuttmill Ponds.

Britty Wood is situated on sandy free draining soil. 80 year old oak plantation, much of the remainder coniferous plantations of various ages from 10 - 30 years old. The area is quite hilly and there are some attractive views to the south.

Crabwood/Cold Blow Shaw
(J Bothamley) **F** 28ha
O.S.S. 187 - TQ 390 600
01883 623038

★6🚻1🦌∪👤Υ🖼

From Farleigh Common (on road between Warlingham and Selsdon) take Farleigh Court Road (brick pillar box) for 3/4 mile to "Newlands

Barn". Free admittance to wood adjacent to farmland.

Semi-ancient mixed woodland. Some very old ash coppice and actively worked chestnut coppice (1ha). New mixed planting on 2ha planted 1995. Several very large beech trees. A quiet mixed woodland with acres of bluebells and new since 1994 - deer!

Hindhead
(National Trust) **F** 500ha
O.S.S. 186 - SU 892 357
01428 683207

Main car park is 400m north of Hindhead traffic lights to west of A3.

Extensive areas of Scots pine, oak and birch woodland with areas of open heathland. Fine walks.

Leith Hill
(National Trust) **F** 269ha
O.S.S. 187 - TQ 132 428
01306 742809

NW of A29, W of A24, S of A25.

Well managed productive woodland together with areas of semi-natural ancient woodland.

*Nower Wood
(Surrey Wildlife Trust) **A** 33ha
O.S.S. 187 - TQ 193 546
01372 379509 or 01483 488055

Off Junction 9 of M25, follow signs to A24. Join A24 S. Turn off 1st exit at "Beaverbrook" roundabout onto B2033. One mile along this road - entrance on L. Variable admission charges - ask for details. Car park, field centre, WCs, nature trail. Refreshments on open days. Phone 01372 379509 for details of charges. Open to public 3rd

---

HAVEN WOODLANDS
Management of woodland, hedgerow & heathland habitats. Management plans & survey.
17 Archers Road, Eastleigh, Hants, SO509AQ.
Tel: 01703 496715

Sunday Apr - Oct, 10 am to 4 pm Otherwise by appointment for school groups, interest groups and clubs/uniformed organisations. Nower Wood provides an excellent nationally-respected education facility for all ages - advance booking. No dogs.

Nower Wood is 81 acres of mixed woodland, mainly broadleaved, with 40 different tree and shrub species. Over 70 species of birds have been seen in this ancient woodland, many of which breed on site. There are also areas of marshland, heath and chalk grassland, and several pools and ponds. The Surrey Wildlife Trust purchased Nower Wood in 1971 and gradually established it as an educational nature reserve.

Ranmore
(National Trust) **F** 266ha
O.S.S. 187 - TQ 142 504
01306 742809

2m NW of Dorking adjoining the S boundary of Polesden Lacey estate.

Extensive wooded common - mostly semi-natural oak, ash and birch with various managed plantations.

*Winterfold Forest
(J A McAllister) **AE** 125ha
O.S.S. 186 - SU 965 435
01483 203474

From A254 Guildford to Dorking road take A248 signposted Godalming. After ½ mile cross small bridge then L into New Road up hill over level crossing to Farley Green, then L at village green

*into Shophouse Lane, then 1 mile to forest sign.
Parking for 25 cars and 2 coaches by
arrangement. There are some WCs on site.
Access for the disabled is particularly good.
Motorised trips for the elderly can be arranged.
Open at any time by booking in advance by
phoning 01483 203474 or 0171 499 6616. Details
can be left on answerphone if unattended.*

Densely planted working forest in the Surrey Hills
(highest point of SE England). 23 different species of
trees, Corsican pine, Douglas fir, cypress, larch,
Japanese cedar etc. Wildlife includes deer, badger, fox,
snakes. Many species of birds including birds of prey.
Hopeful of reintroduction of red squirrel in near future.
Heathland re-creation project in hand. Schools
welcome.

Witley Common
(National Trust) **F** 152ha
O.S.S. 186 - SU 933 407
01428 683207
⬥30🚌🚶 🌲 🦌 WC 🛈 📖 🎋 🗺 🥾 ⛺

*7 miles SW of Guildford between the Portsmouth
(A3) and Haslemere (A286) roads. Information
Centre is open on certain days between April and
October.*

Mixed age Scots pine and some areas of open
heathland.

SUSSEX - EAST

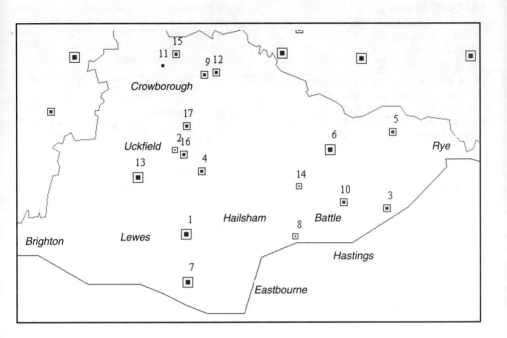

1. *Abbotts Wood*
2. Blackdown Wood
3. Church in the Wood
4. *Coneyburrow
5. Flatropers Wood
6. *Footland Wood*
7. *Friston Forest*
8. Gillham Wood
9. Hoth & Cards Woods
10. Mansers Shaw
11. Marline Wood
12. *Morris's Wood
13. Nap Wood
14. Plashett Wood
15. Powdermill Wood
16. Rocks Wood
17. Selwyn's Wood
18. *Wilderness Wood

Abbots Wood

(Forest Enterprise) **F** 356ha
O.S.S. 199 - TQ 556 074
01528 211044

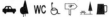

Take the A22 S from the Boship roundabout. Turn R onto minor road after approximately 2 miles, then take the next L. The car park is on the L 400 yds beyond The Oak public house. Facilities waymarked walks. Free access.

Blackdown Wood

(D E Gunner) **F** 3ha
O.S.S. 199 - TQ 538 202
01435 862016

1 mile from Blackboys village on road to Waldron. Park on verge by Countryside Commission board. There are no facilities. Entrance is free but guided walks are £2 per head, by appointment. Open from 0800 hours to sunset, daily. Permissive footpaths and bridleways in wood, with open access to adjoining fields managed under countryside stewardship scheme.

Rotational cutting of chestnut coppice with oak and Scots pine standards. 8 year old amenity planting, with all indigenous species. Excellent display of bluebells in May. Attractive walk by the stream.

Church-in-the-Wood

(Hastings Borough Council) **F** 25ha
O.S.S. 199 - TQ 851 113
01424 722022

Head southwards for approximately 2.5 miles from junction of the A2100 and B2092 (Queensway). Turn left into Churchwood Drive, follow the road for .75 mile before turning right into Church-in-the-Wood Lane. Follow road past church into car park. Information board present detailing main footpaths.

Church-in-the-Wood is an ancient woodland site

formerly managed under a coppice system and dominated by oak, sweet chestnut and hornbeam. Severely damaged by the 1987 hurricane, but coppicing has since been reintroduced under the Forestry Commissions Woodland Grant Scheme.

*Coney Burrow

(Major M R R Goulden) **R** 20ha
O.S.S. 183 - TQ 577 175
01435 812597

£1.50♠30♥2↰⊙♣☀Ψ wc ᕊ
ⓘ 📖 ⻌ Ⓚ FP ♨♣ ☕🍴 🍺 🏧 ⻌ 🎋

On A267 between Heathfield and Hailsham in Horam village. Open every day Easter to October, 1000 to 1700. Winter months by appointment.

Woods, streams and lakes. Part new conifers, part ancient hornbeam woods with open field which give the nature walks a unique and varied interest at all times of the year. Totally unspoilt by exploitation, this is one of the most beautiful parts of Sussex Low Weald. Home of the old Sussex iron industry.

Flatropers Wood

(Sussex Wildlife Trust) **F** 35ha
O.S.S. 199/189 - TQ 861 231
01273 492630

Nearest town is Rye. There is good access throughout along a system of paths and rides linking with the entrance on Bixley Lane, which joins the A268 on a sharp bend just W of Beckley.

A beautiful example of typical E Sussex woodland. In many parts young birch has been cut and regenerates profusely on the sandy soils of this area. Sweet chestnut has been cut as coppice, and there are small plantations of beech and pine. Standard oaks provide a continuity of woodland cover and more are being planted into the area of cut birch - the birch being a timber crop. An open heathy ride crosses the reserve and the sunny woodland tracks and paths support many invertebrates such as the pearl bordered fritillary and the tiger beetle. The spread of heather is encouraged by controlling bracken and birch.

Footland Wood
(Forest Enterprise) **F** 167ha
O.S.S.199 - TQ 764 204
01580 211044

From the A21 take the B2089 S of John's Cross. The car park can be found on the R some 600 yards distant. There is free access and the wood is open permanently.

*Friston Forest
(Forest Enterprise) **F** 858ha
O.S.S. 199 - TQ 519 001
01580 21104

Take the A259 W from Eastbourne. On reaching the Seven Sisters Country Park at Exceat, take the minor road to Litlington on the R. The car park is on the R 100 yards beyond the R turn to West Dean village. There are two car parks, one with toilets. There is free access and the forest is permanently open. Friston Forest is situated on the South Downs between Eastbourne and Seaford. Horse riding by permit.

The woodlands are predominantly beech and were planted mostly between the two world wars. There are waymarked walks from both car parks which are situated on opposite sides of the forest and the extensive network enables the more adventurous walker to venture further afield. There are several sites of botanical interest where typical chalk downland plant communities may be found and there is a National Nature Reserve managed by English Nature on the northern edge of the forest.

Gillham Wood
(Sussex Wildlife Trust) **F** 3.2ha
O.S.S. 199 - TQ 718 069
01273 492630

Off Gillham Wood Road in Bexhill. Access to the woodland is from the lay-by on the N side of Withyham Road, Cooden.

This oak woodland, within a residential area, has little altered over the years. Beneath the trees is a thick shrub layer with bramble beneath. Most of the oak is of similar age and size, indicating that the wood was probably felled about 50 years ago and allowed to redevelop naturally. Management is centred around maintaining the footpath network and opening glades to encourage butterflies and woodland flowers.

Hoth and Cards Woods, Rotherfield
(CS Hall) F 21ha
O.S.S. 188 - TQ 565 318

Take Rotherfield turning off A26 in Eridge. Turn L at first crossroads (2 miles). Woodland on l.

New plantings of hard and softwoods following 1987 storms. Bluebells in spring.

*Mansers Shaw
(Battle Town Council) **R** 2ha
O.S.S. 199 - TQ 742 155
01424 772210

Off A271 and nearly opposite Police Station. Entrance to be found at bottom righthand corner of recreation ground.

Mansers Shaw was once a part of a larger ancient woodland site. The wood is a small L-shaped woodland strip, with two small streams running through it. The dominant tree specis is multi-stemmed hornbeam. There are also standards of oak, ash, and cherry. Management of the wood is for wildlife, education and amenity.

Marline Wood
(Sussex Wildlife Trust) **F** 40ha
O.S.S. 199 - TQ 783 123
01273 492630

Off the Queensway NW of Hastings. Park in

Napier Road and enter by public footpath. Keep out of the Ghyll (river gorge) - it is dangerous and contains many rare mosses and liverworts.

Much of Marline Wood is old hornbeam coppice, now being restored. Part of the wood is a ghyll, a steep sandstone valley with bare rock faces. Here the moist, sheltered microclimate allows a variety of rare mosses and liverworts to flourish. The Marline Valley reserve as a whole includes flower rich meadows and some areas of scrub heavily used by migrant birds.

Ancient woodland with sandstone stream valleys. The oak, whilst the dominant tree in the wood, gives way to areas of chestnut coppice and clumps of pine planted in certain areas. In many parts of the reserve the oaks have grown up as wide spreading standard trees, but near the entrance they have been cut and worked as coppice. Streams have cut steep valleys forming moist habitats for mosses, liverworts and ferns more commonly found in the N and W of Britain. Controlling bracken and rhododendron helps to preserve the oldest beeches which are attractive for both wildlife and visitors.

*Morris's Wood
(George R Fry) **A** 37ha
O.S.S. 188 - TQ 506 332
01892 653047

6 🚗 🔺 ⚹ 🦌 *i* 🌳 ♿ 🏛

Take Groombridge road from Crowborough Cross. After 1.25 miles take drive on L marked "Highfields". Access is necessarily by prior appointment because main entry crosses private garden of house. Some car parking is available.

Morris's Wood is ancient woodland in two south-west valleys on the border of Ashdown Forest. Management is on active silvicultural principles with broadleaf and conifer species. Care is taken to avoid disturbance to wildlife. The forestry work is confined to the main species but there are many specimen trees and at least one of each will be found in the Shakespeare Memorial Garden. There is a wide variety of wildflowers, fungi, butterflies and birds and a nature trail of about 2.5 miles.

Nap Wood
(National Trust, managed by Sussex Wildlife Trust) **F** 45ha
O.S.S. 188 - TQ 583 327
01273 492630

🦌 ♿ 🦌 🌳

Take the A267 south from Tunbridge Wells. Nap Wood is about 2 miles south of Frant, on the left side opposite a minor turning to the right. Park on the verge. Nearest town, Crowborough.

Plashett Wood
(I V Askew Charitable Trust) **A** 150ha
O.S.S. 198 - TQ 460 163
01825 750750

🚗 20 🚌 2-3 ✂ ♿ 🏹

The wood is alongside the A26 half way between Lewes and Uckfield. There is parking for 20 cars or 2 - 3 coaches. Access is by appointment only and with the forester to act as a guide. It is necessary to charge the forester's time for this.

A predominantly broadleaved woodland managed for timber production, nature conservation and shooting. An educational programme is being developed. Plashett Wood is the largest block of broadleaved woodland under one management plan in E Sussex. The wood is managed as a working woodland and has a resident charcoal producer as well as various other value adding activities.

Powdermill Wood
(Sussex Wildlife Trust) **F** 2ha
O.S.S. 199 - TQ 735 144
01273 492630

 🚗 🦌 ♿

Nearest town is Battle. The car park is on the B2095, Battle-Catsfield road, from which starts a circular nature trail which winds through the whole of Powdermill Wood.

Wet alder woodland over tussock sedge. Much of this area of woodland was probably once cut as coppice for charcoal, an ingredient of gunpowder - hence the name "Powdermill Wood". Surrounded by commercially worked chestnut coppice is a wet valley bottom filled with alder. The alder coppice cycle is gradually being restored in some parts of the reserve. Near the eastern causeway, however, the alder carr will be left in its attractive mature state. The plants on the reserve are typical of marshy stream valleys in woodland.

Rocks Wood

(Lord Gibson) **R** 17ha
O.S.S. 188 - TQ 525 350
01892 867434

Off the B2110 between Groombridge and Crowborough, signposted Motts Hill. Through Motts Hill at the top of a very steep hill turn right. Open 9.00am - 4.00pm. Woodland produce available through forester. Visitors requested to respect privacy of local residents.

Approximately 17 hectares of predominantly sweet chestnut coppice with 3 small areas of coniferous woodland. 3 pleasant walks available with glimpses of interesting rock formations. Archaeological excavations in 1982 produced mesolithic "finds", pottery of several periods and also a bowl furnace for iron working. Fallow deer, badgers, foxes and rabbits may be seen and a good variety of birds, flowers and plants are present all year round.

Selwyns Wood

(Sussex Wildlife Trust) **F** 11ha
O.S.S. 199 - TQ 552 206
01273 492630

From the A265 at Cross in Hand, turn off down the minor road to Blackboys. After the small parade of shops turn left down the minor road towards Rosies Cross. The reserve entrance is to the left - look for the white railings.

Mixed woodland with oak, birch, chestnut and leafy glades. The sweet chestnut areas near the entrance are being coppiced, while birch is harvested elsewhere.

The central area was clear-felled of mature pine, fir and larch and has been planted with oak and associated native species. To the west there is more variety, with large Scots pine, beech, oak and chestnut. The wood is actively managed as an example of harmony between forestry operations and wildlife.

*Wilderness Wood

(C & A Yarrow) **RCE** 24ha
O.S.S. 199 - TQ 536 240
01825 830509
Hadlow Farm Near Uckfield Sussex TN22 4HJ

£1.60●40●2 WC & ⓘ ◻︎☂︎
FP ♨︎ ⚓︎ ▦ 🏠

North from Uckfield 1 mile; take A272 eastwards through Buxted to Hadlow Down (4 miles), wood on right (southside) on main road. Two miles from Buxted BR station.The whole wood is open to explore; woodland trails and exhibition in timber barn give an insight into growing and using wood, and woodland wildlife. Guided walks, children's activities and "hands on" demonstrations available for schools and other booked groups (1 weeks notice). Picnic areas, barbecues for hire, adventure playground, teas, souvenirs, WCs. Barn, WCs and yard area are accessible to the disabled. Open access to the wood (10 am to dusk). Admission: Adults £1.60, OAPS £1.10, children 90p (reduced rates Nov-Feb); Booked groups of 15 + people, £1.45, £1, 80p; Guided walks/demonstrations (including admission): £2.60, £2.20, £1.95. Minimum £22 per group. School rates: Children 90p; one free adults per 10 children; extras £1.45. Guided walks/demonstrations £17 per group in addition to admission charge. Teachers pack £2 (refundable).

An ancient working wood, mainly chestnut coppice with mixed age plantations. Set in rolling High Weald AONB, beautiful views. Managed by resident owner-occupier, a professional forester, living on site, to maximise timber, wildlife, education, and recreation benefits.

SUSSEX - WEST

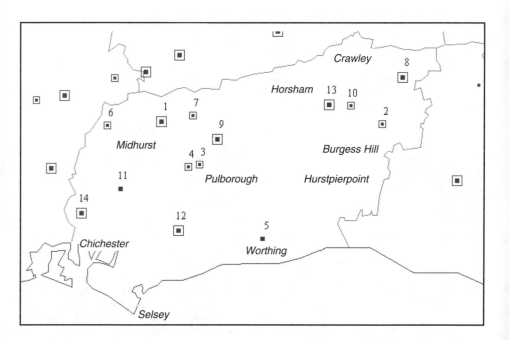

1. Blackdown Wood
2. Borde Hill Gardens
3. Burton Pond Woodlands
4. Burton Rough
5. Clapham Woods
6. Durnford Wood
7. Ebernoe Common Nature Reserve
8. *Gravetye*
9. The Mens Nature Reserve
10. Nymans
11. *Rabbit Warren
12. Slindon Wood
13. *St Leonard's Forest*
14. *Stansted Forest

Blackdown

(National Trust) **F** 303ha

O.S.S 186 - SU 920 308

01428 683207

🚗🏕️🅿️🥾☀️🌲⛺🦌🚶

1 mile SE of Haslemere.

Extensive Scots pine, oak and birch woodlands on sandy heath, with attractive walks.

the Warren - all derive from oak and birch woodlands, though much altered in the past. There are many heathy areas and the Black Hole - a bog on Welch's Common, now partly covered by alder and willow and supports plant species more usually associated with the North and West of Britain. In the drier woodlands, birch has spread into these areas where the felling of oak and lime was once common. These birch blocks are to be replaced with a more natural mix of broad leaved trees including oak. The mill pond is a good place to see wildfowl.

Borde Hill Garden

(Borde Hill Garden) **R** 10ha

O.S.S. 198 - TQ 322 262

01444 450326

🎫 **£3.50** 🚗🚌🥾🥂🦌🍴 WC ♿🚽🚶🔖🛍️🌳🏕️🛍️

1.5 miles from Haywards Heath on Balcombe road. Leaflets available in shop.

The woodland walks cover three separate woods, each composed of splendid mature oaks, interplanted with exotic conifers and deciduous trees up to 100 years old. The range of exotic collections is so wide that no one genus dominates. The woods are a delight in the spring with rhododendrons and bluebells, cool and peaceful in the summer months, turning fiery in the autumn. A replanting programme has been started following storm clearance and will be continued each year.

Burton Pond Woodlands

(Sussex Wildlife Trust) **F** 27ha

O.S.S. 197/198 - SU 978 181

01273 492630

🚗🐴🥂☀️

Head south from Petworth on the A285. Take the second left - after about 2 miles just over the brow of the hill just past a garage. It is signposted Burton Park. Burton Pond is about 1 mile from the A285.

The reserve consists of woodlands enclosing areas of bog and surrounding a large mill pond. The woodlands - Newpiece Wood, Welch's and Crouch Common, and

Burton Rough

(Miss PE Merriman) **F** 22ha

O.S.S. 197- SU 968 186

01234 750927

Take the A285 from Petworth, then the first L after crossing the river. Entrance to the wood is on the left after 300 yards. Open any time.

Mixed conifer plantations, chestnut coppice and a small area of southern beech. (Nothofagus).

Clapham Woods

(J F Somerset) **A** 145ha

O.S.S. 197/198 - TQ 105 059

01903 264686

Off A27 Arundel to Worthing road. The drive to Holt Farm House is on the N side of the road opposite Castle Goring to the W and the Coach and Horses public house to the E. Open by appointment in Apr/May.

Primroses and bluebells beneath the hazel with oak standard trees. No coppicing or cutting has taken place since March 1989, when a blanket tree preservation order was served on the whole wood.

Durford Wood
(National Trust) **F** 25ha
O.S.S 197 - SU 790 260
01243 814554

2.5 miles NE of Petersfield on S side of A3 side.

Mostly oak with some pine. Much is old oak coppice.

Ebernoe Common Nature Reserve
(Sussex Wildlife Trust) **F** 72ha
O.S.S. 197/186 - SU 976 278
01273 492630
🚗9🚉 ●

Take the A283 north from Petworth. After about 3 miles take the minor road to the right (it is the first road outside of the town). Follow this winding road until you reach a red phone box - the entrance is marked "Ebernoe Church", about 10 yards on the right. Take care not to get lost - we strongly advise you keep to paths.

Ancient woodland with grassy glades, ponds and archaeological remains. Once wood pasture for commoners' livestock, Ebernoe has huge oak and beech trees with holly shrub undergrowth, as well as an old furnace pond and a brick kiln - a scheduled ancient monument. There is also an outstanding "unimproved" flower rich meadow. The diverse habitats give rise to over 300 species of plants, 100 of mosses and 400 of fungi; many of the latter flourishing on dead and dying timber. Pond clearance, and the removal of bracken and holly from glades and rides, are annual tasks. In parts of the reserve grazing is to be reintroduced. The woodland areas are deliberately left to continue a natural cycle of growth and decay.

approximately 1 mile. Turn L towards Sharp thorne and L again into Vowells Lane. The car park is on the R 500 yards beyond the entrance to Gravetye Manor. Open permanently.

The Mens Nature Reserve
(Sussex Wildlife Trust) **F** 159ha
O.S.S.197/198 - TQ 023 237
01273 492630
🚗6🚉 ○ ● ☀ 🦌

Head east on the A272 from Petworth. After about 4 miles turn right at crossroads in the middle of a large wood, signposted Hawkhurst. Car park is about 100 yards on right.

A superb ancient beech and oak woodland with medieval woodbanks and "assarts" (clearings). The Mens is unusual in not having been in management for decades, and is reverting to the nature of a "wildwood". The mass of fallen timber and old trees support numerous rare deadwood fungi, beetles and other species. The reserve includes a number of unimproved flower rich meadows.

Nymans Wood
(National Trust) **F** 76ha
O.S.S. 187 - SU 264 295
01444 400321
🚗🦌 ○ ☕

On the B2114 at Handcross just off the London to Brighton (M23/A23) road. Close to Nymans Garden. Visitor facilities (shop, restaurant, information) at Nymans Garden, entrance fee £3.80 to garden.

Mature broadleaved woodland with areas of younger planted woodland. Some fine specimen trees.

Gravetye
(Forest Enterprise) **F** 316ha
O.S.S. 187 - TQ 360 347
01580 211044

From Turner's Hill take the B2028 SE for

*Rabbit Warren
(Trustees of The Edward James Foundation) **A** 130ha
O.S.S. 197 - SU 846 148
01243 811205
🚗12🚐1🏹🦌☀🦌🐾

From Chichester take the A286 in a northerly direction to West Dean. Turn L opposite The Selsey Arms public house and continue until the marked meeting point is reached on the R (about one mile). There is parking for 12 cars and 1 coach. There are no WCs on site. Guided walk on 14 May, 1995. Other guided walks can be arranged by appointment. For all visits, please book two weeks in advance. Please contact I J Odin on above number. Donations to the Forestry Trust.

This woodland is planted on the site of a medieval rabbit warren, hence its name, and is on the dip of the South Downs comprising shallow soils over chalk. The original plantations were severely damaged in the storms of 1987 and 1990 so a large area has been replanted with various species of trees, including Norway spruce, Douglas fir and Japanese larch, since these dates. The remainder of the area has varying age crops, the oldest being 1940s plantings of beech, and also an area of chestnut coppice. Both roe and fallow deer are present in large numbers and nightjars regularly nest in the new plantations. The wide ride through the centre of the area produces a good variety of plant and invertebrate life.

Slindon Woods
(National Trust) **F** 329ha
O.S.S. 197 - SU 952 073 and 960 077
01243 814554
🚗50🚾○⬤ 🌲⬛🏹 🔺

There are car parks. Full and free access. Telephone above number for further information.

Very fine Slindon beech woods mostly destroyed by 1987 storm. Now mixed age with many young trees.

St Leonard's Forest
(Forest Enterprise) **F** 242ha
O.S.S. 187/198 - TQ 207 298
01580 211044
🚗⬤○🌲☂

From Horsham take the A281 to Mannings Heath. Take the minor road running from Mannings Heath. Turn L at the T-junction (just over ½ mile)

and the car park can be found on the R some 400 yards distant. Car park, Waymarked walk. Open permanently. Horse riding by permit.

*Stansted Forest
(Stansted Park Foundation) **R** 400ha
O.S.S. 197 - SU 753 105
01705 412367
🚗35🚾○⬤ ☀🌲 WC 🅸 FP ⬛🏔

From Rowland's Castle SE for 1.5 miles, then L and L again. Stansted Forest is 1 mile N on L, whilst the house is on R. Shop, tea room and WC are in the House Grounds (Bank Holiday Sun and Mon and Sun, Mon and Tues from Jul to end of Sept). There are rights of way on foot through the wood and bridleways through parts. Please contact Head Forester on above number for details and give one month's notice for group visits. The woodlands are open throughout the year with some restrictions during the shooting season.

A large area of multipurpose woodland incorporating wildlife habitats and landscape features. Many large, ancient, environmentally important trees and over 200 species of flowering plants recorded. The main avenue over 1.5 miles long was one of the longest beech avenues in England, now much reduced by disease and storms.

TYNE & WEAR

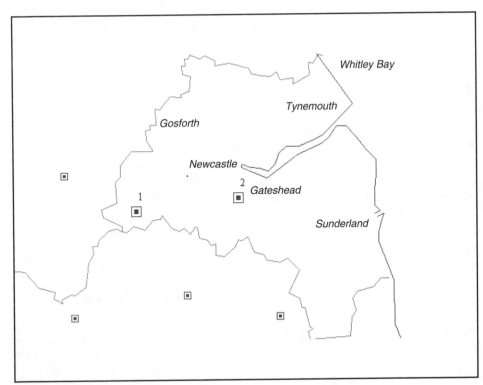

1. *Chopwell Woodland Park*
2. Gibside

Chopwell Woodland Park
(Forest Enterprise) **F** 375ha
O.S.S. 88 - NZ 139 589
01669 620569

➡75🚍6⊷ ∪ ♠ ❋ ☗ ⓘ 📖 ☗ 🏂 ⚓

*From the A1 just south of River Tyne take A694
to Rowlands Gill, then turn R on the B6315 for
1.5 miles. Woodland walks, mountain bikes,
horse riding, orienteering.*

Mixed broadleaf/conifer woodland with views over
the River Derwent.

Gibside
(National Trust) **R** 148.77ha
O.S.S. 88 - NZ 172 583
01207 542255

➡100🚍2⊷ ♠ ❋ ☗ WC ⓘ ☗ 🏂 ⚓ ☕
🛍

*Situated 6 miles SW of Gateshead. A694 to
Rowland's Gill, then B6314 towards Burnopfield.
Car park, picnic area, tea/gift shop and WCs.
Limited wheelchair access. The woodland is
open to the public during the open season for
Gibside Chapel and grounds - Easter to the end
of October.*

Gibside has been described as "one of the grandest
idylls of the 18th century"; the landscape and
associated buildings are a rare survival of the
transitional period in landscape design incorporating
both formal and informal elements. In 1950 the
majority of the parkland was leased to the Forestry
Commission by the then owners. Extensive planting
was carried out; however, most of the original vistas
were left as woodland rides. Snipes Dene Wood is an
SSSI. There are footpaths in Snipes Dene Wood and
along the River Derwent.

WARWICKSHIRE

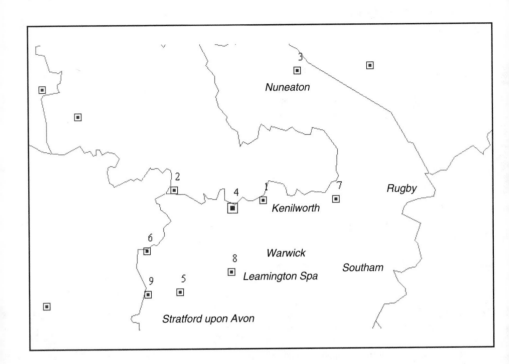

1. *Claywood
2. *ClowesWood
3. Hartshill Hayes & St Lawrence's Wood
4. *Hay Wood*
5. *Oversley Wood*
6. *Rough Hill Wood
7. *Ryton Wood
8. *Snitterfield Bushes
9. Thornhill

*Claywood

(Mr and Mrs Slatem) **F** 14ha
O.S.S. 139 - SP 237 725
01926 484673
🚗6 🚻 WC 🅿 FP ♨♿ ☂

4 miles N of Warwick and just off the A4177. The nearby Honily Court Hotel is a local landmark. Claywood lies on the opposite side of the road 0.5 mile from the hotel. There is fully open access to the wood. Guided visits can be arranged by contacting Mr or Mrs Slatem on the above telephone number. Please allow 7 days notice. Donations received.

Originally an old oak wood and part of the Forest of Arden., formerly known as "Clattylands". Claywood was replanted in the early 60s with mainly conifers. It has now matured into a secluded woodland of different varieties, including regenerated oak and birch. It neatly combines woodland of interest for all, including its own timber conversion for wood products, fencing, furniture, and compost. The site has 2 clay pit diggings from earlier brick making activities, much overgrown. There are plans for cleaning to introduce water habitats into the woodland environment - ideal for children to see the varieties growing in different stages and their practical uses and yet a woodland atmosphere to enjoy.

*Clowes Wood

(Warwickshire Wildlife Trust) **F** 31ha
O.S.S 139 - SP 101 743
01203 302912
🚗10🅿 ♿ ☂ 🅿

From B4102 Solihull to Earlswood, turn right over Earlswood Lake bridge then left into Wood Lane. Park on left after 0.5 mile. Free public car park. Walk through New Fallings Coppice to Clowes Wood.

Clowes Wood, together with the adjacent New Fallings Coppice, form acidic oak-birch woodland with some rowan. The understorey includes lily-of-the-valley, bluebell, woodsage and cowwheat. There is also a damp area of alderwood and two streams. Additional habitats include a small meadow and an area of heathland with heather and bilberry. Over 50 species of birds including wood warbler, woodcock, sparrowhawk and all three woodpeckers. Also good fungi list. Ancient woodland, SSSI, nature reserve.

> **WARWICKSHIRE WILDLIFE TRUST** - For details of our 47 Nature Reserves, and how you can help our conservation work, please send an SAE to Brandon Marsh Nature Centre, Brandon Lane, Coventry CV3 3 GW. The Nature Centre, with its 200 acre wetland Nature Reserve, is open to the public every day.

Hartshill Hayes and St Lawrence's Wood

(Warwickshire County Council) **F** 50 ha
O.S.S. 140 - SP 317 944
01827 872660
🅿£0.70🚗🅿 ♨ ☀WC ♿ ⓘ 🍽 🅿 ♨ ☂
🍴♿ 🛈

B4114 from Nuneaton to Chapel End, turn R to Hartshill and then L (signposted) on Oldbury Lane, or B4111 Atherstone towards Nuneaton, R to Hartshill and R (signposted) on Oldbury Lane. Bus no 776 from Atherstone and Nuneaton, X77 from Atherstone, Nuneaton and Coventry, X76 from Atherstone, Dordon, Polesworth and Tamworth. Car park 70p - charges for 1994/5 yet to be decided. Events, rangers.. Open every day except Christmas Day - closed at dusk.

Reputed to be a remnant of the former Forest of Arden, much of the wood was replanted at the end of the 18th century with oak and lime. The lime was coppiced and used by Atherstone hatmakers for the hat blocks on which felt hats were moulded. Many of the hardwoods were cropped in 1950s and replaced by conifers. The County Council's long term aim is to return woodland to an ancient semi-natural state. Extensive views of four counties across Anker Valley.

Hay Wood

(Managed by Forest Enterprise) **R** 105ha
O.S.S. 139 - SP 205 713
01889 586593

From M42, Junction 5 follow A41 towards Warwick, in 5 miles wood is signposted to the R, at Baddesley Clinton. Car park, picnic area.

Oversley Wood
(Managed by Forest Enterprise) **R** 94ha
O.S.S. 150 - SP 111 568
01889 586593

From Stratford upon Avon take the A422 to Alcester. In 4.5 miles turn R, signposted Oversley Green, in 100 yards turn L up track and drive under new road bridge, forest gate on R. Forest trail and Arboretum. A gate key is available for school parties from Warwick museum.

Very rich display of woodland flowers during the Spring.

*Rough Hill Wood
(Warwickshire Wildlife Trust) **F** 21ha
O.S.S. 150 - SP 053 638
01203 302912

The Wood is on the north side of "the Slough" - the A448 between Redditch and Studley. Park of the road on the verge.

Rough Hill Wood and the adjacent Wire Hill Wood straddle the county boundary (Worcs) south of Redditch. The varied soil conditions support a variety of woodland types, mainly sessile oak with downy and silver birch, but with areas of rowan and some small leaved lime. There is some scattered heather, with bilberry and bluebells, and wetter areas with marshy plants. The wood was purchased by the Trust in 1993 and all records of plants and animals are welcome. A trail is being developed to link the south facing Rough Hill Wood with the north facing Wire Hill Wood and encourage access on foot. Ancient woodland, SSSI, nature reserve.

*Ryton Wood
(Warwickshire Wildlife Trust) **R** 85ha
O.S.S. 140 - SP 384 726
01203 302912

A423 from Coventry to Banbury. Entrance drive 500m south of A445 island, before Bull and Butcher pub. Car park for Wildlife Trust members - details from above number. Waymarked trail and guided walks. Public access on guided walks.

One of the three largest remaining oakwoods in the county. Nature Reserve, ancient woodland. SSSI with diverse flora and fauna, including over 30 species of butterfly and nearly 90 species of birds. Coppicing has been reinstated by Trust volunteers, resulting in excellent ground flora. Pendunculate oak with silver and downy birch, ash, field maple and small leaved lime.

*Snitterfield Bushes
(Warwickshire Wildlife Trust) **F** 50ha
O.S.S. 151 - SP 200 603
01203 302912

From A46 Warwick - Stratford road, go through Snitterfield village towards Bearley. Public access on guided walks.

Snitterfield Bushes was once part of a huge broadleaved wood, reaching as far as Bearley village. A wartime airfield cleared the centre area, leaving a legacy of concrete tracks through Snitterfield Bushes. Extensive felling in the 1940s and 1950s has left tracts of even aged ash and silver birch with occasional oak standards. The shrub layer is mainly hazel - which is being recoppiced - with field maple, wayfaring tree, guelder rose and dogwood. Wildflowers include bluebells, early purple orchid, and herb paris. 26 butterflies and good bird list. Easy going trail. Ancient woodland, SSSI, nature reserve.

Thornhill
(The Marquess of Hertford) **F** 23ha
O.S.S. 150 - SP 055 565
01789 726455

Thornhill is just off the A422 from Worcester to Stratford on Avon, 2 miles W of Alcester. Open May 1st - August 31st.

The wood includes the following stands: 1. Ash and sycamore from which larch and spruce (nurse crop) have been removed, showing how silly it is to plant pure hardwoods. 2. Oak and Norway spruce aged about 25 years. 3. Lodgepole pine, not very successful. 4. Old oak ready to be felled. 5. Corsican pine, planted 1992.

WEST MIDLANDS

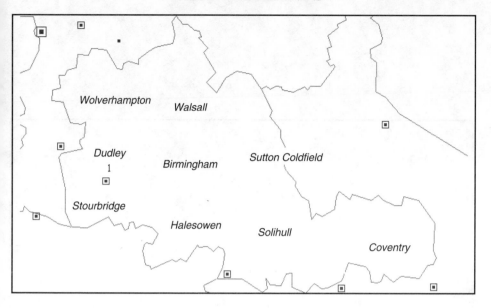

Wolverhampton

Walsall

Dudley
1

Birmingham

Sutton Coldfield

Stourbridge

Halesowen

Solihull

Coventry

1. *Saltwells Wood

*Saltwells Wood
(Dudley Metropolitan Borough Council)
F 40ha
O.S.S. 139 - SO 933 868
01384 261572

🚗🚊●※WC ♿ ⓘ 📖 🐕 ▯

2 miles S of Dudley. Follow signs to Merry Hill Centre: S along A4036 (Pedmore Road); L at island into Coppice Lane; follow signs to Saltwells Inn Car Park. Public car park at meeting point, visitor centre in wood, WCs. Information leaflets and maps, displays. Visitor centre open 0800-1630 hours. Remainder of wood and reserve (100 ha) has open access. Guided walks require pre-booking. Dogs welcome - (must be on lead in SSSI only - Doultons Claypit).

Saltwells Wood is the oldest-established part of the reserve, originally part of Pensnett Chase. The large trees are mainly oak, sycamore and beech. Over 50,000 other native hardwoods have been planted since 1981 within the fenced sections and as underplanting below the mature trees. Typical woodland birds occur, such as nuthatch, great-spotted woodpecker, jay, blackcap and willow warbler. Surprising by their presence, given the nearby urban area, are willow tit, wood warbler, lesser-spotted and green woodpecker and pied flycatcher on migration. Mammals include field vole, common and pygmy shrew, woodmouse, weasel, hedgehog and several species of bat. Foxes are common. In May the floor of the wood is a carpet of bluebells. There were brine baths near the site of the *Saltwells Inn*, using the brackish water which came up in the early mine workings. Saltwells Spa enjoyed its greatest popularity in Victorian times.

WILTSHIRE

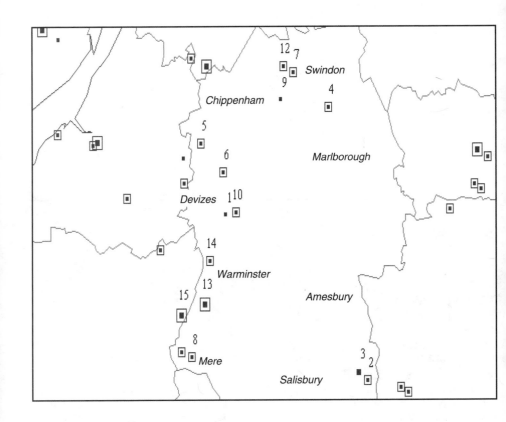

1. Biss Wood
2. Blackmoor Copse
3. *Clarendon Park Estate
4. Clouts Wood
5. Colerne Park & Monks Wood
6. Corsham Court Arboretum
7. *The Firs
8. *Great Combe

9. Great Wood, Grittenham
10. Green Lane Wood
11. *Jack's Castle
12. Ravensroost Wood
13. *Swancombe Wood
14. *Witham Park
15. *The Woodland Park

Biss Wood
(Gilbert W Green) **A** 22ha
O.S.S. 173 - ST 881 567
01380 830369

On the W side of the A350 between Westbury and Semington. Car park at entrance opposite Castle Lodge, West Ashton. (0.5 mile northwards from West Ashton village in direction of Semington). Open by appointment between Mar and Oct.

Ancient pedunculate oak, ash, hazel, maple coppice. Regrown from major felling in 1930-33, active management since 1985. 200 vascular plant species. Numerous bird species, roe deer, 32 butterfly species including white admiral and silver-washed fritillary. 185 fungi species recorded since 1986.

*Clarendon Park Estate
(A W M Christie-Miller) **A** 400ha
O.S.S. 184 - SU 198 30
01722 710233

Take the A30 E of Salisbury. After 2½ miles turn R to Pitton. In Pitton village turn R at crossroads by bus shelter and follow the road to gate and Lodge. No WCs on site. Donations to Forestry Trust.

Formerly a royal forest, this woodland includes the site of Clarendon Palace, a favourite haunt of medieval kings. The woodland is a mixture of conifer and broadleaf and includes large areas of ancient and semi-natural woodland. Oak and ash predominate along with Douglas fir and larch. There are a large number of woodland birds and other fauna, including roe deer.

Blackmoor Copse
(Wiltshire Wildlife Trust) **F** 31ha
O.S.S. 184 - SU 233 288
01380 725670

Six miles E of Salisbury between A30 and A36. On W side of minor road from Winterslow to East Grimstead Entrance at junction with Ben Lane, the road to Farley. Limited parking on wide road verges. Open at all times.

One of the Wiltshire Trust's loveliest ancient woodlands. Mainly oak and birch with hazel coppice, it is particularly noted for its butterflies, including silver-washed fritillary, white admiral and purple emperor. The variety of vegetation results in a rich and varied wildlife. In spring primroses, bluebells and violets abound, whilst in the autumn the paths are bright with berries of the hawthorn, wild rose and honeysuckle. King Charles Pond supports sedges, rushes and wetland flowers and the mossy stumps of ancient oaks provide habitat for a host of invertebrates.

Clouts Wood
(Wiltshire Wildlife Trust) **F** 13ha
O.S.S. 173 - SU 136 801
01380 725670

On A4361 Swindon to Avebury road, 1 mile SW of Wroughton. 2 lay-bys nearby. Open at all times.

Clouts Wood is an outstanding area of ancient ash woodland. Within a mosaic of trees, shrubs and plants may be found the spiked Star of Bethlehem (unusual so far east) and the nettle-leaved bellflower. Decaying wych elms provide habitat for a variety of birds and insects, including woodpeckers, nuthatches and tits. Several mammals inhabit the wood including badgers, foxes and roe deer. In the valley bottom the moist soil supports a variety of wetland plants such as horse tail, goat willow and hemp agrimony.

Colerne Park and Monks Wood
(Woodland Trust) **F** 48.3ha
O.S.S. 173 - ST 838 734
01476 74297

Situated close to junction 17 on the M4, between the A4 main Bath to Chippenham road and the A420 Bristol to Chippenham road. The wood is reached from a no through road, leading off the narrow lane between Slaughterford and Thickwood. Open at all times. National Trust events may take place in this wood during late Nov/Dec. Please phone the Woodland Trust on above number for details in the autumn.

Situated near the Fosse Way in the County of Wiltshire and in the Cotswold Area of Outstanding Natural Beauty. The most attractive features of the woods are the glades and swathes cut through the trees. In the summer, when the meadow flowers are blooming, you will see a great number of butterflies attracted to these open spaces. Also there are a number of different types of bird to be found, including green and great spotted woodpeckers and marsh tits.

Lies between Brinkworth and Purton on Wood Lane, which runs from B4042 at Callow Hill to B4696 near Braydon. Reserve guide available (30p) from Wiltshire Wildlife Trust. Circular walk through wood. Wellingtons advisable.

Lying in the heart of the old royal hunting forest of Braydon, the woodland is owned by Hills of Swindon Ltd, but managed by the Wiltshire Wildlife Trust, through the Braydon Forest Project. Opened to the public in 1992 it offers a circular walk through woodland which is being currently restored to high forest and part coppice management. Oak and ash form the canopy layer with small leaved lime and poplar in places. The field layer is mainly hazel, but on the wetter areas blackthorn and ash regeneration is obvious. Bluebells, early purple and common spotted orchids during spring and summer with small songbirds, buzzards and many butterflies such as the white admiral during the summer.

Corsham Court Arboretum
(James Methuen-Campbell) **R** 10.5ha
O.S.S. 173 - ST 874 705
01249 712214

4 miles W of Chippenham. Signposted from The Cross Leys Inn on the A4 Bath road. Free parking. Historic house on site open to the public. Charges - Adults £2.00, OAPs £1.50, Children £1.00, Group rates for 20 or more. Open daily from 2-4.30 pm. except Mondays and Fridays. From Good Friday to Sept 30 open until 6 pm. including Fridays and Bank Holiday Mondays. Closed Dec. Groups by appointment. Go to cash desk in house for tickets.

Abundance of daffodils and cowslips when in season. Many rare and exotic species in newly planted arboretum. Mature specimen trees in Capability Brown landscape including oriental plane and copper beech.

*The Firs
(Hills of Swindon Ltd) **R** 11.5ha
O.S.S. 173 - SU 048 866
01380 720774

*Great Combe
(HC Hoare Esq) **FE** 40 ha
O.S.S..183 - ST 748 353
01747 840824
40

Turn off the A303 W of Mere, signposted for Stourhead, on the B3092. Take the 4th turning L, after 2 miles, follow signs for Alfred's Tower. After about 2 miles the parking area will be seen on the L, before the road descends a steep hill. Open 365 days per year. There are rights of way on the foot and bridleways through the woodland. Guided tours by arrangement - please phone Jeremy Hoare on above number.

Great Combe is an attractive, steep sided valley, sheltered from the prevailing wind. Its nature trail meanders through a variety of mixed scenery, where around every bend something new meets the eye. Conservation and wild life opportunities are good with something of interest throughout the year.

*Great Wood, Grittenham

(Mr. N. L. Stewart) **A** 75 ha
O.S.S.173 - SU 018 816
01489 877419

Wootton Bassett-Lyneham main road nr M4 junction 16; turn into Trow Lane and travel N for some half mile across main railway line. Roadside parking.

Ancient semi-natural woodland since 1970 restored to include conifer plantations. Size 185 acres. Predominant hardwood species is oak; conifer are Norway spruce with Douglas fir (new and old) and also larch. One acre newly planted with selected ornamental trees. Large excavated pond encourages amphibians. Fine display of bluebells and primroses in spring.

Green Lane Wood

(Wiltshire Wildlife Trust) **F** 25ha
O.S.S. 173 - ST 886 576
01380 725670

Beside W side of A350 between Semington and Westbury. Car park but no coaches. Open at all reasonable times.

Ancient pedunculate oak wood with areas of ash, alder, maple and hazel coppice. Mostly regrown from major felling 1930-33. 160 vascular plant species. Roe deer and muntjac. 31 butterfly species including white admiral and silver-washed fritillary. Electricity pylon line swathe forms a distinctive open habitat, especially valuable for butterflies.

*Jack's Castle

(H C Hoare Esq) **F** 22ha
O.S.S. 183 - ST 748 353
01747 840824

Turn off the A303 west of Mere, signposted for Stourhead, on the B3092. Take the 4th turning on the L, after about 2 miles, following signs for Alfred's Tower. After about 2 miles the parking

area will be found on the L, before the road descends a steep hill. There is parking for up to 40 cars. Open 365 days per year. There are guided tours by arrangement - please phone Jeremy Hoare on above number.

Jack's Castle is steeped in history. The beech clumps quite possibly replaced earlier landscape features, and even the current ones are about 200 years old. The edge of the ridge on a fine day provides spectacular views of Somerset from the Quantocks to the Mendips.

Ravensroost Wood

(Wiltshire Wildlife Trust) **F** 39ha
O.S.S. 173 - SU 024 877
01380 725670

W of Swindon, approximately 1.5 miles S of Minety and 2.5 miles N of Brinkworth. Main car park at S of wood. Open at all times.

Once part of the Royal Forest of Braydon, the wood consists predominantly of matured oak over a hazel-dominated coppice layer. An SSSI, the area is rich in bird and animal life, characteristic of ancient woodlands. Among the rarer species are the wild service tree, small leaved lime and midland thorn. Much of the coppiced area supports a wide variety of butterflies including the silver-washed fritillary. Several ponds provide another important habitat and dragonflies are common.

*Swancombe Wood

(The Marquess of Bath) **FC** 160ha
O.S.S.183 - ST 828 423
01985 213507

From Warminster take the A362 to Frome. At the Longleat roundabout turn L towards Horningham and drive about 1 mile. Nockatt car park is situated on the L. Car parking for cars, surfaced path to Shear Water lake. Open throughout the year. Please use parking provided at Nockatt Car Park on the Horningsham/Warminster road. Educational visits, for which a charge will be made,

can be arranged by contacting John McHardy on the above number.

The part of the wood named Nockatt dates back over 400 years but other areas were planted from the 1820s on what was previously heath land. After the second world war, the emphasis was on commercial softwood management, but more recently a change in emphasis to amenity and conservation values has become effective. Natural regeneration of species is encouraged which include Noble fir, Douglas fir, western red cedar, coastal redwood, oak, birch, wild azalea, sycamore, hornbeam etc. The timber from the wood is marketed to provide saw logs for construction, veneers for furniture, with low grade timber being used on the estate itself. The wood has a wide range of plant and animal life. At Shear Water lake there are water activities, sailing and coarse fishing, and a small restaurant and café.

*Witham Park

(The Duke of Somerset) **F** 240ha

O.S.S. 183 - ST 770 384

01985 844317

⚓20🛏2↜☾🛶☀Ψ🗜FP🕱

From Maiden Bradley village, take lane to Bruton. At T junction, c3 miles turn R, car park 300 yards on L, signposted Witham Park Farm.

Witham Park is part of the ancient forest of Selwood straddling the Wiltshire/Somerset boundary. It is in the North Wessex Downs AONB near the chalk downs on a greensand scarp looking west over the clay of the Witham Vale. Long term woodland management has produced an attractive mixture of species and ages and areas of both native hardwoods and commercial exotic softwoods. Fallow, roe and occasionally muntjac deer, all of which damage younger trees by fraying and browsing, are present with a wide variety of bird species. The woodlands are managed to produce the timber you use, whilst contributing to the landscape and wildlife you enjoy.

*The Woodland Park

(A G Phillips, OBE, CC) **R** 48ha

O.S.S. 183 - ST 840 525

01373 822238

⚓100🛏10↜ ● WC 🛏🚻▲🔌🏕
🔒

Signposted from A361 and A36 roads - brown tourist board signs indicate location from Yarnbrook, Southwick and North Bradley. Open all year. There is fully open access to the wood. Group visits arranged by appointment only. Please contact Mrs S Cap. All the year round admission charge: £2.00 and children £1.00. Accompanied children under 14 free. Other events include: supper evenings with guided walks, dawn chorus walks with continental breakfast in May, all by appointment only. Special events for children include bunny trails, adventure trails and educational activity trails for schools.

Ancient woodland, five groups of owners since 1066. 86 species of trees and shrubs, a lake created in 1960, Museum built in 1970. Shop and tearoom, camping and caravanning facilities, coarse fishing, schools, party visits, supper evenings, special guided walks arranged, wide range of flora and fauna, adventure playground and railway. Garden furniture and sale of forest products. Wide range of bird life. Butterflies include white admiral. 48 types of lichen and moss recorded and a very good specimen of wild service tree. Woodlands felled in late 50s early 60s and now restored.

YORKSHIRE - NORTH

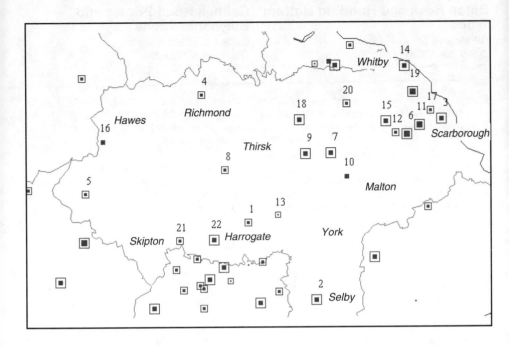

1. Bilton Beck
2. *Bishopswood*
3. *Broxa Forest*
4. Calfhall Round Howe & Billybank Woods
5. *Clapdale
6. *Dalby Forest*
7. *Duncombe Park
8. Hackfall Wood
9. Hambleton Woods
10. *Hovingham High Wood
11. *Langdale Forest*

12. *Levisham Wood
13. Marton Wood
14. Mulgrave Woods
15. *Newtondale*
16. Ranley Gill
17. Scar and Castlebeck Woods
18. *Silton Forest*
19. *Sneaton Forest*
20. Sonley, Sikehill and Hall Woods
21. Strid Wood
22. Swinsty Reservoir

Bilton Beck and Rudding Bottom Wood

(Woodland Trust) **F** 18ha
O.S.S. 104 - SE 315 584
01476 74297

From the A59, in Bilton turn either along Bilton Lane or Woodfield Road. There are no facilities but there is some parking near railway bridge.

This woodland lies along the southern bank of the beautiful River Nidd, eastwards from the impressive, now disused, Nidd Viaduct. Oak, ash and alder are the main tree species with hazel and rowan forming the shrub layer. The wood is home to a large number of plants and animals, including celandine, bluebell, wood sorrel, pink purslane, townhall clock, fungi, roe deer, mink and fox. The combination of river and woodland provides plenty of insect food and roosting sites for several species of bat; also dipper, grey wagtail and kingfisher.

Bishopswood

(Forest Enterprise) **F** 330ha
O.S.S. 105 - SE 561 333
01751 72771
⊕⊶ 🐎 ⫨

Turn R off B1222 3.1 miles E of Sherburn in Elmet, either into wood or 2.8 miles E of Sherburn in Elmet take Wistow road for about 1.25 miles to find Dutchman's car park and picnic place.

Broxa Forest

(Forest Enterprise) **F** 733ha
O.S.S. 94/101 - SE 965 945
01751 72771
⊕⊶🚶⫨☀🦌🐎⫨

Take the Coomboots road SW from Burniston off the A165 for about 1.5 miles turn R at T junction towards Harwood Dale. Car park at Reasty viewpoint Grid Ref - SE 965 945.

Attractive conifer forest with open heath areas and very varied topography. Just reached end of first rotation.

Calfhall Round Howe and Billybank Woods

(National Trust) **F** 38ha
O.S.S. 92 - NZ 153 005
01904 702021

Between Richmond and Hudswell just S of A6l08. Access on foot, 0.5 mile upstream from Richmond bridge. Local Authority car park off the A6108 just W of Richmond.

Ancient semi-natural woodland on the S side of the River Swale to the W of the ancient town of Richmond. Rich and mature calcareous woodland. Part of the property is an SSSI.

*Clapdale

(Dr J A Farrer) **R** 20ha
O.S.S. 98 - SD 749 692
015242 51302
🅱🏹🌙⫨☀🦌🛏 ⓘ 🍴🗺⫨🚩🏕🎿
🛍

A65 Skipton to Kendal road between Settle and Ingleton. Dales car park in the village. An information centre and WC in the village. There is a hard surface for walking and wheelchairs. Part of Estate/Nature trail on way to cave. The wood is open during daylight hours, and charges are Adults 20p, Children 10p (liable to small increase). Student studies by arrangement.

Woodlands consist of mature beech; lake scenery and an area of rhododendrons. Geological fault, new planting, developing woodland views of improving silviculture.

*Dalby Forest

(Forest Enterprise) **FC** 3000ha
O.S.S. 100 - SE 857 874
01751 472771
🅱⊕£2.50🐎🏹🌙🚶☀🦌WC🛏ⓘ🍴
🗺🐎⫨🚜🔵🏕🐎🏕🚩🍴🏠

Eastwards on A170 from Pickering, turn N on the Whitby Road at Thornton le Dale and follow brown signs to Dalby Forest Drive. Turn R about 2 miles from Thornton into Forest Drive. Visitor centre, forest drive, WCs, picnic places, waymarked walks, cycle trails. Parking: £2.50 cars, £12.50 minibuses, £25 coaches. Open all year, 7.30am - 8.30pm. Group visits and coaches by appointment only. Guided visits are available at £10 per hour. Educational visits can be arranged through the Education Ranger who can provide material suitable for students from 5-20 years. For further details telephone the above number.

Dalby Forest is an attractive mixed age conifer woodland. The drive allows motorists to go into the heart of the forest and provides picnic places with waymarked walks to enable exploration on foot. For the energetic visitor there are waymarked cycle routes and a permanent orienteering course, maps of which can be purchased at the visitor centre, which also has souvenirs and leaflets on the Deepdale Habitat Trail starting at the Bickley Forest Garden. The different habitats of the beautiful Deepdale valley are interpreted by a series of information boards.

*Duncombe Park

(The Rt Hon Lord Feversham) **R** 165ha
O.S.S.100 - SE 603 833
01439 770213

🏛️🚗300🚽5🔀♿🌲☀️🦌 WC ♿ ⓘ 📖 🌳
🔥🏕️🍴🌮🕺🎒🛍️

Duncombe Park is in Helmsley off A170 Thirsk/ Scarborough road. Entrance 3 mins from market square. Admission charge is £2.75 (Garden and Park), £1 (Park only). The Park is open from Apr to Oct with the house and garden also open daily in Jul, Aug and Sept. Please telephone above number for details (24 hours) and any restrictions.

On the site of a medieval deer park and landscaped in the 18th century. Duncombe Park contains multi-purpose deciduous and coniferous woodlands. The wooded dale sides form a natural landscape of river, grazing land and forest. The ''green garden'' at the mansion house, with its terrace and temples overlooking the River Rye valley, contains the tallest lime and one of the tallest oak trees in England. The undisturbed hardwood ecosystem hosts a wealth of insect, herbaceous and birdlife with rare species identified and is designated a National Nature Reserve. There are no public rights of way but entry charge gives access to woodland paths, visitor facilities and the garden (when open).

Hackfall Wood

(Woodland Trust) **F** 45ha
O.S.S. 99 - SE 234 773
01476 74297

From Ripon market square, head W on the B6265 (signposted Hackley Bridge). After about 500 yards take the RH fork to Grewelthorpe. Follow this road through the village and on towards Masham for about 0.5 mile. Park in the car park and follow the signs to the wood. There are no facilities. Hackfall Wood remains wet even in the driest summers. Boots or wellingtons are recommended. This ancient woodland, at least 350 years old, forms a remarkable landscape feature on the NW facing side of a 100m deep gorge cut via the River Ure. The wood provides a diversity of habitats for a range of wildlife, including wood warbler, nuthatch and kingfisher. Tree species such as oak, ash and spindle can be found in the wood. The ground flora is also characteristic of old established woodland with dog's mercury, primrose, bluebell and wild garlic. If you move quietly, you may catch a glimpse of roe deer.

Hambleton Woods

(A Bailey) **R** 174ha
O.S.S. 100 - SE 515 830
01845 525460

🚗150🚽4🔀♿🌲☀️🦌 WC ♿ ⓘ 📖 🌳🍴
🔥🏕️🍴🌮🕺🎒

From Thirsk take A170 to Helmsley. Drive up Sutton Bank and park in National Park car park immediately on your L (£1). Walks will be advertised in information centre. The majority of facilities itemised are provided by North York Moors National Park located adjacent to woodlands. Way-marked paths and some picnic tables will be provided within the woodland. Two distinct blocks of mixed coniferous woodland (spruce, larch and pine) planted after the Second World War. Now that many areas have reached maturity some felling will break up the age structure to improve views and wildlife habitats and allow the introduction of modern design features. Other features include permissive way-marked walks and picnic facilities. North York Moors visitor centre adjacent to the woodlands, provide extensive facilities.

*Hovingham High Wood
(Sir Marcus Worsley and Mr William Worsley) **AE** 170ha
O.S.S. 100 - SE 657 753
01653 628771

From Malton follow B1257 to Hovingham (8 miles). In village turn left opposite the Worsley Arms Hotel. Follow road through the park for approx. 0.75 mile. Gated car park on left hand side up track by bend in road. By prior written appointment for groups only (minimum 15), dates by arrangement.

A mixed commercial forest in the Howardian Hills AONB managed continuously since 1897. Centre of Excellence Award 1993 for management improving the quality of the landscape, creating benefits for wildlife and growing timber in environmentally sound ways. A large oak from the estate was recently used in the rebuilding of York Minster. Variety of tree types mostly planted in intimate mixture.

Langdale Forest
(Forest Enterprise) **F** 4256ha
O.S.S. 94/101 - SE 927 926
01751 72771

Follow the road from Hackness to Langdale End. Just after leaving Langdale End turn R towards Birch Hall. Car park and start of mountain trails at Grid Ref - SE 924 929. Mountain bike trails may be closed for motor car rallies etc. Prior notice will be given and further details available by phoning the above number. Mountain bike trails.]

*Levisham Wood
(North York Moors National Park) **F** 64ha
O.S.S. 94/100 - SE 826 897
01439 770657

Take A169 N from Pickering to Whitby. Turn L to Lockton and Levisham after 5 miles. Drive through Lockton to Levisham. At top of Levisham village turn L by church and follow back lane until it becomes track. Park at end where Green Lane begins. Do not obstruct gateway to adjoining fields. Various extraction tracks have been created through woods plus existing Public Rights of Way

giving full access to whole site.

Levisham Woods are all ancient semi-natural woodland within the Newtondale SSSI. Previous ownership/tenancy by the Forestry Commission resulted in extensive felling of broadleaves and conifer planting. Present management objective to revert to native broadleaved species. Has ancient oak coppice. Steep slopes are a management constraint but give exceptional views into Newtondale. The woods adjoin a series of unimproved pastures which together with the woods contain an extensive range of flora and fauna.

Marton Wood
(North Yorkshire County Council) **F** 7ha
O.S.S. 99 - SE 420 617
01609 780780 ext 2460

Take B6265 south from Boroughbridge. Take 3rd L to Marton, approx. 3 miles. Take first L after 1 mile. The wood is on LH side approx. 0.5 mile down this lane. Park on the roadside. Access to the wood can be gained from Legram Lane but visitors may find it easier to go via the adjoining small paddock which is a caravan club certified site. Fully open access throughout the year.

A broadleaved woodland, part of the County Farms Estate. It has been planted in three parts, the eastern third in 1956. The remainder is semi-mature, 80-100 years old. Species include oak, sycamore and ash.

Mulgrave Woods
(Marquis of Normanby) **P** 810ha
O.S.S. 94 - NZ 861 125
01947 893239

Follow the A174 from Whitby into Sandsend village, cross the road bridge over East Row Beck and turn immediately left into the car park. Access to the woodland is through the handgate at the extreme end of the parking area. The woodland is open on Wed, Sat and Sun only. Closed throughout May.

The existing layout of Mulgrave Estate was formulated by Humphrey Repton in 1793. The Estate and its woodland are of great landscape importance. The woodland rises from sea level to 850' on the moorland plantations. All age classes are represented with European/Japanese larch and Scots pine predominating among the conifers and with beech the leading hardwood. The younger plantations have mainly been planted as mixtures. Much of the roadside areas throughout the main wood are of high amenity value and many fine old, as well as more recently planted native and exotic species are easily viewed. Management objectives are to grow good timber crop which is compatible aesthetically with the overall estate landscape.

Newtondale

(Forest Enterprise) **F** 500ha
O.S.S. 100 - SE 824 938
01751 72771

🏠🚗300🚻♿👟☀️☂️🦌🍽️🏕️

North York Moors railway to Newtondale Halt. By road: turn W off A169 at Lockton and drive through Levisham to Newtondale Forest Drive or E of the Stape to Egton Bridge road at Mauley Cross. Forest drive, picnic places and walks. Parking £1.00, no coaches. Special arrangement for school parties and educational groups.

Within the dramatic scenery of Newtondale, mainly conifer woodland well into the second rotation. Superb views of a mixed forest and moorland landscape. Explore the woods by means of the waymarked walks from Newtondale Halt or along one of the many public rights of way which intersect the wood. A rich and varied wildlife population.

Ranley Gill

(Mr L N Tucker) **A** 180ha
O.S.S. 98 - SD 813 872
01524 272249

🦌🏕️☀️☂️

Take A684 to Hawes then B6255 south for approx. 4 miles. Woodland lies to north west, off road. Please write to Tilhill Economic Forestry, Sellet Hall, Via Carnforth, Lancs, LA6 2QF, for access permission. Access will be permitted on forest roads only.

Predominately commercial woodland with Sitka spruce at higher levels and larch and mixed broadleaves at lower levels. Roe deer can be sighted on the property. Views across valley to Snaizeholme Fell from higher ground.

Scar and Castlebeck Woods

(Woodland Trust) **F** 33ha
O.S.S. 94/100 - SE 947 971
01476 74297

🚗🦌🚶

On the main A171 Scarborough to Whitby road, take the road running S to Harwood Dale. Access to the woods is at two points, 1 mile and 1.5 miles along this road at the A171 junction. For the latter entrance follow the bridleway just before Chapel Farm. This leads into the southern part of the property. Cars can be parked on the roadside verge opposite the bridleway. Please DO NOT park in the farmyard. There are no facilities and there is free and full access all year. Paths within the woods can be quite muddy and stout footwear is advisable. Caution should be taken if the stream is crossed at the northern end as the stepping stones can be very slippery.

Scar and Castlebeck Woods lie in a deep, secluded valley in the North York Moors National Park. Alder and rowan line the stream edge with oak, ash and elm also present. The wood has a rich and interesting fauna and flora. On the valley side a wealth of mosses and liverworts, known as bryophytes, flourish in the damp atmosphere. Wood club rush, broad buckler fern, and wavy hair grass grow in abundance. Of special interest is the brimstone butterfly; in Scar and Castlebeck Woods it has reached the most NE point of its range in England.

Silton Forest

(Forest Enterprise) **F** 465ha
O.S.S. 100 - SE 469 943
01751 72771

🚗🚻♿👟☀️☂️🦌🍽️

Turn east off A19 to Over Silton or Nether Silton. Silton Forest is about 5km from A19.

Sneaton Forest

(Forest Enterprise) **F** 1209ha
O.S.S. 94 - NZ 888 036
01751 472771

🚗🦌♿☂️🏕️🍽️

B1416 from Ruswarp and turn S at Red Gate junction down minor road to Falling Foss car park. Waymarked walk, picnic places, car parks. School parties by appointment.

The old woodland around Falling Foss is most attractive, mature broadleaf giving way in the south to young conifer plantations established mostly in the late 1960s on open moor. Much work has been done in the young plantations to soften edges and diversify habitats. Waymarked walks from both the Falling Foss car park and the Maybeck car park (893 024) enable the visitor to explore the forest on foot.

Sonley, Sikehill and Hall Woods; Farndale Woodlands
(National Trust) **R** 13ha
O.S.S. 94/100 - SE 654 994
01904 702021

Access is by foot from minor public highways running N from Church Houses.

Mixed woodlands in Upper Farndale, in the North York Moors National Park, famed for its wild daffodils. Bought in 1991 jointly by the Council for National Parks, the Ramblers' Association, and the Council for Protection of Rural England and Open Spaces Society, with help from the Countryside Commission. Presented to the National Trust to commemorate the life of Francis Ritchie, who campaigned all his life, in a voluntary capacity, for the designation and protection of National Parks.

Strid Wood (Bolton Abbey)
(Trustees of the Chatsworth Settlement)
F 46ha
O.S.S. 104 - SE 077 533
01756 710533
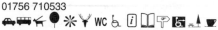

4 miles E of Skipton take the B6160 N from the A59 Skipton-Harrogate road. In 1 mile turn down private drive to the Cavendish Pavilion car park. Car parking for 1500 cars(£2.50) and 50 coaches (free). Height restriction 10'9"). Other facilities include: restaurant and ice cream facilities at the Cavendish Pavilion, shop and interpretation area. There is fully open access to the woodland trails and there are rights of way through the wood on

foot. The woods are open every day of the year. Three electric vehicles are available for less able visitors, free of charge.

The Strid, straddling the River Wharfe has long been a place of legend and beauty. An SSSI, the abundance and variety of species is a result of the management of the ancient woodland by selective felling and regeneration, retaining a continuous canopy with a diversity of species. Records show 62 nesting species of birds, 98 species of mosses, 97 of fungi, 80 lichens, 49 molluscs, 42 liverworts and an abundance of vascular plants. Visitors have been welcomed to the Strid since the early 19th century when a series of views, summerhouses and trails were created by the 6th Duke. These now form the basis of the present nature trails.

Swinsty Reservoir
(Yorkshire Water) **F** 200ha
O.S.S. 104 - SE 197 538
0113 231 2576

From the A59 Harrogate/Skipton road, take the turning to Otley at Blubberhouses. Once on that road take the side road marked "Timble" down to Swinsty and Fewston. Facilities include footpaths. Fishing is also available but there is a charge for this facility. The wood is open all year. Woodland walks with a wide variety of wildlife - especially on the water.

The woods surround Swinsty Reservoir, providing superb views along the Washam Valley.

YORKSHIRE - SOUTH

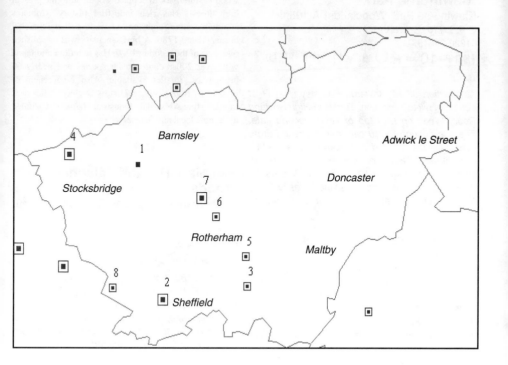

1. *Cawthorne Park
2. Ecclesall Woods
3. Hail Mary Hill & Falconer Woods
4. Langsett Reservoir
5. Roe Woods
6. Scholes Coppice
7. *Wharncliffe Woods*
8. Wyming Brook

*Cawthorne Park

(Cawthorne Park Woodlands) **A** 105ha
O.S.S. 110 - SE 283 102
01226 295197

🔋1🚗10🚌🔥🚶‍♀️( ) ♠ 🦌📖🏕 🍴 FP 📺
🔺

At Junction 38 M1 towards Barnsley, first R at bottom of hill to T junction. Turn R at High Hoyland Road. Wood on L at top of ridge, second gate. There is parking for 10 cars and 1 coach but no other facilities. Guided visits can be arranged by appointment. Please book 2 weeks in advance. Charges: car parking £1. Group visit rates by negotiation. Donations made to the Forestry Trust. For ALL visits please contact Len Batty on the above number.

The wood is a replanted ancient woodland being part of the original Bretton Hall Estate, replanted in the late 50s with a selection of hard and soft woods. Within the stream valley that runs down the centre of the wood is evidence of ancient ironstone workings. There is some hearsay that this iron was used to make cannon balls used against the Spanish Armada. There is also a series of ponds holding a selection of aquatic wildlife. The woodland is being managed on a selective thinning regime with underplanting of hardwoods. The mains species on site are hybrid larch and Corsican pine with a good proportion of mixed hardwoods.

Ecclesall Woods

(Sheffield City Council) **F** 130ha
O.S.S. 110 - SK 309 820
0114 250 0500

🚗🔥( ) 🔺 ⓘ FP 📺

Approximately 4 miles from City Centre - A625 - turn off onto Limb Lane or alternatively A621 opposite Abbeydale Industrial Hamlet (326 820). Across busy main road. There is no crossing point. Car parking and picnic area at Limb Lane meeting point. No WCs. Free access all year round. There is an extensive footpath/bridleway network. Please keep to the paths as much as possible and avoid entering bird sanctuary.

An ancient woodland though much modified. Has passed through various stages from 'wildwood' to

wood pasture/park to coppice woodland to the present high forest. Has rich industrial history. Contains commemorative tombstone of wood collier (charcoal burner) dated 1786. A bird sanctuary was established over part of the wood in 1929. Has rich flora and fauna with over 200 recorded plant species and nearly 60 bryophytes. Leaflet available. Also comprehensive booklet by Sorby Natural History Society. It lies next to interesting Abbeydale Industrial Hamlet. Scheduled to become local nature reserve.

Hail Mary Hill and Falconer Woods

(Rotherham Metropolitan Borough Council)
F 21ha
O.S.S. 111 - SK 440 867
01709 822022

🚗🔥( ) 🔺 ❄ 📺

Follow A618 S from Rotherham, over the M1, past Ulley Country Park to Aughton village. Turn R onto West Lane, follow for 1 mile until junction with Falconer Lane. Turn R and park by entrance to Treeton Dyke, follow footpath to woodland. Horse-riders please keep to the marked horse route.

Ancient semi-natural oak-birch woodland, carpeted with bluebells in springtime. Additional habitats include an alder carr, marshland and acidic grassland, which combined are of considerable wildlife interest. The woodland is situated on a west-facing slope, overlooking Treeton Dyke, a subsidence flash noted for its wildfowl. To date, the main focus of management has been recreation and amenity. It is hoped to introduce a programme of works benefiting the wildlife of the woodland in the near future.

Langsett Reservoir

(Yorkshire Water) **R** 150ha
O.S.S. 110 - SE 212 005
0114-259 2005

🚗🔥🔺❄WC ♿ ⓘ 🏕 🚣 📺

The car park is off the A616 Stockbridge by-pass which links the M1 with the Manchester road (A628). Footpaths, information centre (summer only), café, pub. Open all year.

The wood is mainly coniferous and surrounds Langsett Reservoir. There are spectacular views over the reservoir and onto the moors of the Peak District, especially attractive in September when the heather is in flower.

Roe Woods
(Sheffield City Council) **F** 13.5ha
O.S.S. 110 - SK 358 904
0114 278 7863

Entrance is by junction of Norwood Road and Herries Road, Sheffield S5, opposite Northern General Hospital. Open all hours.

Great Roe is a broadleaf wood, mainly beech and oak. Indicators of its ancient origins include dog's mercury and yellow archangel. In autumn numerous types of fungus abound, with jew's ear and destroying angel. The wood is managed on traditional lines by Sheffield Wildlife Trust in partnership with Sheffield City Council, using, for instance, coppicing and heavy horses. It has a unique tree sculpture and a picnic site, carved by a local sculptor from felled beech trees.

Scholes Coppice
(Rotherham Metropolitan Borough Council) **F** 23ha
O.S.S. 111 - SK 395 955
01709 822022

Follow the A629 NW form Rotherham for 2 miles, and turn R at Admirals Crest, just past Grange Park Golf Course. Park opposite Keppel's Column. The woodland lies to the NE across the open grassland found here.

A well recorded ancient woodland site, Scholes Coppice is now characterised by a mature beech-sweet chestnut woodland, planted at the turn of the century. Active silviculture management has recently been reintroduced with the aim of promoting a more mixed woodland. Other work has been implemented to improve the path network and enhance the wildlife

value of the site. Features of particular interest include Caesar's Camp, a well preserved Iron Age Fort, and close by stands Keppel's Column, an eighteenth century obelisk. Fine views of the historic Wentworth Estate are found throughout the area.

Wharncliffe Woods
(Forest Enterprise) **F** 456ha
O.S.S. 110 - SK 325 950
01623 822447

Wyming Brook
(Sheffield City Council) **F** 50ha
O.S.S. 110 - SK 275 865
01742 500500

A57 Manchester road - turn off by old waterworks house (O.S. Ref - SK 276869) and travel across access road to Rivelin Dam. Alternatively access can be obtained from Redmires Road (O.S. Ref - SK 269858) where there is a small car park. There are no other facilities other than footpath network. Free and full access all year round. Stout footwear required if taking stream-side path. Please keep to paths as much as possible.

A very attractive mixed woodland mainly of native broadleaves but also with significant conifer element, notably Corsican pine and spruces. Valuable wildlife site. Good views obtainable from higher areas; rises to 300m. Adjoins Water Authority woodland and reservoir. Scheduled to become local nature reserve.

YORKSHIRE - WEST

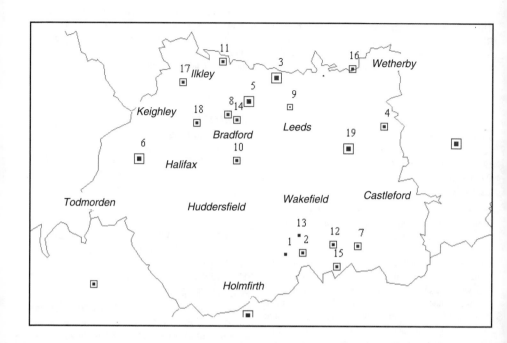

1. Bank Wood
2. Bella Vista
3. *Chevin Forest Park
4. Coburn Hill Wood
5. Esholt Woods
6. Hardcastle Crags
7. Haw Park Wood
8. Hirst Wood
9. Ireland Wood
10. Judy Wood

11. Middleton Wood
12. Newmillerdam Country Park
13. North Wood
14. Northcliffe Wood
15. Notton Wood
16. Ox Close
17. Park Wood
18. St Ives Wood
19. Temple Newsam Estate

Bank Wood

(Job Earnshaw & Bros Ltd) **A** 35ha
O.S.S. 110 - SE 268 139
01924 830099

Junction 38 M1. Take A637 towards Huddersfield. Turn L at West Bretton roundabout and follow A636 for half mile, then turn R. Follow track down to wood. Some public footpaths, all other access by appointment.

Bank Wood is an ancient woodland site although opencast coalmining has affected some areas. Relics of bellpits from 18th century ironstone mining are to be found in the wood. The wide rides support a range of butterfly species. Tree cover is predominantly sycamore, larch and Scots pine, with some ash and occasional beech.

Bella Vista

(Job Earnshaw & Bros Ltd) **R** 16ha
O.S.S. 110 - SE 277 142
01924 830099

Junction 38 M1. Take A637 towards Huddersfield. Turn L along A636 at West Bretton roundabout. Car park is approximately 200 yards on the L hand side. There are rights of way on foot through the woods. Please keep to footpaths. No dogs allowed away from official footpaths. Information sheet available.

Bella Vista plantations were probably planted for visual and sporting purposes by the owners of Bretton Hall in the 19th century. They are bisected by the remains of a medieval road and the relic of a 17th century brickworks can be found in the west of the woodland. Tree cover is predominantly sycamore and Japanese larch with some oak and beech.

*Chevin Forest Park

(Leeds City Council) **FE** 283ha
O.S.S. 104 - SE 216 444
0113 258 6655

⛔200🚻4🅿🔘🚶☀🦌 wc ℹ️ 📖🐾🔥
🚴⛺☕🍴📮

The Park is signposted from Otley town centre. There is a Visitor Centre and a café. There are rights of way, bridleways and self guided trails through the park. All group visits are by appointment only and require 30 days notice; please contact Mr Terry Cree on 01943 465023.

This park of woodlands and crags was designated a Local Nature Reserve in 1989. It is home to a wide range of flora and fauna; of particular interest are green hairstreak butterflies and bog asphodel, roe deer and woodcock. The woodlands are made up of many tree species, both native and exotic, including beech, oak, sweet chestnut, hemlock and Corsican pine. The park is criss-crossed by paths and bridleways, and offers fine views across the Wharfe valley. The site can be explored using the permanent orienteering course and self guided trails. School visits are catered for with the field study centre offering an opportunity for indoor study of the natural environment. Centre of Excellence Award 1994.

*Coburn Hill Wood

(Leeds City Council) **F** 20ha
O.S.S 105 - SE 450 360
0113 281 3068

⛔200🚻6🔘🚶🦌 wc ℹ️ 📖🐾🔥
🚴⛺☕🍴📮🏠🐾🏛️

From Garforth take the A642, after going under the A1 turn R into the B1217. After ½ mile turn R into Lotherton Hall Estate. Coburn Hill Woods are reached by a footpath which runs off to the S of the estate. There are WCs, including WCs for the disabled, a shop, a picnic area, a café, a bird garden, a hall and chapel. There is open access to the woods, rights of way and bridleways. There are also self guided trails. For group visits please allow 2 weeks notice. Contact the Ranger Service on 0113 281 3068.

Coburn Hill Wood is one of a number of woodlands running N to S between Lotherton Hall estate and the Fairburn Ings nature reserve. It lies on a bed of magnesium limestone to the E of Leeds. Many plants and animals which are not seen in other parts of Leeds thrive in the wood. The wood was purchased by Leeds

City Council in the 1980s. It formerly belonged to the Forestry Commission.

Esholt Woods
(Bradford Metropolitan District Council)
F 120ha
O.S.S. 104 - SE 182 404
01274 754826

12🚗4🚌🅿 ♿ ✳🚻👁 ■

From Shipley, take the A6038 and follow the signs for Esholt. Car park is on the L just before the village. There is car parking for 12 cars and 4 coaches. There is open access and bridleways through the wood. Guided visits can be arranged; please contact Richard Dunton on above telephone number.

A number of small conifer plantations and deciduous woods locally known as Esholt Woods, surrounding the village of Esholt, of `Emmerdale Farm' fame. Some of the woods in the bottom of the valley are owned by Yorkshire Water, with restricted access for operational reasons.

Hardcastle Crags
(National Trust) **F** 125ha
O.S.S. 103 - SD 988 295
01422 844518

🚗🚌🐎 ● ▲ 👁🚻 ♿

1.5 miles NW of Hebden Bridge. Parking at entrance, coaches by arrangement only. Guided walks - please contact the Warden on above number. Braille guide available. Information caravan (seasonal weekends). The main path is accessible by wheelchair users.

Woodland, NW of Hebden Bridge, comprising two steep wooded valleys, each with a stream running through it. The woodland is predominantly broadleaved, with areas of conifer. Rock outcrops and millponds are attractive features. Riverside walks beside Hebden Water take you through deciduous woodland and past a disused 19th century cotton mill.

Haw Park Wood
(Wakefield Metropolitan District Council)
F 65ha
O.S. S. 110/111 - SE 375 154
01924 296203

🚗100🚌♿ ♿ 🚻 👁 🚏

Follow brown tourist signs to Anglers country park from either A61 Wakefield/Barnsley road or A638 Wakefield/Doncaster road. Car park at Anglers country park, wood is 1/4 miile. Visitor Centre. Open every day.

Haw Park Wood is an ancient replanted woodland formerly owned by the Forestry Commission. The northern part of the wood was part of the eminent naturalist Charles Walton's estate. Pleasant walks and a bridleway go through the wood. It is predominantly coniferous but the long-term aim is for it to become mixed deciduous. Management is to enhance, diversify and improve the woodland for people and wildlife.

Hirst Wood
(Bradford Metropolitan District Council)
F 15ha
O.S.S. 104 - SE 140 380
01274 754826

🚗30🚌 ● 🚏🚻♿ 🚶‍♂️

Follow the A650 to Saltaire. At the roundabout, take the third L, carry on over the railway bridge to the car park on the L. The picnic area is next to the car park. There is full access to the wood. Guided visits can be arranged by appointment, please contact Richard Dunton on above number.

Hirst Wood is an SSSI due to the presence of a glacial bog. It is bounded by the river Aire and the Leeds-Liverpool canal, next to the historic village of Saltaire. A mature broadleaf woodland with some notable beech trees. A woodland walk is signposted and waymarked within the wood.

Ireland Wood
(Woodland Trust) **F** 4ha
O.S.S. 104 - SE 255 392
01476 74297

🚗🐎 ●

From Leeds take the A660 signposted to Otley through Headingley to the main roundabout (Leeds ring road). Continue on the A660 and take the first main turning L, signposted to Cookridge. Along this road turn L to Cookridge Hospital. The woods are about 500 yards along this road opposite the hospital. Ample roadside parking.

This remnant of long established woodland is situated within a heavily developed residential area and is well used by local people. It is an attractive wood containing oak growing from old coppice stools, along with birch, wild cherry, rowan, beech, holly and sycamore. Robin and thrush are just two of the many common bird species living in this wood.

Judy Woods
(Bradford Metropolitan District Council)
F 40ha
O.S.S. 104 - SE 160 301
01274 754826

🚗20🍴●⛺🛈👤⬚🏠

3 miles from Bradford on the A641, turn R towards Norwood Green, park on the road 200m after the bend. Disabled access into the woods on surfaced paths. There is open access to the wood. Guided visits can be arranged by appointment, please contact Richard Dunton on the above number.

A number of small broadleaf woods known locally as Judy Woods. There has been small scale mineral extraction in the past. Mainly mature beech, planted to supply bobbins for the local textile industries. A woodland walk is signposted and waymarked within the wood.

Middleton Wood
(Bradford Metropolitan District Council)
F 51ha
O.S. S. 104 - SE 110 480
01274 754826

🚗15🍴👤✳⛺👤🏠

From the centre of Ilkley, travel down Brooke Street over the bridge. Take the next R. The entrance is a quarter of a mile on the L. There is open access to the wood. Guided visits can be

arranged by appointment. Please contact Richard Dunton on above number.

An ancient deciduous woodland as noted before Domesday. It is of outstanding landscape value with views over Ilkley Moor and the Wharfe Valley. It is particularly noted for its wildlife and an abundance of bluebells in the spring. A woodland walk is signposted and waymarked within the wood.

Newmillerdam Country Park
(Wakefield Metropolitan District Council)
F 95ha
O.S. S 110/111 - SE 331 157
01924 296203

🚗110🍴○👤 WC 🛈⬚🚽🍽🏠

4 miles from Wakefield on the A61 Barnsley/ Wakefield road. Pay and display car park. Pubs, café etc. in Newmillerdam village. Open every day.

An historical landscape with woodland and lakeside walks. The lakeside walk is suitable for wheelchairs. Marked bridleway and a permanent orienteering course in the wood. There is good wildlife interest at all times. The conifers were planted for the mining industry and are now marketed for saw-logs, fencing etc. The wood is managed to improve, diversify and enhance its character.

North Wood
(Job Earnshaw & Bros Ltd) **A** 35ha
O.S.S. 110/111 - SE 277 153
01924 830099

From junction 38 on M1, follow the A637 towards Huddersfield. Turn R down the B6117 and R again. All access by appointment except for public rights of way.

North Wood is an ancient woodland site. There is some evidence of late 19th century coal mining and the remains of a mineral railway. Badgers are occasionally found in the woods and jays and woodcock both breed. A wide range of tree species occurs - sycamore, oak, Scots pine and larch predominate. Ash, rowan and beech are also present.

Northcliffe Wood
(Bradford Metropolitan District Council)
F 17ha
O.S.S. 104 - SE 150 370
01274 754826

Take the A650 from Bradford to Shipley, after 2.5 miles turn L into Cliffe Wood Avenue. Facilities include children's play area and model railway. There is open access to the wood. Guided visits can be arranged by appointment, please contact Richard Dunton on above number.

A broadleaf woodland with oak as the dominant species. Bounded by playing fields and a golf course with views over the historic village of Saltaire, Salts Mill, and Baildon and Ilkley Moor. There is evidence of small scale mining and charcoal burning pits. A woodland walk is signposted and waymarked within the wood.

Notton Woods
(Wakefield Metropolitan District Council)
F 48ha
O.S.S. 110 - SE 338 123
01924 296203

6 miles from Wakefield on the A61 Wakefield/ Barnsley road. Turn L into Keeper Lane (minor road). Parking 0.5 mile on R as road turns L. Follow track at side of field to wood. Open every day.

Notton is an ancient replanted woodland which has been replanted predominantly with conifers. The long-term aim is to convert it back to a mixed deciduous woodland.

Ox Close
(East Keswick Wildlife Trust) **F** 14ha
O.S.S. 104 - SE 364 459
01937 574140

Follow A659 from Collingham toward Harewood to car park at junction with Crabtree Lane. Bridleway opposite leads in 600m to access gate on R just before footbridge. Open access on foot to rides and paths in the western half of the wood.

The wood was purchased following clear felling of half of the site and is now managed primarily for wildlife. The remaining stands are mainly of ash and sycamore. The clear-felled area is managed to produce a mixed broadleaved woodland with rides and clearings.

Park Wood
(Bradford Metropolitan District Council)
F 14ha
O.S.S. 104 - SE 064 420
01274 754826

Situated quarter of a mile from the centre of Keighley and above the Worth Valley Steam Railway. There is open access to the wood. Guided visits can be arranged by appointment. Please contact Richard Dunton on above number.

A mature broadleaf wood with an old cobbled path running through it. The wood is an important landscape feature with good views along the Aire Valley to the Dales.

St Ives Estate
(Bradford Metropolitan District Council)
F 65ha
O.S.S. 104 - SE 090 390
01274 754826

Take the B6429 Harden road. From Bingley, the entrance is on the R at the top of the hill. Other facilities include ornamental gardens, disabled access to parts of woods, 3 self guided nature trails, golf course and fishing pond. There is open access with bridleways through the wood, and self guided trails. Guided visits can be arranged by appointment, please contact Richard Dunton on above number.

A woodland estate dating back to the 13th century, when it was given to the monks of Rievaulx Abbey. The woodland is mixed with some recent conifer plantations. There is evidence of an entrenchment from the English Civil War and other notable features. A large oak from the estate was used in the recent building of the south transept of York Minster.

*Temple Newsam Estate
(Leeds City Council) **F** 485ha
O.S.S. 104 - SE 358 323
0113 264 5535

🚗1000🚌20↰ ∪ ⌕ WC ♿ ⓘ 📖 ⛺ 🏌

🍴 ☕ 🍴 🏪 ⛺ 🏛

Follow the A64 York road out of Leeds, then take the A63 Selby road (signposted). Nearest locations are Halton and Crossgates. Other facilities include a souvenir shop, tea rooms, adventure play ground, Tudor-Jacobean mansion, ornamental gardens, lakes and good disabled access around the park, Home Farm Museum and Rare Breed Centre. There is fully open access to the woods via rights of way and bridleways. There are also self guided trails. Guided visits can be arranged by contacting M Akers on the above number. Please give 2 weeks notice.

Temple Newsam is a 485 hectare country park with a recorded history as a private estate of 1,000 years. The woodland is of mainly semi-natural appearance although planted with new plantations. Much of it dates from the 18th century when the estate was landscaped by Capability Brown. All the main timber species are represented in clearly defined stands - oak, beech, sycamore etc. The old hazel coppice is currently being brought back into rotation. The arboretum includes gingko, cedars, sorbus and prunus species, also old parkland oaks and sycamore avenues.

WALES - CLWYD

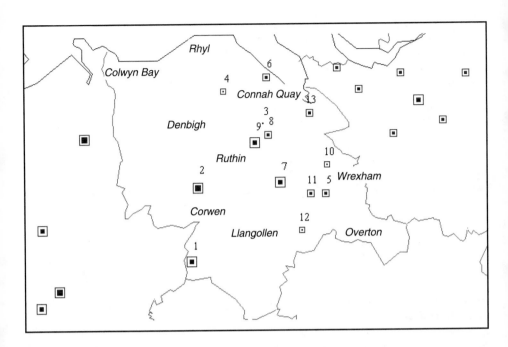

1. Cefn Llwyd
2. *Clocaenog Forest*
3. *Coed Nant Gain
4. Coed Sodom
5. Erddig Wood
6. Greenfield Valley Heritage Park
7. Llandegla
8. Loggerheads Country Park
9. *Moel Famau*
10. Nant-y-Gaer Woods
11. Plas Power Wood
12. Tan-y-Cut Woods
13. Wepre Country Park

Cefn Llwyd
(Shotton Paper Co Ltd) **RM** 439ha
O.S.S. 125 - SH 997 343
01974 261688
🚗6🔭 🛈 ☀

4 miles SE of Bala on the B4391 Bala to Llangynog road. Open all year. Royal Welsh Show Woodlands and Plantations Competition Gold Medal 1993.

A conifer forest planted between 1952 and 1991 as part of a larger woodland estate. Comprises open moor and woodland with great diversity of habitats supporting raptors, black and red grouse, and red squirrels. The forest is managed on a small coupe felling system which will provide a diverse age structure at the end of the restructuring period. Group strip and selection systems are being practised. The views of the forest and moor are impressive with paths leading to the Berwyn mountain. There are also spectacular views down the Dee valley.

Clocaenog Forest
(Forest Enterprise) **F** 6000ha
O.S.S. 116 - SJ 037 510
01492 640578
🚗40(£1)🔭🕙 🛈 ☀ WC ♿ ☂ ▲

The forest lies immediately N of the B5105, which links the A5(T) at Cerrigydruidion with the A525(T) at Ruthin. Open all year.

This large upland forest is the ideal place to get away from it all. Establishment began in 1930, producing the present wide structural diversity and species range. The woodland area is well broken by agricultural land and rough moorland, also enclosing the popular Alwen and Brenig reservoirs. The mature conifer habitat allows a viable population of native red squirrel to prosper. The forest and surrounding moors also support black grouse and fallow deer. A forest visitor centre has been established in a former gamekeepers cottage at Bod Peyrual (SJ 037510) where a car park and picnic area are provided for visitors' convenience. Two public roads threading the forest area allow unlimited opportunity for access to the solitude of the deeper forest.

*Coed Nant Gain
(Iliff Simey) **R** 8ha
O.S.S. 116 - SJ 186 651
01352 741039
🚗🚌🍴 ● ☂ 🛈

4.5 miles W of Mold in Clwydian hills. From Mold take Pantymwyn road, then Cilcain road, cross stone bridge, park on road side. Limited space. Gate at foot of Trial Hill. Access at any time along public footpath overlooking the vallye (Trial Hill to Pentre). Descriptive leaflet available Pantymwyn shop & Loggerheads Countryside Centre. Donations collected for the Woodland Trust and Tree Aid. Guided tours by appointment (forestry, conservation, countryside history, geology etc.) for schools, societies and individuals interested in ancient woodlands. Please telephone as above.

Narrow glacial valley, predominantly oak/ash/ bluebell ancient woodland with meadows, linking river escarpment to open moorland. Exceptionally rich habitat diversity, flora and fauna typical of what was once common. Wild flowers peak late April/early May, autumn colours/fungi late October. Past management evident in the silviculture; land forms reflect rural history (see Journal Royal Forestry Society, April 1993). Management combines forestry and wildlife conservation to restore native broadleaved woodland usuing natural regeneration for long term production of timber.

Coed Sodom
(Mr & Mrs J D Binnian) **F** 8ha
O.S.S. 116 - SJ 097 723
🚗🐎 🛈

From Denbigh take A541 towards Mold. 4 miles on turn L in Bodfari to Tremeirchion on B5429. 1 mile N of Bodari turn R up steep hill; first L, straight over cross road and continue to meeting point. Limited car park only. Donations to the Forestry Trust £2. Please acknowledge donations are from visiting Coed Sodom.

Coed Sodom is alongside Offa's Dyke Path, with views to the sea and to the hills of the vale of Clwyd. The woodland was bought from the Forestry

Commission in 1985 and a winding track leads down through the well thinned sitka spruce and Douglas fir to a lower lane. Young plants and bushes have colonised the ride margins to produce attractive glades. There is a vigorous badger sett; buzzards are present and the russet bark of Californian redwoods can be seen at the lower edge among fine Douglas fir stems.

Erddig Wood
(National Trust) **F** 72ha
O.S.S. 117 - SJ 330 485
01978 355314

On the outskirts of Wrexham; take the A534 from A483 or Wrexham town centre, and follow signs to Erddig House. Car parking at Erddig House including the above facilities.

Erddig Wood comprises several woodlands in Erddig Park, predominantly broadleaved of high landscape value. Some fine mature oak and beech. Most of the woodland is classified ancient semi-natural. Points of interest include the historic Erddig House gardens and park, and Watts Dyke with associated earthworks. There is an extensive network of parkland and woodland paths.

Greenfield Valley Heritage Park
(Delyn Borough Council) **F** 20ha
O.S.S. 116 - SJ 195 775
01352 714172

Free parking is available off the B5121 Greenfield - Holywell road. Exhibitions, woodland trail, museum. Public park. Visitor centre open 10am - 5pm 1 Apr - 31 Oct. Ranger service all year round.

During the 18th century the valley was a hive of industrial activity, its factories producing copper goods, spinning cotton and a wire works. Once industrial activities ceased trees and shrubs colonised the valley. The characteristic and dominant tree species are oak on dry acid slopes and ash in the

damper valley bottom. There is an extremely attractive area of mature beech woodland and much scrub has been colonised by sycamore. 5 reservoirs set in the woodland attract much wildlife.

Llandegla
(Shotton Paper Co Ltd) **R** 653ha
O.S.S. 117 - SJ 228 521
01974 3688

7 miles W of Wrexham, the forest lies to the S of the A525, and 1.5 miles E of the village of Llandegla. Access is off the unclassified "Old Chester Road". Limited car parking. Open all year. Please keep to the paths to avoid disturbance to nesting birds. Dogs to be kept on leads April - June. Royal Welsh Show Woodlands and Plantations Compeition Silver Medal 1994.

A predominantly conifer forest planted in early 1970s. Formerly a grouse moor and adjacent to Llantysillio Mountain and Minera SSSI. The forest is at thinning stage and the intention is to convert this even age plantation into a perpetual forest. A number of footpaths and bridleways have been cleared and improved. The Offas Dyke long distance path runs through the forest.

Loggerheads Country Park
(Clwyd County Council) **F** 35ha
O.S.S. 116/117 - SJ 198 626
01352 810614

Adjacent to A494(T). 3 miles W of Mold. Main car park on R - see brown direction signs. Car park 50p (all day). Main car park closes 9pm.

A mixed woodland with limestone cliffs from which there are superb views westwards to the Clwydian Hills. Evidence of early mining gives added interest. A nature trail and an industrial trail are laid out.

Delightful all the year round but especially in spring (wild flowers) and autumn (colours). River Alyn flows through the site giving added interest, especially where the river disappears into swallow holes.

oak, sycamore and ash and is easily accessible along surfaced footpaths. The woodland is situated half a mile from Alyn Waters Country Park and can form part of a walk in the Alyn Valley.

Moel Famau
(Forest Enterprise) **F** 502ha
O.S.S. 116 - SJ 170 610
01492 640578

 75(£1) ⚲ ⚑ ❋ WC ⅛ ☂ ⚑

2km along minor public road running SE from A494(T), midway between Llanferres and Loggerheads. Open all year.

A mainly coniferous woodland with good species diversity and age range on the slopes of Moel Famau. Within easy reach of Merseyside, the site is deservedly popular with visitors. There are two walks from the well maintained car park and picnic area up the wooded slopes to Jubilee Tower on the summit. From this vantage point, built to commemorate the 50th year of George III's reign, there are panoramic views unequalled in Clwyd. Additionally visitor interest is provided by the Moel Famau and Loggerheads Country Parks, respectively immediately east and west of the woodland. (see previous entry).

Plas Power Wood
(Woodland Trust) **F** 34ha
O.S.S. 117 - SJ 297 495
01476 74297

Take the A525 out of Wrexham towards Ruthin. On entering Coedpoeth turn L onto a minor road towards Nant Mill. Park in the public car park and picnic area at Nant Mill, just before crossing the River Clywedog.

Plas Power Wood is of considerable historical interest, as a well-preserved section of Offa's Dyke runs through the middle of the wood. Offa's Dyke dates from the 8th century and is a scheduled Ancient Monument. Plas Power is a large mixed woodland with mature ash, oak and alder, which have been underplanted with western hemlock and other exotic species. It is a valuable wood in terms of wildlife habitat, due to the variety of woodland, streams and rock face habitats to be found there.

Nant-y-Gaer Woods
(Wrexham Maelor Borough Council) **F** 4ha
O.S.S. 117 - SJ 335 557
01978 292046

Take New Llay Road out of Wrexham (B5425), into Llay village, take 2nd R down Nant-y-Gaer Road, continue for 1/4 mile. Limited parking alongside houses and walk down valley, turn L into woods. There are no facilities and access is free and full all year round.

The wood is a small steep sided river valley adjacent to the village of Llay. The valley is dominated by mature

Tan-y-Cut Woods
(Wrexham Maelor Borough Council) **F** 3ha
O.S.S. 117 - SJ 278 411
01978 822780

Take B5606 through Newbridge, at junction turn R along A5 towards Llangollen. Take 2nd sharp R (before cafe) and follow unmade track alongside canal. Park in the small lay-by, walk underneath canal bridge and follow lane until wood is reached on L. The wood is a mature, mixed, deciduous woodland sloping down towards the River Dee on the opposite bank of the river from Ty Mawr Country Park.

The wood is approached via a trackway adjacent to
Llangollen canal. A boardwalk and footpath have been
created around the woodland which is boggy in places
with a calcerous stream running across the site. Good
displays of spring flowers.

Wepre Country Park

(Alyn & Deeside District Council) **F** 66ha
O.S.S. 117 - SJ 295 685
01244 814931

🚗100🚌4🚐 🌳 WC ♿ ⓘ 📖☂ 🍴 ⛽ 📷
🏕 🔦

*From A55, exit to Mold, turn L at traffic lights in
Northop follow brown tourist signs once in
Connah's Quay. Signposted off A548 in Connah's
Quay. Events programme - ring above number for
details. Free and full access all year round.*

160 acre semi-natural ancient woodland running from
Connah's Quay to Ewloe Castle, a 13th century Welsh
castle. Mixed woodland with good native flora. Well
surfaced footpath network and nature trail. A Visitor
Centre is on the site of Wepre Hall and there is a small
garden and arboretum dating from 1880. The Ranger
Service runs a wide ranging series of events and
activities. School visits are encouraged. Please contact
for more details for groups. Guided visits can be
arranged.

WALES - DYFED

Dyfed

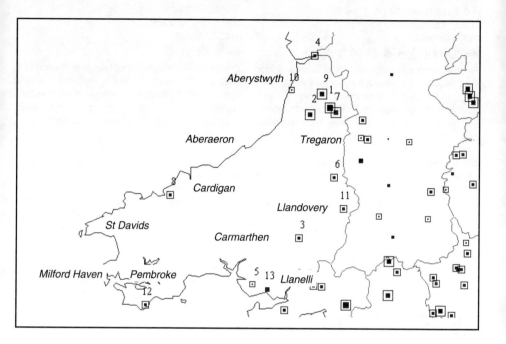

1. *The Arch*
2. *Black Covert and Coed Allt Fedw*
3. Castle Woods Nature Reserve
4. Coed Penrhyn - Mawr
5. Coed Rhyal
6. Dinas
7. *Haford*
8. Llwyngoras Nature Reserve
9. *Nant Yr Arian Visitor Centre*
10. Parc Natur Penglais
11. Poor Man's Wood
12. Stackpole Estate Woodlands
13. Stradey Estate Woodlands

The Arch
(Forest Enterprise) **F** 2100 ha
O.S.S. 135 - SN 765 756
01974 261404
🚐20🚌2/3🐎♦ ☀ WC ₺ ⛱ ♨🅿

From Aberystwyth take A4120 to Devil's Bridge, then B4574 to Cwmystwyth; car park is signed to the L of the road. Three walks of varying length start from the car park and follow woodland rides and tracks with exceptional views down the valley of the Rheidol from the high sections.

The area takes its name from the old masonry Arch which spans the road; it was erected in 1810 by Thomas Johnes, formerly the owner of the nearby Hafod estate, to mark King George III's Golden Jubilee. Some of the beeches in these woods are more than a century old and exotic species such as red oak and western red cedar have also been planted. Because of this diversity the area is rich in bird life, including ravens, crossbills, redpolls and red kites.

Black Covert and Coed Allt Fedw
(Forest Enterprise) **F** 119ha
O.S.S.135 - SN 667 729
01974 261404
🚐10🐎♦ ☀⛱♨🅿

From Aberystwyth take the B4340 signed Trawscoed. At Trawscoed turn R over concrete bridge spanning river Ystwyuth (signed Llanilai) then immediately L - follow the forestry signs.

Black Covert is part of the former Crosswood estate of the Earls of Lisburne. There is a sheltered picnic site amid walks from here; a gentle 1.1/4 mile walk through woodland by the river and adjoining farmland, and the Coed Allt Fedw (Birchgroive) walk of 2 miles which climbs the nearby hill to an ancient hillfort site from which panoramic views may be enjoyed. There is also a butterfly reserve.

Castle Woods Nature Reserve
(Dyfed Wildlife Trust) **F** 28ha
O.S.S. 159 - SN 622 222
01437 765462
🚐● ☀ ⚥ ⛱

On the southern outskirts of Llandeilo Town off the A483 by the River Tywi bridge. Facilities include a visitor centre (disabled access), open Easter - October, weekends/Bank Holidays, no toilets. Programme of guided walks and "watches".

An ancient semi-natural woodland, the reserve is probably the most important in south Wales for its invertebrate and lichen communities. The woods surround the old Dynevor Castle - home to the former Princes of Deheubarth - and overlook flood meadows and oxbow lakes. The flora, which is rich with fine old trees, extensive bluebells and even the parasitic toothwort, supports a diverse fauna of mammals such as badgers and fallow deer, and a wide variety of woodland birds, including all species of British woodpecker. There are also the overwintering wildfowl and numerous butterflies and dragonflies.

Coed Penrhyn - Mawr
(RSPB) **R** 12ha
O.S.S. 135 - SN 683 964
01654 781265
🅿£3🚐30🗝● ☀⚥ WC ⓘ 📖⛱⚥ ♨

6 miles S of Machynlleth on A487. 12 miles N of Aberystwyth on A487. Turnings in Furnace - Ynys-Hir Reserve. Facilities include a visitor centre, information, displays, paths, observation hides. Entrance £3 for non members of RSPB (children 50p); RSPB members free. Open every day 0900 hours to dusk.

The reserve area is 1000 acres. In spring the woods are carpeted with bluebells and wood anemones. Speckled wood and greenveined white butterflies are common here and you can see holly blue butterflies in most years, especially in Cae'r Berllan Wood. The oak woodlands, a mid-Wales speciality, have a rich community of breeding birds in spring including buzzards, pied-flycatchers, wood warblers, redstarts and lesser-spotted woodpeckers. See if you can spot elusive purple hairstreak butterflies fluttering around the top of oak trees in July and August.

Coed Rhyal

(British Coal Opencast) **F** 6ha
O.S.S. 159 - SN 432 028
01267 222933

From Carmarthen, take A484 S, through Kidwelly, and on towards Pembrey. Just before Pembrey take L turn onto B4317 for 1 mile. Turn R at bus stop, along track, past farm and woodland is on RH. Limited parking in lay-by (to be signposted). Permissive paths approx. 1 mile long. No charges. Open all year. Groups by arrangement. Visitors requested to stay on paths for safety reasons - old drift mines and bell pit which are fenced but caution advised. Dogs strictly on leads. Badgers often dig up paths - again care advised of holes, which may turn ankles!

An oak/hazel woodland on a steep slope above coal measures. Abundant spring flora, especially bluebells. Active badgers and dormice. Excellent views across Pembrey peninsula.

Dinas

(RSPB) **F** 45ha
O.S.S.146 - SN 788 471
c/o Troedrhiwgelynen, Rhandirmwyn, Llandovery, SA20 0PN
●30🎋 🔥 ☀ 🌾 *i* 🌳

Follow signs for Llyn Brianne and RSPB Dinas from A483 in Llandovery. There is a car park which is free to RSPB members, £1 per car for non-members. Open all day all year round. Part of the path round wood is very rocky and unsuitable for infirm. See signs in car park for details.

The Dinas is an ancient semi-natural oak wood of high conservation interest. About half the wood has a long history of management; the remainder has been left undisturbed. The wood is an SSSI. Birds like buzzards,

peregrines and ravens are frequently seen and in summer the wood is famous for its populations of pied flycatchers, wood warblers and redstarts. It is probably best known, though, as a site to see the very rare red kite.

Haford

(Forest Enterprise) **F**168ha
O.S.S. 135 - SN 768 737
01974 261404
●15🚾2/3🐎 🔥 ☀ *i* 🌾 🔥

From Aberystwyth take the A4120 to Devil's Bridge, then B4343 as far as hairpin bend when turn L onto B4574 signed Cwmystwyth. The car park is signposted off this road. A Guide Book (price £1) is available from the Forest District - this gives background and history of the estate and has a map of the walks.

Formerly the home of Thomas Johnes, pioneer of upland forestry in Cardiganshire between 1783 and 1816. His foresighted approach to combining commercial afforestation using conifers and broadleaves, with landscape design for the visual benefit of visitors to his estates, may truly be said to encompass multi-purpose forestry as practised by Forest Enterprise today. He developed his gardens and walks to complement the natural beauty of this part of the Ystwyth Valley in a style known as the Picturesque. A programme of partial restoration of the gardens, paths and landscape features was begun by the Forestry Commission in 1987 and will continue in years to come.

Llwyngoras Nature Reserve

(P J & E M Wheeler) **R** 29ha
0.S.S. 145 - SN 083 397
01239 820464
🌾🌙 🔥 ☀ *i* 📖🌾 FP 🔥 🚾🍴 🚪 🌲

On River Nevern up river from Nevern on bridle path from Nevern to Velindre. From Trewern Arms in Nevern to Salutation Inn in Velindre Farchog. A nature reserve run by Dyfed Wildlife Trust for the owners.

Semi-natural ancient woodland on a S facing escarpment overlooking the River Nevern. Oak, ash, sycamore managed for the benefit of wildlife. On the old Pilgrims Walk down river to Newport all within the Pembrokeshire National Park.

Nant Yr Arian Visitor Centre

(Forest Enterprise)**F** 755ha
O.S.S. 135 - SN 716 814
01974 261404

🚗50🚌3-4 ⛺ ♨ ☀ WC –
♿ *i* 📖 ⛷ ⚓ 🚲 🅿 🚾 ⛺

From Aberystwyth take A44 to Llangurig. The Visitor Centre is signposted to L of road after approx. 10 miles (just after village of Cwmbrwyno). No dogs allowed in Centre. The Centre is open Easter to end September 11am - 5pm (longer in summer). Entry to Centre is free: car parking is Pay & Display - 50p per car (1994 cost).

The V.C. houses an exhibition explaining the origins and development of the local landscape; there are also various displays and videos etc. There are two woodland trails, both starting from the V.C. In addition there are 4 orienteering courses (map and booklet available from the V.C. @ £1). The Nant Yr Arian trail winds along the head of the valley following the path of an old leat which once carried water to the nearby lead mines. Kestrels, buzzards and red kites may all be seen here. The Jubilee Trail, so named because it commemorates Queen Elizabeth II's 1977 Silver Jubilee, provides stunning views throughout its length. From the viewpoint high above the V.C. one can see Cardigan Bay, Aberystwyth, the Reidol and Melindwr valleys and the summit of Plynlimon.. The route also passes two small lakes where wildfowl may be observed. Butterflies and woodland birds are also much in evidence throughout the walks.

Parc Natur Penglais

(Cyngor Dosbarth Ceredigion) **F** 8ha
O.S.S. 135 - SN 590 822
01970 634314

The wood is located in the NE fringe of the town of Aberystwyth; main entrance on the corner of Penglais and North Road. Facilities include picnic areas, information and self guided trail leaflet. Access is free, all the year round, but there will be a small charge for schools education pack. School and college field study visits welcome. Please contact the project officer on the above telephone number to arrange times.

The woods form part of Parc Natur Penglais which, together with 4ha of disused quarry are managed by local people and the District Council for nature conservation, public access and recreation. Trees on the quarry edge of the woods have been affected by the strong sea winds and exposed conditions. Sessile oak, sweet chestnut, ash, wild cherry, sycamore, beech, and hazel are some of the tree species to be found. There is an extensive display of bluebells and wildlife includes badger, buzzard, blackcap, jay and pied flycatcher. Prince of Wales Award 1993.

Poor Man's Wood

(Llandovery Town Council) **F** 17ha
O.S.S. 146 - SN 779 344
01437 765462

⛷🅾🕊☀🌿 *i* 🚲⚓🚶🏕🏔⛺

Take A40 Brecon road from Llandovery 0.5 miles from town is a sharp L turn along a track, opposite caravan park. Follow footpath 0.5 mile to reserve entrance. Parking in town, unless by special arrangement with Carmarthenshire reserves officer. There is a circular permissive path. - no horses. Leaflet - apply c/o Llandovery Tourist Office. Dogs strictly on leads. (vulnerable setts).

Typical Welsh upland oak wood - steep slopes with bilberry. Attractive circular walk with valley views. approx. 1 - 1.5 hour duration. Mainly level walking after initial hill! Wild service trees, active badgers, tawny owls, pied flycatchers, buzzards and red kites are often seen.

Stackpole Estate Woodlands
(National Trust) **R** 61ha
O.S.S. 158 - SR 980 965
01646 661359
🛏 ◡ ◢

A477 to Pembroke then B4319 S to Stackpole - the wood is just W of village. Permissive horse traiil. Residential outdoor studies Centre.

Varied mixed woodland with extensive network of trails. Boardwalk through wet woodland section. The woods occupy the valleys in the catchment of the eastern arm of the Bosherston Lakes and are of high nature conservation interest.

Stradey Estate Woodlands
(D C Mansel Lewis) **A** 140ha
O.S.S. 159 - SN 492 014
01554 774626
🛗 2 ✳

Stradey Castle is on the B4308 just NW of town of Llanelli. Visit by arrangement only to societies or recognised forestry bodies. £2 per head to cover cost of donation to the Forestry Trust.

Postwar replanting of softwoods, Japanese larch, Douglas fir, sitka spruce, thuja, tsuga and some sequoia sempervirens - about 250 acres. Old hardwood amenity woodlands recently suffering damage in the 1991 gales and progressively being underplanted and overstocked with similar species with amenity in mind. Essentially an ''old fashioned'' estate woodland of character which still retains some interesting old trees - about 100 acres.

WALES - GLAMORGAN, MID

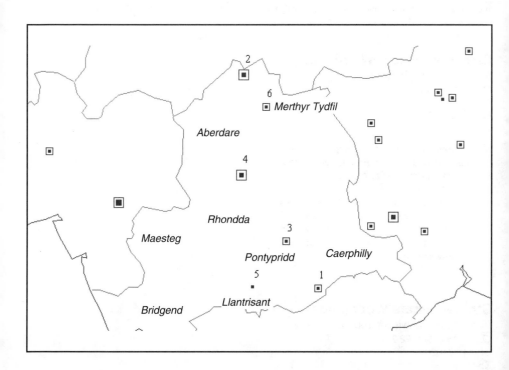

1. Coed-y-Bedw
2. *Garwnant Visitor Centre*
3. Gelliwion Wood
4. *Gethin Woodland Park*
5. *Llanharan Wood
6. Taf Fechan

Coed-y-Bedw

(Glamorgan Wildlife Trust) **R** 16.6ha
O.S.S. 171 - ST 111827
01656 724100

3km NW of Cardiff. On B4262 via the Taffs Well junction off the A470 Cardiff - Merthyr trunk road, just n of M4. A network of paths is maintained.

An SSSI, Coed-y-Bedw is an ancient wet broadleaved woodland, on the boundary between acidic and lime rich soils. It grades from wet oak/ash in the east to drier beechwood in the west, with ash locally dominant on the carboniferous limestone areas to the south. Two lime rich springs arise in the south west of the site and join an acidic stream flowing eastwards along the valley floor. This mix of waters supports an interesting assemblage of aquatic invertebrates. There is a good resident woodland bird population.

Garwnant Visitor Centre

(Forest Enterprise) **F** 500ha
O.S.S. SS 003 131
01685 723060

⇜50🚌5↰ ∪ ⚑ ☀ WC ら ⓘ 📖 ⌐ 🔥
⚐ ⚓🎦 ▮ 🏕 🏠

Set back from the A470, 5 miles N of Merthyr Tydfil. Follow brown and white signs for forest centre. Walks, orienteering, mountain bike routes. Events, school parties arranged by ringing rangers. Open daily 10.00am to 5.00pm, Good Friday - 31st October.

Garwnant Visitor Centre is the focal point of information about wildlife and landscapes of the forests of the Brecon Beacons. It is set in a wonderful woodland setting, nestling close to the Llywn-on reservoir.

Gelliwion Wood

(Mid Glamorgan County Council) **F** 12ha
O.S.S. 170 - ST 064 894
01222 820892

⇜10↰ ● ☀ ⌐ ⚐

To the rear of Sardis Road car park, Pontypridd. Follow the slip road to the rear of the car park and turn L into Woodland Terrace, then R and L into Gelliwion Road. The lower edge of the woodland is facing you. Gate access. Please keep to footpaths which follow drainage berms. Planted areas beyond fencing are steep and rutted following deep ploughing.

The woodland was planted in 1988 as part of a County Council land reclamation scheme. The site consists of colliery spoil and the tree species planted reflect this, being mainly pioneers such as alder, birch, poplar, willow and rowan. The trees are well established and most are thriving The woodland is a good example of what can be achieved in the short term on a rather hostile site and with a minimum of maintenance. Good views of the Taff Valley from the upper part of the site.

Gethin Woodland Park

(Forest Enterprise) **F** 650ha
O.S.S. 170 - ST 000 990
01639 710221

⇜30🚌3↰ ∪ ⚑ ☀ WC ら ⓘ ⌐ ⚐ 🏠

Signposted off the A470 S of Merthyr Tydfil. Walks, events, school parties can be arranged by phoning the rangers on 01685 725060.

The Woodland Park is an area of outstandingly varied woodlands which extend from the outskirts of Merthyr to the summit of Mynydd Gethin. The Forest Enterprise has designated this area as a woodland park and improved access so that the public can more fully enjoy its beauty and take advantage of wider opportunities for outdoor recreation. There are 4 waymarked walks which start and finish at the main car park area.

*Llanharan Wood
(Managed by Sovereign Woodlands)
A 40ha
O.S.S. 170 - ST 016 830
Office 6, 96 Monnow Street, Monmouth, Gwent
NP5 3EQ

From Jn 34 of M4 take the A4119 N. After 2 miles turn L at roundabout at Talbot Green onto A473. The wood is some 2 miles on, on the R. There are no facilities and all visits are by appointment only. Please write to Sovereign Woodlands at the above address. Educational / Schools visits particularly welcome.

Llanharan is a productive wood, predominantly coniferous with the main species being Japanese larch, but there is a belt of ancient semi-natural woodland within it where sessile oak, holly and yew are amongst the main native species that have been retained.

Taf Fechan
(Glamorgan Wildlife Trust) **F** 42ha
O.S.S. 160 - SO 035 085
01656 724100

In the Taf Fechan valley between Old River Bridge at Cefn Coed y Cymru and the river bridge at Pontsarn, about 2.5kms N of Merthyr Tydfil.

Taf Fechan is ancient limestone broadleaf woodland consisting of mainly ash, alder, beech, birch and grey willow. Tawny owl, buzzards, great spotted woodpeckers and dippers are frequently present and the flora includes wild thyme, rough hawkbit and mouse ear hawkweed.

WALES - GLAMORGAN, SOUTH

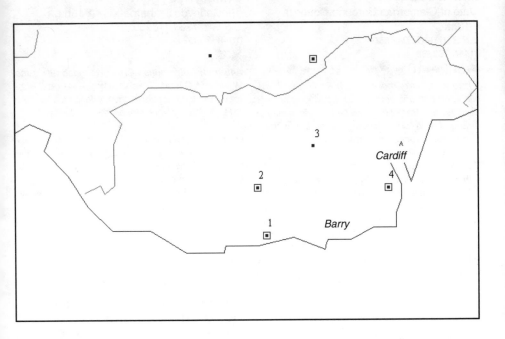

1. Cliff Wood
2. Coed Garnllwyd
3. Coedarhydglyn
4. Cogan Wood

Cliff Wood

(Vale of Glamorgan Borough Council)
F 13ha
O.S.S. 170 - ST 087 660
01446 733589

1 mile W of Barry, access from Park road, Barry. pitch and putt golf course. Car parking charge on Sundays and Bank Holidays. Guided visits may be arranged with prior bookings with the warden. School parties accommodated.

Cliff Wood is an ancient woodland site and an SSSI with dominant oak, ash and yew. It has corresponding rich shrub and floral layers. Notable is purple gromwell. Home to a wide variety of mammals and birds including badgers, foxes, weasels, sparrowhawks, tawny owl and woodcock. Contained within the wood is the remains of a 14th century corn mill and water course and 17th century cottages and footpath.

Coed Garnllwyd

(Glamorgan Wildlife Trust) **R** 13ha
O.S.S. 170 - ST 058 713
01656 724100

Park in Llancarfan village. Access by footpath via Garnllwyd Farm. A public right of way cuts across the wood, although there is an informal footpath within the wood.

Coed Garnllwyd forms part of a large woodland block underlain by Lias limestone. The whole woodland is an SSSI. Primarily an ash/oak coppice with standards woodland. The understorey is hazel, field maple, holly, crab apple, hawthorn, spindle and wayfaring tree, making a rich shrub layer. A coppice cycle has been reintroduced to part of the wood. The ground flora is particularly rich, with herbparis and early purple orchid. Within the woodland dead timber (predominantly elm) supports invertebrates and fungi.

Coedarhydyglyn

(Sir Cennydd Traherne KG) **A** 15ha
O.S.S. 171 - ST 110 750
01446 760321

A48 from Culverhouse Cross Roundabout on the W side of Cardiff. Take Cowbridge - Port Talbot road. About half a mile up the hill take small turning to R. marked by white stones, then to Lodge.

Open by appointment only. Early 19th century landscaped wood planted in 1810 as a feature in the building of the present house completed in 1820. Pinetum and cypress garden planted 1944 and 1947. Larch plantations planted 1940 and 1953. Chestnut with some beech planted 1987.

Cogan Wood (within Cosmeston Lakes Country Park)

(Vale of Glamorgan Borough Council)
F 20 ha
O.S.S. 171 - ST 178 693
01222 701678

5 miles S of Cardiff, Cosmeston Lakes country park can be reached via the B4267 from Penarth to Sully. Reconstructed medieval village. Open all year. Access for walkers only.

Designated an SSSI in the early 1980s, Cogan Wood is a mixed broadleaf, wood, predominantly mature hawthorn but with ash, poplar, field maple and birch. Of interest is an ancient parish boundary. An area of English elm cleared in the early 1980s was replanted with indigenous species. In recent years the elm is rejuvenating through suckering. This area is now under management review and experimental monitoring on the possible recurrence of Dutch Elm disease.The wood helps to support badgers, foxes, little and tawny owl and is home to pipistrelle and noctule bats, green and great spotted woodpeckers.

WALES - GLAMORGAN, WEST

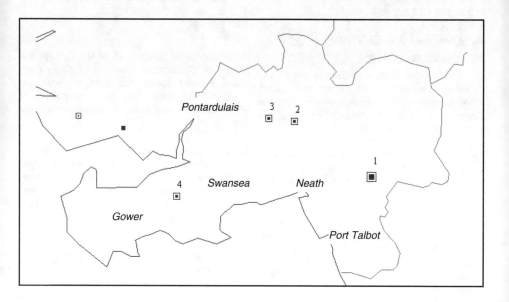

1. *Afan Forest Park*
2. Craig Cilhendre Woods
3. Cwm Clydach
4. Gelli-Hir Wood

Afan Forest Park
(Forest Enterprise) **F** 3250ha
O.S.S. 170 - SS 822 951
01639 850564

🚐50🚻5🔺🔱🛏☀️🦌 WC ♿ ⓘ 🏕🍽

📷 ⚓ 🚤🍴🏔🎣👤 🎒

On the A4107 between Pontrhydyfen and Cynonville, some 5 miles N of Port Talbot. Walks leaflets and information available from the Countryside Centre. Phone rangers for information about events..

The Afan Valley is one of the narrowest and shortest valleys in South Wales, being about 15 miles long from its head at Bwlch yr Afan to the sea at Aberfan. It is very beautiful, and is often referred to as "Little Switzerland". Mature forests embrace relics of abandoned mines, tramways and railways. Native broadleaved trees thrive on the lower slopes, intersected by the numerous mountain streams. The forest park and its focal point, the Countryside Centre, are managed by Forest Enterprise and West Glamorgan County Council.

Craig Cilhendre Woods
(Glamorgan Wildlife Trust) **F** 16ha
O.S.S. 170 - SN 719 022
01656 724100

🚐6🛏♿ 👤 ☀️

1.5km south of Pontardawe. Access from unclassified road to Bryn Coch, a made up track opposite Cilhendre - Fawr Farm leads to a small car park. No public right of way but paths, mainly on old tramways, maintained, allowing circular route.

Ancient semi natural broadleaved woodland situated on a steep north facing hillside. There is evidence of earlier coal extraction, including an old tramway. A sandstone cliff, about 8m high and over 0.5 mile long runs along the top of the reserve and fine views can be gained from the top. The woodland canopy comprises a mosaic of sessile oak, beech, birch, ash, sycamore and alder.

Cwm Clydach
(Lt. Col AD Holland and RSPB) **R** 91ha
O.S.S. 159 - SN 684 026
01792 842927

🛏 👤

Four miles N of Junction 45 of M4, through the village of Clydach, at New Inn in Craig Cefn Parc. Parking, toilets and food at New Inn. Access at all times along public footpaths and RSPB trails. Please keep to marked paths at all times.

Nesting buzzard, sparrowhawk and raven are common. Nestboxes are used by pied flycatcher, redstart and tits, while wood warbler, all three species of woodpecker, nuthatch, tree-creeper and tawny owl also breed. Dipper and grey wagtail frequent the river and tree pipit and wheatear the higher ground. Snipe, woodcock, redpoll and siskin are frequent in winter. 28 species of butterfly are present, including purple hairstreak and silver-washed fritillary.

Gelli-Hir Wood
(Glamorgan Wildlife Trust) **F** 29ha
O.S.S. 159 - SS 562925
01656 724100

🚐12🛏 👤 🍴📷

The woodland lies on the N edge of Fairwood Common, Gower. Access from a small car park on the unclassified road which runs from the B4271 N to Cil-Onen. A disabled access track runs from the car park through the wood to a pond. A number of rides and circular paths exist in the woods.

The reserve grades from wet oak/birch woodland in the S and E to drier ash/elm woodland in the N and W. There is a variety of associated habitats including open rides, streams, and a pond. Fallen timber and rotting stumps support an abundance of lower plants and invertebrates. There is a large and varied population of birds. Coppicing has been reintroduced to parts of the wood.

WALES - GWENT

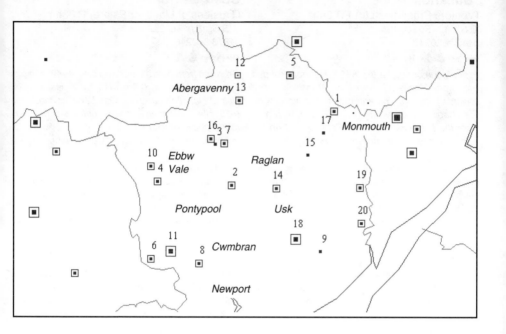

1. *Buckholt
2. Coed Bryntovey
3. Coed y Prior
4. Coedcae Cendle
5. Craig Farm Wood
6. Craig Goch
7. Craig Syddi
8. Craig y Wenallt Wood
9. *Cwm
10. Cwm Merddog
11. *Cwmcarn Forest Drive*

12. Great Triley Wood
13. Pant Skirrid Wood
14. *Parkwood
15. *Penyclawdd
16. The Punchbowl
17. Treowen
18. *Wentwood*
19. *Whitestone*
20. *Wyndcliff*

*Buckholt

(Venture Properties Ltd) **FD** 84ha
O.S. 162 - SO 500 168
01497 820242

*From Monmouth take the A466, Hereford road, 1
mile from Monmouth turn L at Mansons Cross
towards Oldshop. The entrance to the wood is on
the R approximately 1.5 miles. Leaflet with map
from the Manager, Fountain Forestry Ltd on the
above number. Donations to the Forestry Trust.*

This woodland is splendidly set amid rolling Border
countryside, commanding fine views to all points but
notably W over the Monnow valley and E and S over
the Wye Valley. Originally oak and beech coppice with
standards, European larch was first introduced around
1860 and following a substantial felling during World
War two higher yielding conifers were used in the
restocking. The main objects of management have
been the commercial production of timber. The current
mix of broadleaves with conifers makes for a diverse
woodland landscape, rich in fauna and ground flora.

Coed y Prior

(Trustees of Llanover Estate) **P** 33ha
O.S.S. 161 - SO 292 096
01873 880246

*Go south from Abergavenny on the A4042 towards
Pontypool. Approx. 0.5 miles after crossing river
Usk at Llanellen turn R up Oak Lane, continue for
0.75 miles. Parking at bottom of the wood. Open
to the public on Bank Holidays only. Parking in a
lay-by at the entrance to Coed y Prior wood.*

The wood was originally planted in the early 1920s
with crops of Corsican pine, Sitka spruce, Douglas fir,
European and Japanese larches. Further planting
carried out in 1938 and 1942 and the site was felled in
the early 1990s and late 1980s, to be replanted with
Japanese larch, Scots pine and Douglas fir. The more
sheltered areas of plantation have won awards.
Outstanding views of the Usk valley and the
surrounding countryside may be obtained from the
summit. Management objectives are timber production
and silvicultural improvement. Conservation of the
landscape and wildlife is also very important.

Coed Bryntovey

(R Hanbury-Tenison) **FD** 33ha
O.S.S. 171 - SO 317 022
01495 762921

*A 4042 (T) Newport/Abergavenny. Exit to New Inn
at roundabout S of Pontypool. First R in village and
follow Jerusalem Lane for 2 miles. Turn L into
Cwmhir Road and keep on to the end. Park well
beyond cottage. Not suitable for coaches. Open 1
March to 1 October. Access to wood on foot only.
Keep to marked paths, which constitute a circular
route.*

Replanted with ash and larch since the second World
War. Below the line of pylons the ground was dug for
brick clay during the war and has since been partly
replanted and partly allowed to regenerate naturally.
Look out for buzzards and if lucky you may see a
visiting fallow deer. There are damp patches in the
wood in rainy weather, so gum boots are
recommended.

Coedcae Cendle

(John and Susan Russell) **F** 11ha
O.S.S. 161 - SO 188 058

*On the A4046 2.5 miles S from Ebbwvale you enter
the village of Cwm. At the police station you turn L.
Park car on the hill, follow footpath sign to woods.
There are no facilities.*

Coedcae Cendle is an attractive little wood
overlooking the village of Cwm. The wood was
planted in 1971 with spruce and pine. There are nice
areas of beech and oaks throughout the woods
including a rich variety of wildlife and plants. There
are interesting paths through the woods with seats and
picnic tables. There are stiles leading to the mountain
side. To the N is the Cwm Merddog nature reserve.

Gwent

Craig Farm Wood
(Miss P E Merriman) **F** 46ha
O.S.S. 161 - SO 410 224

🏕 🛆 ✳ 🌳

From Abergavenny B4521 to Cross Ash then N on the minor country road.

The woodland is mainly conifer planted in 1963 by the Forestry Commission. The plateau area is dominated by Sitka spruce with lodgepole pine, Norway spruce and Japanese larch at the southern end. There is an impressive view point looking W - it is worth the walk to see this. Fallow deer are regularly seen within the wood or heard crashing into the undergrowth.

Craig Goch
(Islwyn Borough Council) **F** 16ha
O.S.S. 171 - ST 187 911
01495 200113

🚐100🚐4🏹◡🛆✳🌳wc ㏒ ⓘ⛺️
🛤🚌🍴🏪🍻

At junction 28 M4, take A467 then A4048 to Cwmfelinfach. Follow signs to Ynys Hywel. Ignore turning area and go to Wishing Stone picnic site car park. Alternatively, park at Ynys Hywel Countryside Centre and walk. It is a pleasant walk through farmland with superb views. Access is free and facilities include tea room, WCs etc at countryside centre.

A remnant of the ancient woodland which once covered south Wales, Craig Goch is now a local nature reserve. It had been badly managed before acquisition, with bracken infestation and little regeneration. An active management programme is ensuring its survival. Forty species of birds breed in Craig Goch, including the redstart, which has been taken as the symbol of Ynys Hymel countryside centre. There are signs of old charcoal hearths. The woodland contains some very old trees and consists mainly of beech and oak with some birch, ash, rowan and holly. Public access is being improved with the help of conservation volunteers and there is some on-site interpretation. The nearby countryside centre runs a programme of courses and events related to woodland management, willow craft and hedge laying.

Craig Syddi
(Monmouth Woodland Trust) **F** 28ha
O.S.S. 161 - SO 295 108
01600 772904

🚐2🏹●🛆✳🌳ⓘ⛺️

From A4042, near Abergavenny,take the B4269. Turn L after 0.25 mile into the "No Through Road". Go up the hill and over the canal. The woodland is on the L. Marked footpaths and an explanatory leaflet available. Caution is necessary when forestry operations are in progress. Signs will be erected. A leaflet guide and description of the woodland and its management is available from above telephone number or the Tourist Information Centre in Abergavenny. Craig Syddi is situated above Abergavenny.

The woodland comprises well grown conifers planted in the early sixties including Douglas fir, western hemlock, larch and spruce. This primarily commercial woodland demonstrates how productive forestry can enhance the landscape and be of value to the local community. There are spectacular views over the Usk valley and a wide range of birds. Look for the old hardwoods which were retained when the woodland was replanted.

Craig y Wenallt Wood
(Woodland Trust) **F** 6ha
O.S.S. 171 - ST 265 909
01476 74297

🏕●

From the M4 take the B4591 towards Risca. Turn R onto the road leading to Risca school. Just past the school turn R onto a narrow lane. At the T junction turn L, then take the R fork. This track leads up to the wood. There is no parking; do not park on the track leading to Craig y Wenallt.

Craig y Wenallt is a hillside wood on the outskirts of Risca above the Ebbw River. It contains some fine trees and there is an attractive display of bluebells in the spring. This woodland is a prominent feature in the landscape and is composed mainly of beech and birch with mature oak coppice and scrub, gorse and broom. There is a small area of open land within the wood which has been planted with native trees and shrubs.

*Cwm

(Richard Micklethwait) **A** 10ha
O.S.S. 171 - ST 460 928
01633 400213

*Leave M4 immediately N of Severn Bridge, 1 mile
N turn W on A48, after about 5 miles turn N to
Llanvair Discoed, Wentwood and Usk, then take
2nd R and immediately L to Penhein. (Drive 1 mile
long). Open by appointment only and charges by
agreement. Parties will meet at Penhein for tour of
sites of interest on farm trailer(s).*

Semi-natural ancient woodland (SSSI) being managed
to vary canopy which was uniform. Also sites of land
in various stages of regeneration. Land last cultivated
in 1918. Land grazed until 20 years ago. Land last
grazed in 1954. Part of wood from which stock was
excluded in about 1985.

Cwm Merddog

(Gwent Wildlife Trust) **R** 22ha
O.S.S. 161 - SO 187 062
01600 715501

*On the A4046, and 2.5 miles S from Ebbw Vale,
there is a one-way system in Cwm; come out of this
on the N side and turn R by a corner shop; 0.3
miles up this road there is a car park just SW of
Cwm cemetery. From the car park walk northwards
across a flat grass playing area and along a path to
the entrance of the reserve. There is car parking
for 8 cars. There are no WCs on the site. Nearest
shops are in Cwm. There are rights of way on foot
throughout the wood. Guided visits can be
arranged by appointment, please contact Mr J
Winder on the above number.*

The reserve is the most westerly, and forms part of the
highest natural beech woodland in the British Isles.
The splendid greater tussock sedge is worth looking
out for as is the broad leaved helleborine and the heath
spotted orchid. An old dragline is present that used to
take coal from the surrounding hills. Nature has
reclaimed the old coal tip with mosses and lichens,
young hawthorns and other young trees are
establishing themselves and a natural woodland is

developing. Beech and alder dominate most of the
woodlands but there is an area of young mixed
woodland where ant hills can be found suggesting that
this area was once pasture. The green woodpecker,
pied flycatcher and the redstart nest in the woodland.

Cwmcarn Forest Drive

(Forest Enterprise) **F** 345ha
O.S.S. 171 - ST 220 930
01633 400205

*Follow signs from M4 (exit 40). There is fully open
access to the woods with rights of way on foot and
bridleways throughout. There are self guided trails,
please apply to the visitor centre for details.
Donations made to the Forestry Trust. There is
parking available for cars and coaches. The forest
drive (a guide is available for 60p) is open from
Easter to Oct, 11am to 7pm. There are picnic
areas, barbecue sites, children's play area, and a
path for the disabled.*

Cwmcarn is part of Ebbw Forest which dates back
beyond the 13th century. The valleys of south Wales
had most of the tree cover removed for charcoal
making and agricultural use. The industrial revolution
hit the area, especially coal mining and the approach to
the forest drive runs over the old colliery. The 7 mile
long forest drive provides a rare opportunity for the
less able to get deep into a working forest with
spectacular views over the Bristol Channel. There is a
diversity of tree species and age structure together with
associated flora and fauna.

Great Triley Wood

(Woodland Trust) **F** 6ha
O.S.S. 161 - SO 338 233
01476 74297

*The wood lies just between the main Abergavenny
to Hereford road, the A465 and the railway line just
inside the National Park boundary. Parking is in the
lay-by on the Abergavenny side of the site. As the
woodland is wet and boggy in places, visitors are
advised to walk with care.*

The woodland lies on the marshy banks of the river Gavenny, just inside the Brecon Beacons National Park. It is a most attractive area of woodland containing many fine oaks and ash trees. The marshy area of wood supports some very large alder and willow. The ground flora is varied and rich and among the more interesting plants is the unusual flower, herb paris.

commemorative rides lined with hardwood species. There is an abundance of wildlife including foxes, buzzards, herons and ravens. The woods are at their best in the spring with wood anemones, then bluebells. Larch, Douglas fir, western hemlock, sweet chestnut, oak and red oak are mongst the main species grown and marketed. There is a particularly fine grove of redwoods planted in 1949 given as a wedding plantation by Richard St Barbe Baker (the founder of Men of the Trees - now International Tree Foundation).

Pant Skirrid Wood
(National Trust) **R** 14ha
O.S.S. 161 - S0 329 164
01874 625515

The car park below Pant Skirrid wood is situated on the B4521 (old Hereford road) leading out of Abergavenny. There is one public path and an extensive network of woodland rides which are permissive paths. All are waymarked.

Mixed hardwoods and conifers.

*Parkwood
(J H L Humphreys) **FC** 36ha
O.S.S. 171 - S0 389 027
01291 672563

From Usk take the old Raglan road, fork L signed Gwehelog and the lay-by is on the L one mile up the road after sharp bend. There are no facilities but there is parking at the lay-by on old Usk/Raglan road. Walk 300 yards up stone track to information shed and start of walk, except on open days when the gate will be open and parking will be up in the wood. There is a marked circular walk of approx 40 mins; and permitted access for walkers on paths and tracks within the wood. Guided visits can be arranged by appointment from Apr to the end of Oct. Please contact owner on the above telephone number 3 weeks in advance. Rates by negotiation. Donations made to the Forestry Trust.

Park Wood was only scrubland prior to 1936 and was planted by the present owner's father. A special feature of the wood is the way it has been laid out in

*Penyclawdd
(S A J P Bosanquet) **A** 24ha
O.S.S. 161 - S0 440 080
01600 740238
£2/£1🚶**10**

Midway between Monmouth and Raglan - turn S off old A40 at Blue Door Corner. The wood is at top of the Graig Lees hill (map essential). There is parking for 10 cars. There is a right of way on foot through the wood. The owner would be particularly happy to arrange group visits and separate school visits, for which 6 weeks notice is required. Details from Mr Bosanquet on the above number. Cost of guided visits: Adults £2, children £1: no charge for schools. Donations to the Forestry Trust.

An ex-Forestry Commission wood with about two thirds conifers - Norway spruce, hemlock, Douglas fir and larch - and one third mixed age hardwoods - oak ash, beech and birch. The conifers have just been thinned now being about 30 years old. Many wildflowers and butterflies in the rides. A very interesting amalgam of woodland species in a small area.

The Punchbowl
(Woodland Trust) **F** 36ha
O.S.S. 161 - SO 284 115
01476 74297

From A4042 leave at Llanellen onto the B4269 to Llanfoist. Take the lane to the L 1.25 miles along this road. Follow the lane steeply upwards for 1.5 miles take the R fork in the road and then proceed

a further mile until the roadside rest area of the Brecon Beacons National Park is reached. Parking is available. V isitors are advised to keep close to the public footpaths within this wood, as much of the site above the lake is steep or sheer.

The Punchbowl is the largest of several hollows set in the side of Mount Blorenge. Undoubtedly the most striking trees are the huge ancient beeches some up to six foot in diameter, most of which have been pollarded in the past. Ash, hazel, oak and field maple are the other predominant tree species. The wood supports a variety of plant life including wood sorrel, wood avens and enchanters nightshade. The buzzard, green woodpecker and tawny owl, along with the noctule bat, are just some of the birds and mammals that frequent this site.

Treowen

(RA & JP Wheelock) **A** 38ha
O.S.S. 161 - SO 465 114
01600 712031

🚗6🚐1🐕🦯

From Monmouth take B4293 signposted Trellech. After 1/2 mile keep straight on for Mitchel Troy and follow road through village. Follow signs to Dingestow. Turn right in Dingestow and left at top of hill into private road. Very limited access by public footpath/bridlepath through wood which is 1/2 mile from public road. More general access and parking at entrance to wood by appointment only.

Small area of semi natural woodland surrounded by former agricultural land. Probably planted in 19th century. The original wood is largely oak with hazel coppice. The more recent plantings are largely softwood with some ash, oak, cherry and sweet chestnut.

Wentwood

(Forest Enterprise) **F** 279ha
O.S.S. 171 - ST 421 949
01633 400205

🏷️£0.50🚗(£0.50)◡🦯☀️WC♿ⓘ
📖⛺🚐

5 miles W of Chepstow on A48, R turn signed Llanvair Discoed, Wentwood Usk 4 miles. Car and coach park at very top of hill. There are some WCs on site, including facilties for the disabled. There are picnic and barbecue sites, children's play area and a trim trail. There is fully open access to the wood with bridleways and rights of way on foot throughout the wood. A facts book is available at £1, covered barbecues cost £5. Donations made to the Forestry Trust.

In the early days Wentwood belonged to the native Welsh princes and was much larger growing mainly oak and beech with many local people depending on the forest. There were local laws and justice dispensed at Foresters Oaks. Sheep stealing carried the death penalty with the last hanging at Foresters Oaks in 1829. The oak and beech were heavily cut with little left when the Forest Enterprise acquired part of the forest on lease in 1941. Wentwood is a popular walking area with good recreational facilities. Trails pass through the stands of larch, Norway spruce, Douglas fir and beech with a variety of wildlife.

Whitestone

(Forest Enterprise) **F** 98ha
O.S.S. 171 - S0 523 028
01633 400205

🚗🦯◡🦯☀️WC♿ⓘ⛺📷🚶

On the A466 in Tintern village take the road which runs by the side of the Wye Valley Hotel signed Catbrook for some 2 miles. Car park opposite road junction. WCs on site along with facilities for the disabled. Picnic areas, barbecues, a children's play area and less abled trail. Full open access to the wood with rights of way and bridlepaths throughout. Self guided trails available. Please contact above for further details. A guide to walks in Tintern Woods is available for 60p. Donations to the Forestry Trust.

Whitestone Wood is where the productive coniferous woods of the plateau meet the ancient woodland of the Wye Valley AONB. The Tall Trees walk runs through magnificent Douglas fir and Norway spruce to the Jubilee Grove which celebrated the diamond jubilee of the Forestry Commission. The Grove, planted in 1979, includes oak, cherry, sweet chestnut and beech. There are lovely views over the Wye Valley which are accessible to wheelchair users with a strong pusher! Very varied flora and fauna with many different species of butterfly and a variety of fungi. Birds abound with some rare species present.

Wyndcliff
(Forest Enterprise) **F** 95ha
O.S.S. 162 - ST 524 972
01633 400205

🚗🏕🔥 ☀🎪 🚻

From Chepstow take A466 N towards Monmouth. Fork left N of St Arvans to Wyndcliff. Fully open access to the woods with rights of way and self-guided trails. Walks in Tintern Woods guide 60p, contact above. Donations to the Forestry Trust.

Wyndcliff is part of the remnant primeval forest of the Wye valley which has been worked by man for thousands of years. Forest Enterprise owns and manages this woodland to a plan agreed with the Countryside Council for Wales, the area being an SSSI. There are spectacular views from the Eagles Nest lookout and the 365 steps over the Wye Valley. This ancient woodland has a wide variety of trees including whitebeam, yew and giant coppiced lime in the lower wood. Flora and fauna abound with a rich variety of fungi growing in the autumnal fallen leaves.

WALES - GWYNEDD

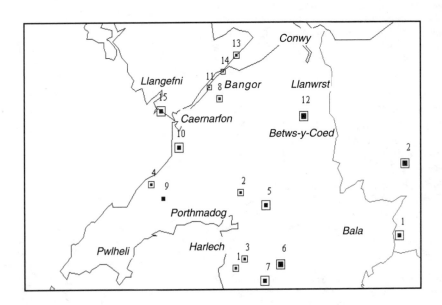

1. Coed Aber Artro
2. Coed Cae Fali
3. Coed Crafnant
4. Coed Elernion
5. *Coed Llyn y Garnedd
6. *Coed y Brenin Forest Park
7. *Cwm Mynach
8. Glan Faenol
9. *Glasfryn Forestry Estate
10. Glynllifon
11. The Greenwood Centre
12. *Gwydyr Forest Park
13. Henllys Hall
14. Nantporth
15. Newborough Forest

Coed Aber Artro
(Woodland Trust) **F** 27.43ha
O.S.S. 124 - SH 597 267
01476 74297

The wood is located in the Artro valley approximate 1.5 miles E of Llanbedr. From A496 in Llanbedr take the minor road E towards Pentre Gwyfryn. After 1 mile turn R onto another minor road, which runs through the centre of Coed Aber Artro - park on the verge. Please take care in the vicinity of the Afon Cwmnantcol gorge, which is very steep.

This is a superb gently sloping area of woodland containing some very fine trees, and a magnificent gorge through which the Afon Cwmnantcol runs. While walking through the wood look out for the large monkey puzzle tree. Other trees to be seen are oak, beech and ash. Several species of fern grow in the sheer sided gorge with bluebell, wavy hair grass, bilberry and cow-wheat making up the ground flora.

Coed Cae Fali
(National Trust) **F** 58ha
O.S.S. 124 - SH 629 407
01766 86293
20

Midway between Penrhyndeudraeth and Maentwrog. Adjacent and N of the A487. Parking in lay-by for 20 cars and woodland interpretation. No WCs. There are public and permitted paths which are open freely all year.

Part of the extensively wooded Maentwrog valley in Snowdonia. Former Forestry Commission predominantly sessile oak woodland with conifer plantations; Norway spruce and Scots pine. Hardwoods being gradually reinstated by group felling with natural regeneration. Rich in typical western oakwood flora and fauna, particularly mosses and liverworts.

Coed Crafnant
(North Wales Wildlife Trust) **R** 48.5ha
O.S.S. 124 - SH 619 289
01248 351541
2

From A496 Harlech - Barmouth road take minor road to Cwm Bychan in Llanbadr. Uphill for 1.7 miles to Penybont. Then either A: Turn R over bridge, through gate and down track for 0.3 miles, then R through gate to Y Fron, uphill, through gate, bear L continue 150m; or B: past Penybont for 0.9 miles towards Cwm Bychan, park on roadside overlooking Pont Crafant. There are no obvious paths and the ground is steep.

A fine example of an ancient woodland with a rich flora of mosses, liverworts and ferns. Many interesting plants, including heath-spotted orchid and common cow wheat, and a number of bird species, including pied flycatcher, goldcrest and buzzard.

Coed Elernion
(Woodland Trust) **F** 20.27ha
O.S.S. 123 - SH 378 462
01476 74297

Turn off the main A499 Pwllheli to Caernarfon road onto the more southerly of the two minor roads leading to Trefor. The entrance is 200m from this junction on the LH side.

This is a good example of a wet oak-ash woodland. In the wetter areas look out for bogbean and heath-spotted orchid. On the drier soils sessile oak is the main tree species, with a shrub storey of hazel below it. A spring visit to the wood is especially recommended, when the whole wood is a sea of bluebells; later honeysuckle covers the ground. A good variety of woodland birds can be spotted in this wood, including choughs.

*Coed Llyn y Garnedd
(Managed by Tilhill Economic Forestry Ltd)
Fd 200ha
O.S.S. 124 - SH 646 415
01678 530206

From Porthmadog take A487 (T) towards Dolgellau. At Oakley Arms pub Maentwrog turn L to Rhyd. Entrance is 200m on L after passing under railway bridge. Full and free access at all times except 28 Feb. Certain paths closed from time to time when forest operations in progress. Please park leaving gateway clear for lorry access.

A mixed wood predominantly conifer and including two reservoirs. Adjacent to the Ffestiniog Railway and including short and long distance walks with spectacular views of the Dwyryd Estuary, Southern Snowdonia and Cardigan Bay. A joint footpath network links with woodlands owned by Woodland Trust, CCW, NT and Snowdonia National Park. Leaflet with waymarked route available from local Tourist Office and Ffestiniog Railway station entitled Dyffryn Maentwrog Llyn Mair.

*Coed y Brenin Forest Park

(Forest Enterprise) **F** 6300ha
O.S.S. 124 - SH 715 277
01341 422289
🚗🐎🔺 [i] WC ♿ ⛺ 🚻 ⚓ 🚾◑🏞🛍

8 miles N of Dolgellau, near Ganllwyd, on the A470 (T) road and well signposted. Facilities include: mountain bike trails, orienteering course, forest nature reserve, forest garden and mining trails (gold and copper), sign writing workshop and wildlife observation hide. Car parking - Pay and display 50p for 2 hours, £1 all day, annual permit £5. Please ring above number for opening times. For prearranged educational group visits please write to the Forest District Manager, Dolgellau Forest District, Government Buildings, Arran Road, Dolgellau, Gwynedd LL40 1LW.

The forest was formerly part of the Nannau estate, founded by Cadwgan, Prince of Powys, in 1100 AD. It has some of the most varied and beautiful landscapes in the southern part of Snowdonia National Park. An extraordinary diversity of rock and soil has enabled the forester to introduce a wide variety of tree species which are enriched by some of the original cover of semi-natural oak woodland. Richly varied plant, animal and bird communities have become established.

Cwm Mynach

(C J Mygind and R G A Youard) **F** 450ha
O.S.S. 124 - SH 683 219
01678 3206
🚗5🚻🔺☀🚶

From Dolgellau head for Barmouth along N side of estuary. Head N opposite toll bridge up steep single track road to end of tarmac. There is parking for 5 cars but no other facilities.

Cym Mynach, although primarily a commercial conifer plantation, contains significant areas of oakwood and upland heather, supported by a Special Management Grant. Its views S to Cader Idris and W towards the Rhinogs make its location particularly attractive. It also features a lake, visited by migrating swans in winter; and numerous former mine workings, in particular a 100 year old tramway to a now-disused manganese mine. Birdlife on the estate is monitored by the RSPB who also carry out conservation work (contact RSPB warden, Reg Thorpe, on 01341 250650).

Glan Faenol

(National Trust) **F** 55ha
O.S.S. 114 - SH 530 695
01690 710636
🚗10🚶🔺☀[i]⛺🚾

Access is via Parc Menai between Bangor and Felinheli/Port Dinorwic on A487. There is parking for 10 vehicles with visitor information. Nearby Plas Newydd house (2 miles) has WC, shop and tearoom, house open 31 Mar to 31 Oct, selected days. There are permitted paths leading from car park; they are freely open all year.

Divided into eight woodland blocks, part of the formerly extensive and landscaped Vaynol Park, adjacent to the Menai Straits. Woods are a mixture of softwood and hardwood, some on ancient woodland sites where conifer is being converted back to hardwoods. Some impressive young plantations of sycamore. Network of woodland and parkland paths with fine views of Plas Newydd and Lleyn peninsula.

*Glasfryn Forestry & Fencing Centre

(R C Williams-Ellis) **A** 250ha
O.S.S. 123 - SH 391 431
01758 750 623

£1←20🚻1✕◡▲⌇🍴 FP 🔘

Find Fencing Centre on the A499 (Caenarfon/ Pwllheli) road 1/4 mile S of Llanaelhaearn 5 miles N of Pwllheli. Facilities include a toilet. parking area, 5 miles Class 30 tonne forest roads. Charges for group visits are £10 per hour - any number of visitors. Appointment with owner - Mon to Fri.

The only fully economical post war forest holding in Wales. It started with 2 hectares planted in 1926 which came into production in 1948. By 1972 195 hectares had been planted. The Fencing Centre was opened in 1989. A further 80 hectares which had recently been felled were bought in 1992. Llyn Glasfryn, within the estate, is an SSSI, but the forest as a whole supports a far richer wildlife community than it did before. Glasfryn now once more employs a workforce of 14 and produces timber, mainly Sitka spruce, averaging 20 tonnes per hectare per year, on sub-standard agricultural land, even though it is inside an Environmentally Sensitive Area.

Glynllifon

(The Principal, Coleg Meirion Dwyfor)
F 300ha
O.S.S. 115 - SH 452 550
01286 830261

←50(£0.50)🚻6🔀 WC ☖ 🏠

From Caernarfon, follow signs to Pwllheli, Glynllifon is approximately 7 miles from Caernarfon and is clearly signed. Other facilities include a country park, countryside museum, craft workshops and a cycleway. The park is open from dawn to dusk and during these times there is fully open access, to the park only. Group visits to the forest by appointment only. Please contact the Associate Principal on the above number, giving one months notice for group visits. Group rates will be negotiable. The site is shared with a country park which provides public access to part of the estate.

Woodland interest is varied, from amenity and landscape to timber production.

The Greenwood Centre

(S & A Bristow) **R** 6.5ha
O.S.S. 115 - SH 530 670
01248 671493

£2.95/£1.95←60🚻2🔀▲☀- WC ☖ ⓘ 📖⌇🍴▲☂🔘🏠🏠

Off the B4366 between Bangor and Caernarfon. Look for brown and white signs near Bethel. 15 minutes from Anglesey, Caernarfon and Llanberis. Large oak framed Visitor Centre with interactive exhibitions about the World of Trees. Open 10.00 - 5.30 daily from March to end of October.

Mixed woodland with a range of habitats, from wetland wood (with boardwalk access) to young beech/oak hilltop planting to new arboretum. Managed for conservation/recreation with sheep access to half the site. Interpretation of various aspects of woodland - rhododendron, Douglas fir, coppice systems.

*Gwydyr Forest Park

(Forest Enterprise) **F** 7250ha
O.S.S. 115/116 - SH 795 566
01492 640578

←🐕▲ⓘ📖⌇🍴🚲▲🏠

Centre of Betws y Coed on the A5 (T) road. Facilities include Pay and Display at all car parks. Visitor Centre "Y Stablau", exhibition and shop, waymarked walks including one for the visually disadvantaged and another for the ambient disabled, mountain bike routes, picnic sites, wayfaring courses, fishing and forest coach tours, mining archaeological trail. Open all year round 10.00am to 5.45pm (summer): 10.00am to 5.00pm (winter). For prearranged educational group visits, please write to the Forest District Manager, Gwydyr Uchaf, Llanrwst, Gwynedd, LL26 0PN.

Gwydyr Forest Park ranges across the hills on Snowdownia's eastern flank. High wooded ramparts rise steeply from the level pastures of the Conwy valley. Salmon abounding in the healthy vital rivers, enfolded by the forest are a tribute to woodland and landscape management and conservation methods used since the Forestry Commission began work here in 1921. A legacy of old engine houses, waste tips and reservoirs are charactersitic features of the forest landscape today. They bear witness to three centuries of mineral exploitation, developed by Sir John Wynn of Gwydyr Castle in the early 17th century.

Henllys Hall
(Country Moment Hotels) **F** 10ha
O.S.S. 114/115 - SH 600 776
01248 810412

⬤50⟵ ▲ ❄ WC *i* ⛺ ⌁▲ ▼◐ ▣ ⋀

In the centre of Beaumaris turn L on B5109 towards Pentraeth. After 300 yards turn R (sign to Henllys Hall Hotel). After 0.5 mile take second L (again signposted) and park behind hotel. No entrance charge and the wood is open 1 hour after sunrise to 1 hour before sunset all year. Walks not suitable for the disabled.

An ancient woodland, it was part of the estate of the Sheriff of Beaumaris Castle; the family lived there for over 400 years. The woodland is varied, dominated by sycamore, but there are many other species present including some very large beech and a lime avenue. The spring flora is partculariy interesting with carpets of wild daffodils, bluebells and wild garlic. There is a 1.5 mile waymarked walk which forms a circular path through the woodland with fine views across the Menai Strait to Snowdownia. The woodland has not been managed for over 20 years but is entering into a programme of management for amenity, conservation and timber production.

Nantporth
(North Wales Wildlife Trust) **R** 8ha
O.S.S. 115 - SH 566 721
01248 351541

⬤10⟵ ⬤ *i* ⋔ ▣

Leave A5122 near the Normal College sports ground, and take first turn towards the Strait. Cars can be left at the small car park at the end of this

lane. A footpath towards the Strait leads into the reserve.

A small disused limestone quarry together with some woodland and foreshore. On the NW facing slope above the Strait and part of the botanically rich declivity which lies along the Strait-side between Normal College and Gorad-y-Gyt. The soil is a calcareous boulder clay and supports an interesting calcicole flora. Some of the more uncommon plants are yellow-wort, in one of its very few Caernarfonshire localities, a species of whitebeam (Sorbus porrigentiformis) confined to a few localities in western Britain, and the bee orchid which is very erratic in its appearance. The flora of the woodland floor is typical of shady base rich habits, including wood violet, wood sedge, woodruff, and soft shield fern. Only about 20 species of invertebrates have so far been recorded.

Newborough Forest
(Forest Enterprise) **F** 948ha
O.S.S. 114 - SH 406 634
01492 640578

⬤380(£1.20)⟵ ▲ WC ♿ ⛺ 🅿 ⌁▲

The forest lies SW of Newborough village, on the A4080(T), 16.5 km from A55 Expressway. open all year.

Predoninantly pine forest established on a previously mobile sand dune system, planted btween 1947-69. Almost entirely an SSSI, noted for its floral diversity and particularly its range of orchids. The Malltreach salt marshes, internationally important as a sea bird and wader habitat, forms the western flank of the forest. Llanddwyn beach, accessed from main forest car park at SH 406634 was awarded a blue flag in July 1994. Additional interest is provided by Llyn Parc Mawr, an award winning 4ha lake specially constructed for European Year of the Environment. Car park at SH 415673 gives access to it and two bird hides, one of which provides for disabled visitors.

WALES - POWYS

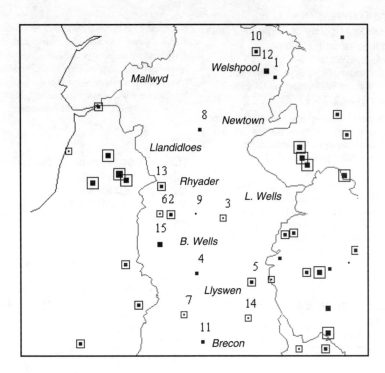

1. *Ackers Grove
2. Allt Ddu/Cwm yr Esgob/Bedw Caemelyn
3. Bailey Einon
4. *Cefnllysgwynne Estate
5. Cilcenni Dingle Wood
6. Cnwch Wood
7. Coed Dyrysiog
8. *Craigfryn Caeau-Bach Wood
9. Doldowlod Woods
10. Gaer Fawr Wood
11. *Held Wood
12. Leighton Estate - Big Wood
13. Penygarreg Wood
14. Pwll y Wrach
15. *Trallwm Forest

*Ackers Grove

(Royal Forestry Society of England, Wales and Northern Ireland) **P** 12ha

O.S.S. 126 - SJ 225 075

The (RFS) Warden, Tan y Bryn, Wellington Road, Llandrindod Wells, Powys LD1 5NG

🏠£2🚗10🚶🌲🌳

Meet at car park adjoining Spar shop in Welshpool where there are WCs - there are no facilities at Ackers Grove. Charge for school children £1. There are no public rights of way

A private collection of fine specimen conifers in the Naylor Pinetum, and the adjacent Charles Ackers Redwood Grove, the oldest and largest stand of coast redwoods in Britain. Because of the private ownership and the delicate nature of the habitat, the property is not normally open to the public. Please respect this.

Allt Ddu/Cwm yr Esgob/Bedw Caemelyn

(RSPB) **R** 40ha

O.S.S. 147 - SN 936 652

🌳🍽️🌲🌿

Off B4518, from Rhayader, at Elan village. Nearest rail station at Llandrindod Wells (14 miles) with are bus and taxi services. The woodland is located on the hill slopes behind the village. There are no facilities but full and free access all year.

An oak woodland with some trees over 350 years old. Very quiet for wildlife during winter months but from mid April to early June it supports large numbers of birds - of special interest are pied flycatchers, redstarts, wood warblers, tree pipits and woodpeckers.

Bailey Einon

(Radnorshire Wildlife Trust) **F** 5ha

O.S.S. 147 - SO 085 614

01597 823298

🚗10🚶🍽️🌲🌿

From Llandrindod Wells take Cefnllys Lane for about 2 miles, after steep descent park in picnic area. Woodland is downstream of picnic area.

A mixed broadleaved woodland, dominated in the wetter flushes by ash and alder, the drier areas dominated by sessile oak and hazel. A wide variety of plants and birds can be seen in the woodland which borders the river Ithon. A short walk lasting about 3/4 hour has been laid out in the woodland. Management is as high forest and coppice with standards.

*Cefnllysgwynne Estate

(C R Woosnam CBE) **A** 64ha

O.S.S. 147 - SO 001 501

01982 552237 or 01982 553248

🚗2🌲🌿

W of Builth Wells. A location plan will be sent to those making appointments. Parking for 2 or 3 cars and a picnic site. No other facilities. Donations to the Forestry Trust. Visits on 14 May, 11 Jun, 9 Jul, are by arrangement with at least 1 months notice. No smoking. Groups of 5 to 10 preferred. Guided tours by the owner between 10am and 4pm. Local schools particularly welcome.

The woods represent one third of the estate, the rest being permanent pasture. On the S side of the Irfon, a tributary of the Wye, 500-1000 feet above sea level. The bulk of the wood has been planted and managed by the owner since 1947, mainly conifers which will reach maturity over the next 15 to 20 years. The wood illustrates how wildlife and landscape can be well served by good silvicultural management. Coupled with a small pheasant shoot and the development over the next few years of a network of footpaths and bridleways, both public and permissive, the woods show the many benefits that forestry offers.

Cilcenni Dingle Wood

(Woodland Trust) **F** 14ha

O.S.S. 161 - SO 175 414

01476 74297

🚗🐎🌲

Just off the A438 Hereford to Glasbury road, not far from Hay-on-Wye on the Welsh-English border. From Glasbury, travel 0.5 mile beyond the turning to Maesyronen Chapel and look for a no-through

road on the LH side. Turn on to this and park on the verge running parallel to the A438. There are no facilities.

Cilcenni Dingle is a secluded valley woodland, lying along the steep slopes of a tributary of the River Wye. Mature oak and ash trees now dominate the wood and plant lovers can expect to find an excellent range of herbaceous plants, including the locally uncommon herb paris, slender St John's wort and soft shield fern. Many birds such as pied flycatcher, woodpecker, tree creeper and nuthatch inhabit the woodland, encouraged by the wealth of varied habitats.

Cnwch Wood
(Dwr Cymru Welsh Water) **F** 5ha
O.S.S. 147 - SN 931 648
01597 810449

 100(£0.50) ⚲ ● ✳ WC ♿ ⓘ 📖 🍴
ȴ ⚲ 🛈 🚻 🏠

Take the B4518 out of Rhayader in the direction of the Elan Valley - follow the signs for the Elan Valley visitor centre - approximately 3.5 miles. Nature trail with interpretative panels and leaflet but no other facilities. There is free and full access all the year. Please observe the country code and treat the area and other visitors with consideration.

A mainly sessile oak woodland situated below the Elan Valley reservoir complex. Wide variety of bird species present. The wood has recently been fenced to exclude sheep with a view to encouraging natural regeneration. The woodland is designated as an SSSI.

Coed Dyrysiog
(Brecknock Wildlife Trust) **F** 7ha
O.S.S. 160 - SN 980 310
01874 625708
🐾 ●

From Brecon take the A40 W towards Sennybridge. After just over 3 miles turn N on minor road to Aberbran. At T junction turn R to Aberyscir/Cradoc, after 500m take 1st L to Llanfihangel Nant Bran. Woodland is on L after just under 1 mile. There is a footpath.

A mixed broadleaved woodland developed on steeply sloping old red sandstone. One of the few afforested commons in Brecknock, the wood is ungrazed and has a diverse ground flora. The drier banks support mainly oak of mixed ages, whilst ash is most common in wetter flushed areas. The rich shrub layer includes honeysuckle, hawthorn, field maple and guelder rose. A variable ground flora includes bilberry, common cow-wheat, wild strawberry and marsh marigold.

*Craigfryn Caeau-Bach Wood, part of Dinam Woods
(Rt Hon Lord Davies) **AC** 54ha
O.S.S. 136 - SO 031 891
01591 620309
⚲ 10 🐾 1 ȴ Ᵹ

A470 7 miles W of Newton and 6 miles E of Llanidloes, across river Severn at "Davies" statue in Llandinam, turn L - old railway line for one mile to meeting point at the wood. Guided visits can be arranged by contacting Mr Kahars on the above number. Donations to the Forestry Trust.

The wood consists of 15 hectares of broadleaved oak, ash, beech and others, mainly 50 to 120 years old, and 39 hectares of conifers, larch, Douglas fir and others, mainly 7 to over 30 years old. The site is partially old woodland and previously rough grazing on the River Severn valley side, rising steeply from 500 to 1000 ft, with a SE aspect. The objects of management are timber production, landscaping and conservation of wildlife. The silvicultural practice is directed towards a perpetual uneven aged mixed group forest. Duke of Cornwall's Award winner.

Doldowlod Woods
(The Gibson-Watt Family) **AM** 10+ha
O.S.S. 147 - SN 995 627
01597 89208
On the A470, 5 miles S of Rhayader. Visits by appointment only for individuals or parties with Lord Gibson-Watt.

Doldowlod Woods consists of 42 woods on both sides of the A470 between Builth Wells and Rhayader. Some of the woods are very small but the estate specialises in growing fine oak together with a variety of conifers.

Gaer Fawr Wood
(Woodland Trust) **F** 30ha
O.S.S. 126 - SJ 219 125
01476 74297

Take the minor road off the B4392 at Sarn Bridge on the northern edge of the village of Guilsfield. Climb the hill for about 0.5 mile to the quarry car park. There are no facilities. Stout footwear is advisable especially in winter.

Gaer Fawr Wood is a striking landscape feature, overlooking the Severn valley. The wood covers most of the hilltop and is a Scheduled Ancient Monument. The variety of trees and shrubs especially those with scented flowers, nuts and berries such as rowan, hazel and wild cherry provide food for many insects and birds. Among the birds you can see are nuthatch and spotted flycatcher. Also buzzards are often seen and, if you are quiet, you may see a tawny owl.

*Held Wood, part of Ffrwdgrech Woods
(Mr M D D Evans) **AcM** 24ha
O.S.S. 160 - SO 029 273
01591 620309

From A40 at W end of Brecon town turn S along Ffrwdgrech road opposite Drovers Arms. Meet at Ffwdgrech House - enter at lodge on L. Guided visits can be arranged by contacting Mr Kalnars on the above telephone number, or write 6 weeks in advance to, Ffrwdgrech House, Brecon Powys, LD3 8LB. There are picnic facilities and 4 acres of gardens and lawn.

Woodland cover for about 200 years. Altitude 620 to 920 feet. All on old red sandstone. 40% compulsory clear fell First War and 60% Second War. Replanted in small compartments of various species now managed

as a perpetual forest, multi storey in parts. Full exposure to SW winds. Ravens and hawks nested annually in old Scots pine for at least 100 years. Very wide variety of small birds in spring and summer. Carpets of bluebells in some areas. Main tree species: Douglas fir, Japanese larch, Corsican pine, red cedar, ash, beech, oak. Marked increase in butterflies in recent years. Forestry Authority Merit Award.

Leighton Estate - Big Wood
(Mr C F E Shakerley) **A** 100ha
O.S.S. 126 - SJ 225 075

Redwood Grove car park. Kind permission of RFS. Take mountain road at Cock Hotel off A490. Follow RFS signs. Guided tour on 4/6/95 lasting approx 3 hours, starting 2pm.

A mixed woodland block with over 50 species. Some very fine ash, Douglas fir and over 3 acres of Metasequoia. Many large trees including a 200ft Abies grandis. Planting began in 1875 by John Naylor and many of his achievements still grace the woods. Charles Ackers bought the estate in 1931 and the present owner in 1972.

Penygarreg Wood
(Dwr Cymru Welsh Water) **F** 11ha
O.S.S. 147 - SN 915 674
01597 810449

Take the B4518 out of Rhayader in the direction of the Elan Valley - continue for approximately 6 miles. The wood is situated below Penygarreg Dam and adjacent to the guest house known as the "Flickering Lamp". There are no facilities but there are waymarked and leafletted walks. Free and full access all the year round.

A mixed broadleaved woodland which is being positively managed to favour the broadleaved species and during 1993 was fenced to exclude stock and encourage natural regeneration. The wood abounds in birdlife.

Pwll y Wrach
(Brecknock Wildlife Trust) **F** 8ha
O.S.S. 161 - SO 165 328
01874 625708

🚗 ⛏ ● *i* ☎ 🔥

From Brecon take the A470 and A438 to Bronllys (12km) and then the A479 to Talgarth (2kms). Pass through Talgarth taking the minor road signposted to the Mid Wales hospital. The car park is 500 metres past the hospital. Wheelchair route, car park, interpretatiive panels, leaflet from Trust office.

A fine broadleaved woodland of considerable botanical interest. The upper leached parts of the valley side support sessile oak over acid-loving species such as heather. Ash/elm woodland has developed lower down the valley side. The rich ground flora includes dogwood, spindle, herb paris and toothwort. In July 1991 the Pwll y Wrach geology trail was opened in this reserve which explores and explains the environment of 400 million years ago.

*Trallwm Forest
(George Johnson) **P** 175ha
O.S.S. 146/147 - SN 881 543
01591 3229

🚗20 ⛏ ∪ 🔺 📖 🔥 🦌

Turn off the A483 between Builth Wells and Llanwrtyd Wells at Beulah, signposted Abergwesyn - Trallwm is 3.5 miles on R. There is parking for 20 + cars but no other facilities. The wood is open on advertised days or by appointment.

There is a variety of conifer crops, producing quality timber as well as providing a home for many species of bird, mammal, insect and reptile along edges of roads, rides, lake and farmland. We also have accommodation for up to 40 guests in s/c stone and slate cottages.

Extending Your Enjoyment

WOODLAND AND FOREST VISITOR CENTRES

Many of the larger forests have visitor centres near the main approach. Find out if the forest you intend to visit has one. You will find displays and publications to heighten your understanding of the forest. Facilities including car park, lavatories, shop and refreshments are usually provided on site so the centre makes an ideal starting point for your walk. There may be staff on hand to answer questions and lead guided walks, also special facilities for school groups. Often there is a seasonal programme of events and activities to do with the forest including cycle rides, treasure hunts, deer spotting trips, orienteering and natural history days. Ask for details locally.

The buildings have been carefully designed to suit their woodland surrounds and to provide a focal point for visitors. They can provide much appreciated warmth and shelter on occasions! But do not expect to find centres everywhere for they are expensive to build, equip and staff so most private woodlands will not have one. Large Forest Enterprise woods, those near country parks or on National Trust estates are the most likely places. Here are two:

2. WESTONBIRT ARBORETUM, Gloucestershire. One of the jewels in the Forest Enterprise Crown, Westonbirt is internationally renowned and justly famed for its spectacular autumn colours. The centre has a wide range of facilities to complete a rewarding visit.

Forest Enterprise Centres

ENGLAND

Alice Holt Visitor Centre: Bedgebury National Pinetum: Border Forest Park: Cannock Visitor Centre: Dalby Visitor Centre: Forest of Dean Information Centre: Grizedale Forest Park: Hamsterley Visitor Centre: Kielder Castle Visitor Centre: North Riding Forest Park: Thetford Forest Park: Westonbirt Arboretum: Whinlatter Visitor Centre: Wyre Visitor Centre.

WALES

Afan Argoed Countryside Centre: Bod Petrual Visitor Centre: Bwlch Nant Yr Arian Visitor Centre: Coed y Brenin Forest Park & Visitor Centre: Cwmcarn Visitor Centre: Garwnant Visitor Centre: Y Stablau Snowdonian National Park Information Centre.

1.THE LOOK OUT , Nine Mile Ride, Bracknell, Berkshire, RG12 4QW. Off the A322 south of Bracknell. An ideal starting point for walks in Bracknell and Swinley & Bagshot Forests which are part of the larger Windsor Forest. (see page 24). Enjoy the exhibition exploring life in the forest, the video and slide shows, the look-out tower, gift shop, coffee shop and picnic area. Summer or winter there is always something to enjoy.

Private Sector Centres

Privately owned forest visitor centres, apart from the Lookout, can be found at - New Forest, Hants - Combe Sydenham, Somerset, - Wilderness Wood, East Sussex - Woodland Park, Wilts. More will be listed in 1996.

🍂 FOREST ACCOMODATION

Outside Forest Enterprise and, in the private sector, Center Parcs, we are only aware of two places, Craig Farm Wood in Gwent and Trallwm Forest in Powys, that offer forest accomodation. We would welcome information of other sites that have forest cabins, chalets or bed and breakfast accomodation in a forest environment for inclusion in the 1996 book.

▣ PUBS & WOODLAND WALKS

Walking in the forest generates a healthy appetite and a decided thirst! There is no better plan than to begin or end your woodland visit with refreshment at a pub or small hotel. Public Houses (PH) are shown on the Landranger OS maps so you can easily see if there is one near the wood you have selected. Often you can leave your car in the pub car park if you have a drink or take a meal there. Some entries in this book suggest a nearby inn - often with a name like "The Foresters Arms", "The Woodcutters", or, of course, "The Royal Oak". Look in the Yellow Pages for pubs with names like these as many are in or near well known woodlands. In this book, where a handy pub makes the most convenient rendezvous for a forest visit, the map reference you will find for the wood is, in fact, the pub. Do patronise these pubs near the following woods and encourage the pub wood scheme to succeed.

Berkshire, Poyle Poplars Community Woodland, Round Oak Piece, Westrop Wood.

Buckinghamshire, Bottom Wood, Burnham Beeches.

Cambridgeshire, Waresley Wood.

Cheshire, Church Wood and Clayhill Wood, Risely Moss, Stanney Wood.

Cleveland, Thorpe Wood.

Cumbria, Baysbrown Wood, Bryerswood Woodlands, Grizedale Forest Park, Hows Wood, Rayrigg Wood, Skelghyll Wood, Talkin Wood, Whinhill

Derbyshire, Firth Wood, Snake Pass, Whitwell Wood.

Devon, Clovelly Wood, Dunsford Wood, Heddon Valley, Holne Woods, Marridge/Elberry/The Grove Woods, Milber Wood, Occombe Wood, Riding Parks & Lawelldown Woods, Salcombe Hill, Scadson/Ten Acre Brake, Teign Valley, Watersmeet.

Dorset, Melcombe Park.

Durham, Durham Riverbanks, West Plantation.

Essex, Belfairs, Rawreth Hall Wood.

Gloucestershire, Nagshead Nature Reserve.

Greater Manchester, Hulmes and Hardy Wood.

Hampshire & Isle of Wight, The Chase, Phrympth Wood.

Hereford & Worcester, Coedgwen, Langdale Wood & The Lills, Monk Wood, Queensland Country Park, Shrawley Wood, Tiddesley Wood.

Hertfordshire, Broxbourne & Bencroft Woods, Bullens Green Wood, The Bushes, Hardings, Home Park, Monken Hadley Common, Wall Hall Estate Woods.

Humberside, Elsham Hall Country & Wildlife Park.

Kent, Batfold, Bushy & Kilnhouse Woods: Bore Place, Octavia Hill Woodlands: Toys Hill, Toys Hill.

Lancashire, Roddlesworth & Tockholes Woodlands.

Lincolnshire, Bourne Wood, Hartsholme Country Park, Park Gate Plantation.

Norfolk, Gayton Thorpe Wood, Warren.

Northants, Fineshade Wood, Irchester Country Park, Salcey Forest, Short Wood, Wakerley Great Wood.

Northumberland, Priestclose Wood.

Nottinghamshire, Blidworth Woods Complex, Rufford Country Park & Abbey, Sherwood Forest Country Park, Sherwood Pines Forest Park.

Shropshire, Hurst Woodlands, Longdon & Withybed

Somerset, Coombe Sydenham.

Staffordshire, Jacksons Bank.

Suffolk, Bradfield Woods, Bonny Wood.

Surrey, Alice Holt Woodland Park, Ashtead Common, Crabwood/Cold Blow Shaw, Leith Hill, Ranmore.

Sussex - East, Abbots Wood, Blackdown Wood, Coney Burrow, Morris's Wood, Wilderness Wood.

Sussex - West, Borde Hill Gardens.

Warwickshire, Ryton Wood, Snitterfield Bushes.

West Midlands, Saltwells Wood.

Yorkshire - North, Clapdale, Dalby Forest, Duncombe Park, Hambleton Woods, Hovingham High Wood, Levisham Wood, Marton Wood, Mulgrave Wood, Strid Wood (Bolton Abbey), Swinsty Reservoir.

Yorkshire - South, Cawthorne Park, Eccleshall Woods, Hail Mary Hill & Falconer Woods, Langsett Reservoir, Scholes Coppice, Wyming Brook.

Yorkshire - West, Chevin Forest Park, Coburn Hill Wood, Esholt Woods, Middleton Wood, Newmillerdam Country Park, Northcliffe Wood, Park Wood, St Ives Estate, Temple Newsham Estate.

Clwyd, Loggerheads Country Park, Wepre Country Park.

Dyfed, Llwyngoras Nature Reserve, Park Natur Penglais, Poor Man's Wood.

Glamorgan - Mid, Garwnant Visitor Centre.

Glamorgan - South, Cogan Wood, Coed Garnllwyd.

Gwent, Craig Goch.

Gwynedd, The Greenwood Centre, Henllys Hall.

PUBLIC TRANSPORT

Very few entries this year have significant details of access by public transport, but Hampstead Heath, Highgate Wood, Lesnes Abbey Woods and Sydenham Hill Wood in Greater London. We would welcome help in compiling this level of data for more rural areas for 1996.

U Woods with Bridleways or Riding Facilities

Beds,Maulden Wood, Rowney Warren, West Wood
Berks, Fencewood, Round Oak Piece, Rushall Woods, Swinley and Bagshot Forest
Bucks, Bottom Wood
Cleveland, Guisborough Forest
Clwyd, Clocaenog Forest
Cornwall, Cardinham Woods, Costislost & Polgeel Woods, Idless Woods
Cumbria, Baysbrown Wood, Ennerdale Forest, Grizedale Forest Park, Hardknott Forest, High Stand, Higham and Setmurthy, Lowther Park and Sillathwaite, Miterdale Forest, Old Hall Wood, Sowerby, Whinlatter Forest Park
Derbyshire, Farley Moor
Devon, Abbeyford Woods, Burrator Wood, Buzzards, Dunsford Wood, Eggesford Woods, Heathercombe Wood, Lydford Wood, Riding Parks and Lawelldown Woods, Scadson / Ten Acre Brake
Dyfed, Poor Man's Wood, Stackpole Estate Woodlands
Essex, Broads Walk
Glamorgan Mid, Garwnant, Gethin Woodland Park
Glamorgan West, Afan Forest Park
Greater London, Chalk Wood, Hampstead Heath
Greater Manchester, Hulmes Wood
Gwent, Craig Goch, Cwmcarn Forest Drive, Wentwood, Whitestone
Gwynedd, Glasfryn Forestry Estate
Hants & IOW, The Holt
Hereford &Worcester, Dymock Wood, Langdale Wood & The Lills, Queensland Country Park,Tedstone Court **Humberside,** Allerthorpe Wood
Kent,Batfold, Bushy & Kilnhouse Woods, Clowes Wood, Hemsted Forest, Kings Wood, Octavia Hill Woodlands, Perry Wood, Toys Hill
Lancs, Gisburn Forest, Longridge Fell, Lords Lot, Roddlesworth & Tockholes Woods
Leics, Burbage Wood and Sheepy Wood Norfolk, Bintree, Thetford Forest Park
Northants, Brigstock, Fineshade Wood, Harry's Park , Salcey Forest, Wakerley Great Wood
Northumberland, Chillingham Woods
Notts, Bestwood Country Park, Blidworth Woods Complex, Sherwood Pines Forest Park
Shropshire, Edge Wood
Staffs, Cannock Forest, Jacksons Bank
Suffolk, Rendlesham Forest, Sudbourne,Tunstall Forest

Surrey, Alice Holt Forest, Box Hill, Crabwood & Cold Blow Shaw, Hindhead, Leith Hill, Ranmore, Winterfold Forest
Sussex East, Blackdown Wood, Coneyburrow, Flatropers Wood, Friston Forest, Hoth & Cards Woods
Sussex West, Blackdown Sussex West, The Mens Nature Reserve, Slindon Woods, Stansted Forest
Tyne & Wear, Chopwell Woodland Park
Wiltshire, Witham Park Woods
Yorkshire - North, Broxa Forest, Clapdale, Dalby Forest, Langdale Forest, Levisham, Newtondale, Silton Forest, Sneaton Forest
Yorkshire - South, Cawthorne Park, Ecclesall Woods, Hail Mary Hill & Falconer Wood, Scholes Coppice
Yorkshire - West, Chevin Forest Park, Coburn Hill Wood, Esholt Woods, Haw Park Wood, St Ives Estate, Temple Newsam Estate

♿ Woods with WCs for the Disabled

Berks, Rushall Woods, Swinley and Bagshot Forest
Bucks, Black Park Country Park Cheshire, Little Budworth Country Park Woods,Risley Moss, Stanney Wood
Cleveland, Thorpe Wood
Clwyd, Clocaenog Forest, Loggerheads Country Park, Moel Famau, Wepre Country Park
Cornwall, Cardinham Woods, Mount Edgcumbe Country Park Cumbria, Ennerdale Forest, Grizedale Forest Park, Mirehouse and Catstocks Woods, Talkin Wood, Whinlatter Forest Park
Derbyshire, Goyt Valley, Stand Wood, Upper Derwent Woodlands
Devon, Arlington, Burrator Wood, Dunsford Wood, Heddon Valley, Holne Woods(2), Parke Estate
Durham, Hamsterley Forest
Essex, Marks Hall Estate, Norsey Wood
Glamorgan Mid, Garwnant, Gethin Woodland Park
Glamorgan South, Cliff Wood,Cogan Wood
Glamorgan West, Afan Forest Park

Glos, Beechenhurst
Greater London, Hampstead Heath
Gwent, Craig Goch, Wentwood, Whitestone
Gwynedd, The Greenwood Centre, Newborough Forest
Hants & IOW, The New Forest, Queen Elizabeth Country Park
Hereford & Worcester, Queensland Country Park
Herts, The Bushes, Home Park
Humberside, Elsham Hall
Kent, Batfold Bushy & Kilnhouse Woods
Leics , Staunton Harold Estate Woodlands
Lincs, Hartsholme Country Park
Norfolk, Mannington Woods, Thetford Forest Park
Northants, Brigstock, Irchester Country Park, Salcey Forest, Wakerley Great Wood, The Wilderness-Boughton Park
Northumberland, Cragside, Wallington - East & West Woods
Notts, Bestwood Country Park,Harlow Wood , Rufford Country Park and Abbey, Sherwood Forest Country Park, Sherwood Pines Forest Park
Powys, Cnwch Wood
Shropshire, Haughmond Hill, Helmeth Wood
Somerset, Luccombe and Horner Plantations
Suffolk, Rendlesham Forest
Surrey,Alice Holt Forest, Box Hill, Winterfold Forest
Sussex East, Coneyburrow, Friston Forest, Wilderness Wood,
Sussex West, Borde Hill Gardens
Warwicks, Hartshill Hayes and St Lawrence's Wood
West Midlands, Saltwells Wood
Yorkshire - North, Clapdale, Dalby Forest, Duncombe Park, Hambleton Woods, Strid Wood
Yorkshire - South, Langsett Reservoir
Yorkshire - West, Coburn Hill Wood, Ox Close, St Ives Estate, Temple Newsam Estate

Cornwall, Cardinham Woods
Cumbria, Grizedale Forest Park, Mirehouse and Catstocks Wood, Talkin Wood, Whinlatter Forest Park
Devon, Abbeyford Woods, Arlington, Cookworthy Forest, Heathercombe Wood, Parke Estate, Salcombe Hill, Teign Valley Woods
Essex, Hatfield Forest, Marks Hall Estate
Glamorgan Mid, Garwnant
Glamorgan West, Afan Forest Park, Gelli-Hir Wood
Gwent, Cwmcarn Forest Drive, Whitestone
Gwynedd, Coed Cae Fali, Gwydyr Forest Park, Newborough Forest
Hereford & Worcester, Queensland Country Park
Humberside, Elsham Hall
Kent, Batfold, Bushy & Kilnhouse Woods, Toys Hill
Lancs, Roddlesworth & Tockholes Woods
Leics, Martinshaw Wood
Lincs, Bourne Wood Lincs, Hartsholme Country Park
Norfolk, Hockering,Honeypot Wood, Mannington Woods, Thetford Forest Park
Northants, Brigstock, Grafton Park , Irchester Country Park, Salcey Forest
Northumberland, Cragside, Wallington - East & West Woods
Notts, Sherwood Forest Country Park, Sherwood Pines Forest Park
Shropshire, Haughmond Hill, Mortimer Forest
Staffs, Dimmings Dale
Suffolk, Rendlesham Forest
Surrey, Alice Holt Forest, Box Hill, Leith Hill, Winterfold Forest, Witley Common
Sussex West, Burton Pond Woodlands, Slindon Woods
Warwicks, Clowes Wood, Snitterfield Bushes
Wilts, The Woodland Park
Yorkshire - North, Clapdale, Dalby Forest, Duncombe Park, Hambleton Woods, Strid Wood
Yorkshire - West, Chevin Forest Park, Coburn Hill Wood, Esholt Woods, Hardcastle Crags, Hirst Wood, Judy Woods, Newmillerdam Country Park, Northcliffe Wood, Ox Close, St Ives Estate

Woods with Trails for the Disabled

Berks, Rushall Woods
Bucks, Linford Wood
Cheshire, Little Budworth Country Park Woods, Risley Moss
Clwyd,Loggerheads Country Park

FORESTS FOR LEARNING

All the woods in this book offer opportunities for enjoyable learning. Those which make special provision for education and welcome school groups are shown as *Study Woods*. We hope that these will grow in number as the value of studying at first-hand in the forest becomes fully recognised. Many woodland parks and nature reserves are already used for teaching natural history. The Trust, however, is keen to demonstrate the particular excitement of using woods which produce timber and other forest products and are rich in wildlife and landscape. Such woodlands offer an even wider range of study topics which will appeal to children. They show how producing things that people need can - with skill - be integrated with conservation.

Topics immediately suggest themselves.

The variety of trees; how to recognise them; where they come from, both at home and abroad; trees and soil; trees and the weather; leaf shapes and textures; bark studies; how fast trees grow; how long they live; how they spread; how they die; what they provide for us like timber, paper, bark and resin...

Forests - how old are they; the forest in the past; the forest today; kinds of forest; how forests look; enter the forester; forest management; planting trees; caring for trees; felling trees; forest produce in the forest (gates, stiles, hides, bridges, bird boxes...); using wood; making paper...

Wildlife - forest ecology; what plants and animals can we find; where are they living; how are they suited to their habitats; food chains in the forest; birds of prey; forest deer; helping wildlife - unplanted areas, rides, streams, bat boxes, dead trees left...; the wildlife of broadleaved, conifer and mixed woodlands..

Inspiration - woodlands in words; photography in the woods; drawing and painting; music; sculpture; design and craftsmanship in wood...

The relevance of all of these - and many more - to the drier language of the school curriculum is obvious. Science, mathematics, geography, history, technology, economics and art can all be served by the experience of a well-managed multi-puprose forest environment.

Many of the individual study topics and attainment targets specified in the national curriculum and public examination syllabuses can be achieved with the help of the forest experience. Where better to undertake environmental education! Or teach field study skills.

The Trust - and many of the woodland owners featured in this book - want to help. At the listed *Study Woods* you will find trees being grown to produce timber and / or small forest produce and evidence of woodland management for conservation. There will be a variety of types and ages of tree and you will be able to see how felled trees are replaced by a new generation in accordance with the principle of sustainability. The owner, whether private or public, (notably Forest Enterprise), is keen to provide some opportunities for teachers to bring pupils to learn about the wood. Usually there will be either a self-guided trail, perhaps with explanatory posters provided by the Forestry Trust, or guided visits led by a forester or ranger. To make the visits as profitable as possible, teachers are encouraged to visit and discuss in advance so that the time can be spent as you decide. The forest is seen as an educational resource with learning programmes kept fully flexible to meet curricular needs. Obviously the input that a small private woodland owner can give will be less than organisations like Forest Enterprise and the National Trust where facilities - including study centres and lavatories - as well as educational staff will often be on hand. Look carefully at the individual entry in this book to see what may be available and the arrangements you need to make in advance of the visit.

Educational materials are vital for use both in the forest and in the classroom before and after. The range is increasing and you may well find a pack about the local forest, especially if it is well-known and publicly owned, already available locally. The Trust publishes educational materials itself and details of a few are given on page 258. Others are available from Forest Enterprise and the organisations listed on pages 266 - 267. Do contact the Trust for further help and information. We are here to assist teachers who are keen to take their pupils to learn from the forest environment.

FOR THE TEACHER
Preparing for a School Visit to a Study Wood

To ensure a successful and enjoyable study visit the secret is to **BE PREPARED**. The following points will help you with your advance preparation:

1. Contact the Forester and arrange to meet him/her for a preliminary visit, and/or invite him/her to talk to the pupils at the school.

2. Obtain from the Forestry Trust a copy of "YOUR LINK WOOD" and teaching materials appropriate to age and subject - if not held by the forester at your local wood.

3. Discuss the scope and objectives of the visit and obtain a map of the area and a plan of the wood showing all paths, rides, and details of forest plantations. (In the appropriate space in YOUR LINK WOOD note down any additional information about the wood provided by the Forester.)

4. Make a date and time for the visit and determine the duration and whether it will be a guided or a self-guided visit.

5. If a car/coach park is not available, arrange for a suitable site to park the vehicles adjacent to the wood.

6. Ascertain the proximity of WCs (if any).

7. Make visit preparations including the assembly of the following equipment: camera, compass, secateurs (for collecting specimens - consult Forester first), clipboard, notebook and pencil, metre rule, measuring tape, hand lens, light/temperature meter, quadrat, plastic container or bag for collecting specimens, suitable clothing and footwear.

8. Ascertain from the Forester which materials are suitable for collecting and taking back to the classroom.

9. Ensure that safety considerations have been fully addressed. The pupil to adult ratio should be as low as possible but should at the very least conform to LEA or school regulations. If unescorted, check with the Forester that there are no safety hazards (ie windblow, unsafe trees etc..)where you will be visiting. First aid kit should always be taken, not because the forest is inherently dangerous, but you will frequently be some distance from habitation should anyone require first aid. Finally check your school's liability insurance cover. Woodland owners should have liability to cover for most eventualities but the onus is on the visitor to take adequate steps to ensure that accidents that might subsequently be construed as the responsibility of the visitor do not carry financial penalties as well.

10. Allow sufficient time for study at the site(s). An overambitious programme will result in a route march to different areas with only superficial knowledge gained from each stop. A few well planned activities will always be preferable to many rushed ones - diversity and interest will come from unexpected discoveries as you walk through the wood.

Educational Materials

THE FORESTRY TRUST. The Forestry Trust produces a range of educational materials that are specifically geared for use on field visits to any working wood and forest. The principal publication, Your Link Wood, provides a template for all woodland study visits with detailed project work for Key Stages 1, 2 and 3 given in Trees and Leaves, Trees and Woodlands and Trees in the Forest respectively. Some of the woods in this book will have samples of these which you can see or they can be obtained from the Trust direct (all priced at £3 each except Trees in the Forest (£4). Please add £1.00 postage for orders under £5, £2.00 for orders under £10.00 and £3.00 for orders over £10. Cheques should be made payable to the Forestry Trust.

OTHER ORGANISATIONS

Many of the woods listed in the book have their own educational materials and some of the larger organisations whose addresses are given in Where to Find Out More produce education packs or programmes which can be used in the woods or on forest related studies. In the same way that our materials have a forestry emphasis they will tend to be geared to a different perspective of trees and forests. The Forest Enterprise, who are strong advocates of multi-purpose forestry publish a number of packs for their major forests. The National Trust is actively developing educational programmes for many of its properties including some which are woodlands. Other sources include the Wildlife Trusts, the Royal Society for the Protection of Birds and the Tree Council.

THE FOREST EDUCATION INITIATIVE

Together with the Forestry Authority, the Forestry Industry Committee of Great Britain and the Timber Trade Federation, the Forestry Trust is a founder member of the Forest Education Initiative which was formed in 1992 to bring together those who grow and use timber to increase young people's understanding of forestry, the forestry industry and the timber trade.

ⓘ Woods with Information Literature

Avon, Avon Gorge, Browns Folly
Beds, Maulden Wood
Berks, Baynes Reserve, Bowdown Woods, Moor Copse, Round Oak Piece, Swinley and Bagshot Forest
Bucks, Black Park Country Park, Bottom Wood, Dancersend, Finemere Wood, Gomm's Wood, Little Linford Wood, Millfield Wood, Rushbeds Wood
Cheshire, Church Wood & Clayhill Wood, Marbury Country Park Woods, Risley Moss, Stanney Wood
Cleveland, Thorpe Wood
Clwyd, Erddig Wood, Greenfield Valley Heritage Park, Loggerheads Country Park, Wepre Country Park
Cornwall, Cardinham Woods, Horse Wood, Mount Edgcumbe Country Park
Cumbria, Brigsteer Park, Grizedale Forest Park, Mirehouse and Catstocks Woods, Talkin Wood, Whinhill, Whinlatter Forest Park
Derbyshire, Goyt Valley, Linacre Woodlands, Longshaw Estate, Stand Wood, Upper Derwent Woodlands
Devon, Abbeyford Woods, Arlington, Cookworthy Forest, Dart Valley Woods, Dunsford Wood, Eggesford Woods, Heathercombe Wood, Heddon Valley, Knott's & Parsonage Woods, Marridge/Elberry/The Grove Woods, Parke Estate, Scadson / Ten Acre Brake, Teign Valley Woods, Torquay Coastal Woodlands, Watersmeet Wood
Dorset, Moors Valley Forest
Durham, Durham Riverbanks, Hamsterley Forest
Dyfed, Coed Penrhyn-Mawr, Dinas, Parc Natur Penglais, Poor Man's Wood
Essex, Belfairs, Marks Hall Estate
Glamorgan Mid, Garwnant, Gethin Woodland Park
Glamorgan South, Cogan Wood
Glamorgan West, Afan Forest Park
Glos, Midger, Owlpen Estate, Westonbirt Arboretum
Greater London, Fryent Country Park, Highgate Wood, Lesnes Abbey Wood, Sheen Common, Sydenham Hill Wood
Greater Manchester, Hulmes Wood
Gwent, The Buckholt, Craig Goch, Craig Syddi, Cwmcarn Forest Drive, Wentwood, Whitestone
Gwynedd, Coed Cae Fali, Coed Crafnant, Glan Faenol, The Greenwood Centre, Gwydyr Forest Park, Henllys Hall, Nantporth
Hants & IOW, The New Forest
Hereford & Worcester, Coedgwen, Langdale Wood & The Lills, Queenswood Country Park, Tiddesley Wood, Wyre Forest

Herts, The Bushes, Hardings, Home Park, Northaw Great Wood, Sherrardspark Woods, Wall Hall Estate Woods
Kent, Scotney Estate, Toys Hill
Lancs, Roddlesworth & Tockholes Woods
Leics, Burbage Wood and Sheepy Wood
Lincs, Bourne Wood, Chambers Farm Wood, Hartsholme Country Park, Park Gate Plantation
Norfolk, Ashwellthorpe Wood, Felbrigg Great Wood, Foxley Wood, Mannington Woods, Sandringham Country Park, Thetford Forest Park, Wolterton
Northants, Brigstock, Fineshade Wood, Irchester Country Park, Kings Wood, Rotary Wildlife Corridor, Salcey Forest, Short Wood, Wakerley Great Wood, The Wilderness - Boughton Park
Northumberland, Briarwood Banks, Chillingham Woods, Cragside, Priestclose Wood, Wallington, East & West Woods
Notts, Bestwood Country Park, Blidworth Woods Complex, Rufford Country Park and Abbey, Sherwood Forest Country Park, Sherwood Pines Forest Park,
Oxon, Cowleaze Wood, Foxholes, Warburg Reserve, Whitecross Green Wood
Powys, Cnwch Wood, Leighton Estate - Big Wood, Pwll y Wrach
Shropshire, Leaton Knolls, Mortimer Forest
Somerset, Combe Sydenham, Hadborough Plantation, Luccombe and Horner Plantations
Staffs, Cannock Forest, Coombes Valley
Suffolk, Bonny Wood, Bradfield Woods, Ickworth Estate, Rendlesham Forest, Wolves Wood
Surrey, Alice Holt Forest, Box Hill, Britty Wood, Leith Hill, Winterfold Forest, Witley Common
Sussex East, Coneyburrow, Morris's Wood, Wilderness Wood
Sussex West, Stansted Forest
Tyne & Wear, Gibside
Warwicks, Hartshill Hayes and St Lawrence's Wood, Ryton Wood, Snitterfield Bushes
West Midlands, Saltwells Wood
Wilts, Biss Wood, The Woodland Park, The Firs
Yorkshire - North, Clapdale, Dalby Forest, Duncombe Park, Hambleton Woods, Strid Wood, Swinsty Reservoir
Yorkshire - South, Ecclesall Woods, Langsett Reservoir
Yorkshire - West, Chevin Forest Park, Coburn Hill Wood, Hardcastle Crags, Haw Park Wood, Newmillerdam Country Park, St Ives Estate, Temple Newsam Estate

📖 Woods with Educational Materials

Avon, Rocks East Woodlands

Beds, Rowney Warren

Berks, Rushall Woods, Sulham Wood, Swinley and Bagshot Forest

Bucks, Black Park Country Park, Bottom Wood, Gomm's Wood, Hockeridge and Pancake Woods, Wendover Woodland Park

Cheshire, Risley Moss

Cleveland, Thorpe Wood

Clwyd, Loggerheads Country Park, Wepre Country Park

Cornwall, Mount Edgcumbe Country Park

Cumbria, Brundholme, Grizedale Forest Park, Talkin Wood, Whinhill, Whinlatter Forest Park

Derbyshire, Goyt Valley

Devon, Arlington, Cookworthy Forest, Heddon Valley

Dorset, Garston Wood, Moors Valley Forest

Durham, Hamsterley Forest, Hardwick Hall Fen Carr

Dyfed, Coed Penrhyn-Mawr, Parc Natur Penglais

Essex, Gernon Bushes, Hockley Woods, Marks Hall Estate, Stour Wood

Glamorgan Mid, Garwnant

Glamorgan South, Cogan Wood

Glamorgan West, Afan Forest Park

Gwent, Craig Goch, Cwmcarn Forest Drive, Wentwood

Gwynedd, The Greenwood Centre, Gwydyr Forest Park

Hants & IOW, Parkhurst - IOW, The New Forest

Hereford & Worcester, Queenswood Country Park, Wyre Forest

Herts, Broxbourne and Bencroft Woods, The Bushes, Home Park

Humberside, Elsham Hall

Kent, Batfold, Bushy & Kilnhouse Woods

Lancs, Roddlesworth & Tockholes Woods

Lincs, Chambers Farm Wood, Hartsholme Country Park, Park Gate Plantation

Merseyside, Acornfield Plantation, Halewood Triangle Country Park, Littlewood Community Wood

Norfolk, Mannington Woods, Sandringham Country Park, Thetford Forest Park

Northants, Brigstock, Irchester Country Park, Salcey Forest, Wakerley Great Wood, The Wilderness - Boughton Park

Northumberland, Cragside

Notts, Bestwood Country Park, Rufford Country Park and Abbey, Sherwood Forest Country Park, Sherwood

Pines Forest Park

Powys, Cnwch Wood

Shropshire, Leaton Knolls

Somerset, Combe Sydenham, Luccombe and Horner Plantations, Moor Wood

Staffs, Coombes Valley

Suffolk, Bonny Wood, Bradfield Woods, Dunwich Forest, Ickworth Estate, Rendlesham Forest, Tunstall Forest, Wolves Wood

Surrey, Alice Holt Forest, Box Hill, Winterfold Forest, Witley Common

Sussex East, Coneyburrow, Marline Wood, Wilderness Wood

West Midlands, Saltwells Wood

Yorkshire - North, Dalby Forest, Duncombe Park, Hambleton Woods, Strid Wood

Yorkshire - South, Cawthorne Park

Yorkshire - West, Bella Vista, Chevin Forest Park, Coburn Hill Wood, Temple Newsam Estate

🌳 Woods with Self Guided Trails

Avon, Rocks East Woodlands

Beds, Maulden Wood, Rowney Warren

Berks, Round Oak Piece, Rushall Woods, Swinley and Bagshot Forest,

Bucks, Black Park Country Park, Common Wood, Dancersend, Gomm's Wood, Hockeridge and Pancake Woods, Howe Park Wood, Little Linford Wood, Millfield Wood, Wendover Woodland Park

Cheshire, Delamere Forest Park, Risley Moss

Cleveland, Thorpe Wood

Clwyd, Clocaenog Forest, Coed Nant Gain, Erddig Wood,Greenfield Valley Heritage Park, Loggerheads Country Park, Moel Famau,Wepre Country Park

Cornwall, Cardinham Woods, Costislost & Polgeel Woods, Horse Wood, Idless Woods, Trelowarren

Cumbria, Brigsteer Park, Brundholme, Ennerdale Forest, Giggle Alley, Grizedale Forest Park, Mirehouse and Catstocks Woods, Rainsbarrow, Talkin Wood, Whinlatter Forest Park

Derbyshire, Black Rocks, Goyt Valley, Snake Plantation, Stand Wood, Whitwell Wood

Devon, Abbeyford Woods, Arlington, Buzzards, Cookworthy Forest, Eggesford Woods, Harcombe Estate, Heathercombe Wood, Heddon Valley, Hembury Wood, Holne Wood(1), Lydford Wood, Marridge/Elberry/The Grove Woods, Occombe Wood, Parke Estate, Pool Down Wood, Salcombe Hill, Scadson / Ten Acre Brake, Teign Valley Woods, Torquay Coastal Woodlands, Watersmeet Wood

Durham, Hamsterley Forest

Dyfed, Coed Penrhyn-Mawr, Dinas, Parc Natur Penglais, Poor Man's Wood

Essex, Belfairs, Broads Walk, Chalkney Wood, Hatfield Forest, Hockley Woods, Marks Hall Estate

Glamorgan Mid, Garwnant, Gelliwion Wood, Gethin Woodland Park

Glamorgan South, Cliff Wood

Glamorgan West, Afan Forest Park, Gelli-Hir Wood

Glos, Nagshead Nature Reserve

Greater London, Chalk Wood, Sydenham Hill Wood

Gwent, Buckholt, The, Craig Goch, Cwmcarn Forest Drive, Parkwood, Wentwood, Whitestone,Wyndcliff

Gwynedd, Coed Cae Fali, Glan Faenol, Glasfryn Forestry Estate, Greenwood Centre, The, Gwydyr Forest Park, Henllys Hall, Newborough Forest

Hants & IOW, Mottisfont Woods, Queen Elizabeth Country Park

Hereford & Worcester, Coedgwen, Garnons Hill Wood, Langdale Wood & The Lills, Queenswood Country Park

Herts, Broxbourne and Bencroft Woods, Bullens Green Wood, Bushes, The, Home Park

Humberside, Elsham Hall

Kent, Batfold, Bushy & Kilnhouse Woods, Blean Woods Nature Reserve, Kings Wood, Orlestone Forest, Toys Hill

Lancs, Gisburn Forest, Roddlesworth & Tockholes Woods,

Lincs, Bourne Wood, Chambers Farm Wood, Hartsholme Country Park, Ostlers Plantation, Ropsley Rise Wood

Norfolk, Felbrigg Great Wood, Horsford Wood, Mannington Woods, Sandringham Country Park, Thetford Forest Park,

Northants, Brigstock, Irchester Country Park, Rotary Wildlife Corridor, Wakerley Great Wood,Wilderness, Boughton Park, The

Northumberland, Allen Banks/Staward Gorge, Briarwood Banks, Chillingham Woods, Cragside, Kielder Forest, Priestclose Wood, Wallington, East & West Woods

Notts, Bestwood Country Park, Blidworth Woods Complex, Harlow Wood, Rufford Country Park and Abbey, Sherwood Forest Country Park, Sherwood Pines Forest Park,

Oxon, Cowleaze Wood, Shabbington Wood

Powys, Cnwch Wood, Penygarreg Wood, Pwll y Wrach

Shropshire, Bury Ditches, Edge Wood, Haughmond Hill, Mortimer Forest,

Somerset, Combe Sydenham, Great Wood, Luccombe and Horner Plantations

Staffs, Big Wood, Black Firs, Cannock Forest, Coombes Valley, Dimmings Dale, Jacksons Bank

Suffolk, Bradfield Woods, Dunwich Forest, Ickworth Estate, Rendlesham Forest, Tunstall Forest, Wolves Wood

Surrey, Alice Holt Forest, Box Hill, Britty Wood, Hindhead, Leith Hill, Witley Common

Sussex East, Abbots Wood, Coneyburrow, Friston Forest, Marline Wood, Morris's Wood, Wilderness Wood

Sussex West, Blackdown, Borde Hill Gardens, Gravetye, St Leonard's Forest

Tyne & Wear, Chopwell Woodland Park, Gibside

Warwicks, Hartshill Hayes and St Lawrence's Wood, Rough Hill Wood, Snitterfield Bushes, **Wiltshire**, Firs, The, Witham Park Woods

Yorkshire - North, Clapdale, Dalby Forest, Duncombe Park, Hambleton Woods, Langdale Forest, Newtondale, Sneaton Forest, Strid Wood

Yorkshire - South, Cawthorne Park, Langsett Reservoir

Yorkshire - West, Chevin Forest Park, Coburn Hill Wood, Haw Park Wood, West Hirst Wood, tJudy Woods, Middleton Wood, Northcliffe Wood, St Ives Estate, Temple Newsam Estate

↑ **Woods with Guided Walks**

Avon, Rocks East Woodlands

Beds, Maulden Wood

Berks,Bowdown Woods, Moor Copse, Round Oak Piece, Rushall Woods, Ufton Park

Bucks,Black Park Country Park, Bottom Wood, Dancersend, Finemere Wood, Gomm's Wood, Little Linford Wood, Millfield Wood, Priestfield Arboretum, Rushbeds Wood, Wendover Woodland Park

Cambs, Bedford Purlieus, Lady's Wood, Lower Wood, Raveley Wood, Waresley Wood

Cheshire, Church Wood & Clayhill Wood, Risley Moss, Stanney Wood

Cleveland, Errington Wood,Guisborough Forest, Thorpe Wood

Clwyd, Coed Nant Gain, Llandegla, Wepre Country Park

Cornwall, Horse Wood, Mount Edgcumbe Country Park

Cumbria, Bryerswood Woodlands, Grizedale Forest Park, Talkin Wood

Derbyshire, Norbury Estate Woodlands

Devon, Burrator Wood, Eastcottdown Plantation, Heath Wood, Heathercombe Wood, Heddon Valley, Holne Woods(2), Knott's & Parsonage Woods, Lukesland Cleave, Marridge/Elberry/The Grove Woods, Occombe Wood, Pool Down Wood, Roadford Lake Woods, Scadson / Ten Acre Brake, Tavistock Woodlands, Torquay Coastal Woodlands, Whitehills Plantation, Wray Cleave

Dorset, Garston Wood

Durham, Hamsterley Forest, West Plantation

Dyfed,Coed Penrhyn-Mawr, Coed Rhyal, Parc Natur Penglais

Essex, Belfairs, Broads Walk, Chalkney Wood, Epping Forest, Marks Hall Estate, Norsey Wood,Stour Wood

Glamorgan Mid, Llanharan Wood

Glamorgan South, Cliff Wood

Glos, Midger

Greater London, Fryent Country Park, Hampstead Heath, Greater London, Highgate Wood, Sydenham Hill Wood

Greater Manchester, Hulmes Wood

Gwent, Cwm, Cwm Merddog, Parkwood

Gwynedd, Crafnant, Cwm Mynach, Glasfryn Forestry Estate, Greenwood Centre, The, Nantporth

Hants & IOW, Borthwood Copse, Mottisfont Woods, Queen Elizabeth Country Park

Hereford & Worcester, Coedgwen, Langdale Wood

& The Lills, Queenswood Country Park, Whitfield Woods

Herts, Broxbourne and Bencroft Woods, Bullens Green Wood, Wall Hall Estate Woods

Humberside, Allerthorpe Wood, Elsham Hall

Lancs, Witchwood

Lincs, Chambers Farm Wood, Hartsholme Country Park

Norfolk, Felbrigg Great Wood, Horsford Wood, Mannington Woods, Thetford Forest Park, Warren

Northants, Brigstock, Drayton Estate Woodlands, Fineshade Wood, Irchester Country Park, Salcey Forest, Wakerley Great Wood

Northumberland, Allen Banks/Staward Gorge, Briarwood Banks, Cragside, Priestclose Wood

Notts, Bestwood Country Park, Rufford Country Park and Abbey, Sherwood Forest Country Park, Sherwood Pines Forest Park

Oxon, Warburg Reserve, Whitecross Green Wood,

Powys, Ackers Grove, PowysCnwch Wood,Craigfryn Caeau-Bach Wood, Penygarreg Wood

Shropshire, Bury Ditches, Haughmond Hill, Leaton Knolls, Mortimer Forest

SomersetBittiscombe

Staffs, Somerford, Stafford Plantation, Shugborough Park

Suffolk, Bradfield Woods, Dunwich Forest, Rendlesham Forest, Sudbourne, Theberton Woods, Tunstall Forest, Wolves Wood

Surrey, Ashtead Common, Box Hill, Hindhead, Leith Hill, Ranmore, Winterfold Forest, Witley Common

Sussex East, Blackdown Wood, Coneyburrow, Friston Forest, Wilderness Wood

Sussex West, Blackdown, Rabbit Warren, Slindon Woods

Tyne & Wear, Gibside

Warwicks, Claywood, Hartshill Hayes and St Lawrence's Wood, Rough Hill Wood, Ryton Wood, Snitterfield Bushes

West Midlands, Saltwells Wood

Wilts, Great Combe, Jack's Castle

Yorkshire - North, Bishopswood, Broxa Forest, Dalby Forest, Hambleton Woods, Hovingham High, Langdale Forest, Sneaton Forest

Yorkshire - South, Cawthorne Park

Yorkshire - West, Chevin Forest Park, Coburn Hill Wood, Esholt Woods, Hardcastle Crags, Hirst Wood, Judy Woods, Middleton Wood, Northcliffe Wood, Park Wood, St Ives Estate, Temple Newsam Estate

* Study Woods

Avon, Rocks East Woodlands

Beds, Maulden Wood, Park Wood,

Berks, Ashley Hill, Bearwood, Fencewood, Round Oak Piece, Rushall Woods, Swinley and Bagshot Forest, Ufton Park

Bucks, Bottom Wood, Cockshoots, Hockeridge and Pancake Woods, Howe Park Wood, Pavis Wood, Wendover Woodland Park

Cambs, Perry Woods

Cheshire, Delamere Forest Park, Little Budworth Country Park Woods, Marbury Country Park Woods, Riseley Moss

Cleveland, Gisborough Woods, Guisborough Forest

Clwyd, Coed Nant Gain

Cornwall, Cardinham Woods, Horse Wood, Trelowarren

Cumbria, Beacon Wood, Brundholme, Grizedale Forest Park, Mirehouse and Catstocks Woods, Whinlatter Forest Park

Derbyshire, Stand Wood

Devon, Bovey Donn & Bovey Warren, Cookworthy Forest, Eastcottdown Plantation, Gatherley North, Gatherley South, Harpford Wood, Heath Wood, Heathercombe Wood, Hillersdon Woods, Holne Woods(2), Huntshaw, Kedworthy Wood, Kennerleigh Wood, Kiddens Wood - Bullers Hill, Knott's & Parsonage Woods, Lukesland Cleave, Pool Down Wood, Quicke Estate Woodlands, Riding Parks and Lawelldown Woods, Shute Hill, Townleigh Wood, West Bowerland, Whitehills Plantation

Dorset, Belstone, Warren and Chaffins Copse, Hooke Park, Moors Valley Forest, Slepe Wood, Stony Down, Wareham Forest

Durham, Hamsterley Forest, West Plantation

Essex, Hockley Woods, Marks Hall Estate, Norsey Wood, Stour Wood

Glamorgan Mid, Llanharan Wood

Glamorgan West, Afan Forest Park

Glos, Beechenhurst, Broomhill, Miserden Estate Woodlands, Newent Woods, Owlpen Estate,Queen's Wood - Southam

Greater London, Fryent Country Park

Gwent, Buckholt, The, Craig Goch, Cwm, Parkwood, Penyclawdd

Gwynedd, Coed Llyn y Garnedd, Coed y Brenin Forest Park, Cwm Mynach, Glasfryn Forestry Estate,Gwydyr Forest Park

Hants & IOW, Ashridge, Benyons Inclosure, New Forest, Pamber, Phrympth Wood, Queen Elizabeth Country Park

Hereford & Worcester, Garnons Hill Wood, Kiln Ground Wood, Langdale Wood & The Lills, Monk Wood, Monnington Wood, Nunnery Wood, Queenswood Country Park, Tedstone Court, Whitfield Woods, Wyre Forest

Herts, Broxbourne and Bencroft Woods, Bullens Green Wood, Hardings, Monken Hadley Common, Tring Park Estate, Wall Hall Estate Woods

Kent, Batfold, Bushy & Kilnhouse Woods, Blean Woods Nature Reserve, Cutlers Wood, Hemsted Forest

Lincs, Bourne Wood, Park Gate Plantation

Norfolk, Sandringham Country Park, Thetford Forest Park, Weasenham Azalea Wood,

Northants, Fineshade Wood, Grafton Park, Irchester Country Park, Salcey Forest

Northumberland, Chillingham Woods, Cragside, Harwood, Kielder Forest, Kyloe

Notts,Sherwood Pines Forest Park

Oxon, Blenheim Estates

Powys, Ackers Grove, Cefnllysgwynne Estate, Craigfryn Caeau-Bach Wood, Held Wood. Trallwm Forest

Shropshire, Edge Woods, Leaton Knolls

Somerset, Bittiscombe, Combe Sydenham, Dunster Wood, Hadborough Plantation, Moor Wood

Staffs, Cannock Forest, Jacksons Bank

Suffolk, Bradfield Woods NNR, Dunwich Forest, Rendlesham Forest, Sudbourne, Theberton Woods, Tunstall Forest

Surrey, Alice Holt Forest, Britty Wood, Nower Wood, Winterfold Forest

Sussex East, Coney Burrow, Friston Forest, Mansers Shaw, Morris's Wood, Wilderness Wood

Sussex West, Rabbit Warren, Stansted Forest

Tyne & Wear, Chopwell Woodland Park

Warwicks, Claywood, Clowes Wood, Rough Hill Wood, Ryton Wood, Saltwells Wood, Snitterfield Bushes

Wilts, Clarendon Park Estate, The Firs, Great Combe, Great Wood, Grittenham, Jack's Castle, Swancombe Wood, Witham Park, Woodland Park, The

Yorkshire - North, Clapdale, Dalby Forest, Duncombe Park, Hovingham High, Levisham Wood

Yorkshire - South, Cawthorne Park

Yorkshire - West, Chevin Forest Park, Coburn Hill Wood, Temple Newsam Estate

READ ALL ABOUT IT

To make all your forest visits more enjoyable and to extend your knowledge of trees and woodlands here are some books you may like to look at. Your local library will be pleased to help you obtain your chosen titles.

IDENTIFYING TREES

Allen J Coombes   Trees. Dorling Kindersley Eyewitness Handbook. 1992
E H M Harris (Ed)   Field Guide to the Trees and Shrubs of Britain. Reader's Digest. 1988
A Mitchell   Field Guide to the Trees of Britain & Europe. Collins
K Rushforth   The Mitchell Beazley pocket guide to Trees. 1986
Forestry Commission   Broadleaves (Booklet 20) & Conifers (Booklet 15)

MAINLY FOR CHILDREN

D Bellamy   Bellamy's Changing World : The Forest. Macdonald
D Burnie   Eyewitness Guides : Tree. Dorling Kindersley
L Gamlin   Eyewitness Explorer : Trees. Dorling Kindersley. 1993
T Greenaway   Look Closer Tree Life. Dorling Kindersley. 1992
E H M Harris (Ed)   Nature Trail Book of Trees & Leaves; Nature Trail Book of Woodland; Spotter's guide to Woodland Life; Spotter's Guide to Trees; and First Book of Nature: Trees. Usborne.
R Lewington & D Streeter   The Natural History of the Oak Tree. Dorling Kindersley and The National Trust. 1993
R Mabey   Oak and Company.   Kestrel.
Forestry Commission   The Forest Adventure Pack for Teachers of children aged 8-14 years.

READING AT LEISURE

S Dalton   The Secret Life of an Oakwood. Century
H Edlin   Trees, Woods and Man. Collins
H Edlin   Illustrated Encyclopaedia of Trees, Timber and Forests of the World.
E H M Harris & J Harris   Wildlife Conservation in Managed Woodlands & Forests. Blackwell
N D G James   The Forester's Companion. Blackwell
ND G James   A History of English Forests. Blackwell. 1990
H Johnson   Encyclopaedia of Trees. Mitchell Beazley

G L Jones & R Mabey   The Wildwood: In search of Britain's Ancient Forests. Arum Press. 1993.
P Marren   Woodland Heritage. David & Charles. 1990
J E Milner   The Tree Book. Acacia & Channel 4.
O Rackham   Illustrated History of the British Countryside. Weidenfeld & Nicholson 1994
O Rackham   Trees & Woodland in the British Landscape. Dent
C Watkins   Woodland Management & Conservation. David & Charles
P Wood (Ed)   The Tree. David & Charles and the Woodland Trust

DEER IN THE FOREST

R Prior   Trees & Deer. Swan Hill Press. 1994
Publications from the British Deer Society and the Mammal Society

GUIDES & WALKS

M Allaby   The Woodland Trust Book of British Woodlands. David & Charles
D Bellamy   Woodland Walks. Hamlyn and the RSNC
P Marren   The Wildwoods: a Regional Guide. David & Charles. 1992
National Trust   The Countryside Handbook. NT Publication
C Wilkinson   Woodland Walks. Webb & Bower
Woodland Trust Visitors Guide to Woodland Trust Woods

There are also many publications about individual forests and woodland walks that you will find in local bookshops, forest centres and Tourist Information Centres.

WOODLAND MANAGEMENT TITLES

The Forestry Commission publishes a wealth of interesting books and pamphlets on aspects of forest management. Some are technical but you may like to look at the Guidelines series which are attractively illustrated. Titles include: Nature Conservation: Recreation: Landscape and Water. The Wildlife Rangers Handbook and the Guides to major forests will also be of interest.

WHERE TO FIND OUT MORE

ARBORICULTURAL ASSOCIATION
Ampfield House, Ampfield, ROMSEY, Hants SO51 9PA
01794 68717

ARBORICULTURAL ADVISORY AND INFOR-MATION SERVICE
Forest Research Station, Alice Holt Lodge, Wreccle-sham, FARNHAM, Surrey GU10 4LH
01420 22022

ASSOCIATION OF PROFESSIONAL FOREST-ERS
7/9 West Street, BELFORD, Northumberland NE70 7QA
01668 213937

BRITISH TRUST FOR CONSERVATION VOL-UNTEERS
36 St Mary's Street, WALLINGFORD, Oxon OX10 0EU
01491 839766

BRITISH DEER SOCIETY
Beale Centre, Lower Basildon, READING, Berks RG7 5DZ
01734 844094

COED CYMRU
The Old Sawmill, Tregynon, NEWTOWN, Powys SY16 3PL
01686 650777

COUNCIL FOR THE PROTECTION OF RU-RAL ENGLAND
25 Buckingham Palace Road, London SW1
0171 976 6433

CAMPAIGN FOR THE PROTECTION OF RURAL WALES
Ty Gwyn, 31 High Street, WELSHPOOL, Powys SY21 7JP
01938 552525

COUNTRY LANDOWNERS ASSOCIATION
16 Belgrave Square, LONDON SW1X 8PQ
0171 235 0511

THE COUNTRY TRUST
Stratford Grange, Stratford St Andrew, SAXMUND-HAM, Suffolk IP17 1LF
01728 604818

COUNTRYSIDE COMMISSION
John Dower House, Crescent Place, CHELTENHAM, Glos GL50 3RA
01242 521381

COUNTRYSIDE COUNCIL FOR WALES
Plas Penrhos, Ffordd Penrhos, BANGOR, Gwynedd LL57 2LQ
01248 370444

COUNTRYSIDE RECREATION NETWORK
Department of City & Regional Planning, University of Wales College of Cardiff, PO Box 906, CARDIFF CF1 3YN
01222 874970

THE DENDROLOGIST
PO Box 341, CHESHAM, Bucks HP5 2RD
01494 784888

ENGLISH NATURE
Northminster House, Northminster Road, PETER-BOROUGH, Cambs PE1 1UA
01733 340345

ENGLISH TOURIST BOARD
Thames Tower, Blacks Road, LONDON W6 9EL
0181 846 9000

FORESTRY COMMISSION / FORESTRY AU-THORITY / FOREST ENTERPRISE
231 Corstorphine Road, EDINBURGH EH12 7AT
0131 334 0303

FOREST EDUCATION INITIATIVE
c/o Forestry Authority England, Great Eastern House, Tenison Road,, CAMBRIDGE, Cambs CB1 2DU
01223-314546

FORESTRY TRUST FOR CONSERVATION AND EDUCATION
The Old Estate Office, Englefield Road, Theale, READING, Berks RG7 5DZ
01734 323523

FORESTS FOREVER CAMPAIGN / TIMBER TRADE FEDERATION
4th Floor, Clareville House, 26/27 Oxendon Street, LONDON SW1Y 4EL
0171 839 1891

INSTITUTE OF CHARTERED FORESTERS
7a St Colme Street, EDINBURGH EH3 6AA
0131 225 2705

INTERNATIONAL TREE FOUNDATION
Sandy Lane, CRAWLEY DOWN, W Sussex RH10 4HS
01342 712536

THE NATIONAL FOREST
Stanleigh House, Chapel Street, Donisthorpe, SWADLINCOTE, Derbyshire DE12 7PS
01530 273816

NATIONAL SMALL WOODS ASSOCIATION
Hall Farm House, Preston Capes, Northants
01327 36387

NATIONAL TRUST
36 Queen Anne's Gate, LONDON SW1H 9AS
0171 222 9251

PARNHAM TRUST
Parnham House, BEAMINSTER, Dorset DT8 3NA
01308 862204

RAMBLERS' ASSOCIATION
1-5 Wandsworth Road, LONDON SW8 2XX
0171 582 6878

ROYAL FORESTRY SOCIETY OF ENGLAND, WALES AND NORTHERN IRELAND
102 High Street, TRING, Herts HP23 4AH
01442 822028

ROYAL SCOTTISH FORESTRY SOCIETY
62 Queen Street, EDINBURGH EH2 4NA
0131 225 8142

ROYAL SOCIETY FOR THE PROTECTION OF BIRDS
The Lodge, SANDY, Beds SG19 2DL
01767 680551

TIMBER GROWERS ASSOCIATION
5 Dublin Street Lane South, EDINBURGH EH1 3PX
0131 557 0944

TREE AID
Room 1B, Temple House, Temple Street, Keynsham, BRISTOL, Avon BS18 1EJ
01272 860662

THE TREE COUNCIL
35 Belgrave Square, LONDON SW1X 8QN
0171 235 8854

TREE LINK
Ardmore House, 11-15 High Street, MARLOW-on-THAMES, Bucks
01628 890060

WALES TOURIST BOARD
Brunel House, 2 Fitzalan Road, CARDIFF, S Glam CF2 1UY
01222 499909

THE WILDLIFE TRUSTS
The Green, Waterside South, LINCOLN, Lincs LN5 7JR
01522 544400

WOODLAND HERITAGE MUSEUM
Brokerswood, WESTBURY, Wilts BA13 4EH
01373 823880

WOODLAND TRUST
Autumn Park, Dysart Road, GRANTHAM, Lincs NG31 6LL
01476 74297

WORLDWIDE FUND FOR NATURE
Panda House, Weyside Park, GODALMING, Surrey GU17 1XR
01483 426444

BSB

HOLDINGS (CUDWORTH) LTD.

18 Lancaster Street, Barnsley S70 6DX.

Telephone: 01226-242069 or 295197
Fax: 01226-244283

THE ROYAL FORESTRY SOCIETY
of England, Wales and Northern Ireland

Do you care about trees?

We do!

Joining the Royal Forestry Society is an excellent idea for all who care about trees, their husbandry and their future. For over a century the RFS has spread knowledge about trees, woodlands and forests, and encouraged the multi-purpose, sustainable management of this vital renewable natural resource.

What is the Royal Forestry Society?

It is
- ✦ an independent registered charity founded in 1882;
- ✦ the largest forestry association in Britain with over 4000 members;
- ✦ a broad-based body with open membership bringing together thinking people interested in trees, both **professional and amateur**;
- ✦ a way of learning more about trees and woodlands;
- ✦ a body which believes that tree resources are best conserved and extended through wise management compatible with wildlife, landscape and recreation considerations.

What are the benefits for members?

You can
- ✦ go to local national **field meetings** (over 70 each year) held in a variety of woods, forests and arboreta;
- ✦ meet and exchange news and views with other enthusiasts;
- ✦ attend **RFS symposia** with expert speakers on tree topics;
- ✦ read and understand more about trees, woodland and forests through our **Quarterly Journal of Forestry** (free to members);
- ✦ participate in our annual week-long **study tour** in the UK;
- ✦ join our **visits to other countries** to discover how their woods work;
- ✦ enjoy our famous redwood grove and pinetum at **Leighton** and our demonstration wood at **Hockeridge**;
- ✦ consult our extensive **library**;
- ✦ help influence Britain's policies on wooded environments.

What wider role does the RFS play?

We   ✧ founded the **Forestry Trust for Conservation and Education**

✧ take every opportunity to increase knowledge and appreciation of trees;

✧ participate on influential environmental boards, education committees and safety councils, both locally and nationally;

✧ conduct arboricultural examinations;

✧ conceived and run the **Duke of Cornwall's Award for Forestry and Conservation;**

✧ support **Tree Aid** in the Sahel;

✧ use our mixed Chiltern woodland at **Hockeridge** for practical demonstration purposes;

✧ comment and advise, as a well-informed and impartial NGO, on environmental policies and practices involving trees.

How can I join?

Simply complete the application slip and send it with your cheque to:
The Director, The Royal Forestry Society, 102 High Street, Tring, Herts. HP23 4AF. Why not act now?

1995 subscription rates: **Individuals** - £22 (concessionary rate of £11 available to students and OAP's); **corporate bodies £66; a half year's payment is acceptable after 1st July.**

What happens then?

We will send your membership pack and the address of your local RFS secretary who will keep you informed about events near you.

We look forward to welcoming you.

— —

Membership Application

Name _____

Address _____

_____

Post Code _____ **Membership category** _____

Any special interests _____

I wish to become a member of The Royal Forestry Society and enclose a cheque for £.............

Signature _____ **Date** _____

THE FORESTRY TRUST
FOR CONSERVATION AND EDUCATION

The Trust, a registered charity, was established by the Royal Forestry Society of England, Wales & Northern Ireland in 1988. Its aim is "to advance the education of the public (including those engaged in forestry or silviculture) by the creation of wider public appreciation of the role and importance of productive forestry, the promotion of a greater public understanding of silviculture and forestry management, and the demonstration that productive forestry is compatible with the conservation of wildlife and enhancement of the landscape."

This book is the basic building block for the Trust's work. We aim to promote formal and informal education and enjoyment through the generosity of woodland owners who make their woods available for study and exploration, and through the provision of educational materials for use both in the forest and classroom.. The woodlands listed in this book vary greatly. Not all produce timber. Some may be entirely unmanaged and left to nature. Whilst there will be occasions where this is the appropriate treatment, the Trust encourages forest and woodland managers to exploit every opportunity to combine conservation with timber production and recreation to create a truly multi-purpose forest. Our resources are used for forest education in this country. As and when the Trust's funds allow, any surplus will be directed towards projects that promote sustainable forest management in this country and abroad provided these are based on the compatibility of timber production and wildlife conservation..

Membership. The Trust is launching its membership scheme in 1995. Open to all, this includes for £10 per annum, in addition to a copy of *Woodlands to Visit in England and Wales*, 2 newsletters, up to 12 information sheets on forestry conservation topics, a calendar of events, a publications list and membership card. Family or corporate membership is £1 for every extra family or staff member for which an additional members card will be issued. Most importantly, however, by becoming a member you will help to promote the work of the Trust. Please turn to the last page in this book for the membership form. Requests for a publications list should be accompanied by a stamped addressed envelope.

FORESTRY TRUST STAFF

Chairman
BN Howell MA MICFor
Trustees
His Grace the Duke of Somerset FRICS (Chairman designate)
IH Branton OBE (Deputy Chairman)
EHM Harris BSc FICFor MIBiol
I Mercer BA
Rachel Thomas BA FRGS
MC Webb BA FCA (Hon Treasurer)
Ex Officio Trustee
CR Woosnam CBE BA FRICS (Vice President of the Royal Forestry Society)

Trust Secretary CRL Gray MIMgt
Educational Adviser WO Copland BSc
Solicitor Capt JD Hope RN
Auditors Evans Rankin, 20-22 Bedford Row, LONDON WC1R 4ER
Bankers Lloyds Bank, 1 Market Place, READING, Berks RG1 2EQ

Editorial Team - Woodlands to Visit in England and Wales 1995
Co-Editors Charles Gray and Bill Copland
Compilation Pamela Stratford
Cover Illustration Forestry Commission
Printers Severn Print, Ashville Industrial Estate, Bristol Road, GLOUCESTER, Glos GL2 6EV
Distributors Springfield Books, Norman Road, Denby Dale, HUDDERSFIELD, W Yorks HD8 8TH

Thanks are also due to the following for assistance in compiling data for the book, identifying contacts to include in it, to support it and to sell it and for helping with a myriad of connected tasks; Mark Sixsmith, John Tanner, Gordon Robertson, John Stratford, William Stewart, Annabelle and Henry Gray.

Trust offices The Forestry Trust for Conservation and Education, The Old Estate Office, Englefield Road, Theale, READING, Berks RG7 5DZ
Telephone 01734 323523 Registered Charity 327856

SUPPORTERS OF THE FORESTRY TRUST

HM THE QUEEN
The Royal Forestry Society of England Wales and Northern Ireland
Countryside Commission
Countryside Council for Wales
Forestry Authority

Arjo Wiggins
Associated Newspapers plc
Association of Professional Foresters
BSW Sawmills
Barclays Bank
Bernard Sunley Charitable Foundation
The Boots Co plc
Cawthorne Park Woodlands
The Chatsworth Settlement
CLA Charitable Trust
Coutts Bank
Donald Randle Charitable Trust
Dulverton Trust
Englefield Charitable Trust
English China Clays
Ernest Cook Trust
Esmee Fairbairn Trust
Esso UK plc
Fountain Forestry
Game Fair Committee
Gerald Palmer Trust
Golden Bottle Trust
Green Scene
John S Cohen Foundation
Leopold de Rothschild Charitable Trust
Lloyds Bank plc
McRobert Trusts
Marks and Spencer plc
Mitsubishi UK
National Westminster Bank plc
Nextbase
Nicholson Nurseries
Norwich Union Life Insurance Group
Pitney Bowes plc
Plessey Pension Trust Ltd
Provincial Insurance
Prudential
Pye Settlement
Refuge Assurance
Ronaash Ltd
NM Rothschild & Son Ltd

Royal Bank of Scotland
Shotton Paper Company plc
Smallwood
Smith Kline Beecham plc
Tilhill Nurseries
United Newspapers plc
University College of North Wales
Watts Blake, Bearne & Co plc
Whitaker Charitable Trust
WH Smith Ltd
Willis Faber
Woodland Improvements
Yattendon Estates Ltd
Yorkshire Agricultural Society
Yorkshire Electricity

All the above organisations have made recent significant donations or contributed generously or consistently to the Trust during the last five and a half years. For the first time this year we are not listing our individual supporters. It would be invidious to acknowledge some and not all, many of whom wish to remain anonymous or, whilst making a contribution below an arbitrary limit, have made proportionately large donations in relation to their wealth. Without their help this book would not have been possible. To all of them the Trust remains deeply indebted.

Finally these acknowledgements would not be complete without thanking the woodland owners who have agreed to list their woods in this book. In particular those members of the Royal Forestry Society of England, Wales and Northern Ireland and of the Timber Growers Association and other private owners for whom there is no personal benefit in making this offer and often considerable cost. As the years go by we hope that their number will increase significantly, thereby spreading the burden between owners, and the opportunities for visitors to enjoy and appreciate the many values of our woods and forests.

This book was first produced in a pilot version in 1993. It has been extensively revised and added to both in 1994 and 1995 but we would welcome any suggestions for improvements, whilst bearing in mind that changes are likely to be evolutionary and dependent on the limited budget at the disposal of the Forestry Trust.

In order to cater for a wide range of interests it will not be possible to tailor this book to everyone's liking but we would ask you to give your name, address and specific interest in woodland so we can provide a balance for all interest groups.

Most woodland owners know what is growing and/or breeding in their woods but would welcome specialist information, constructive suggestions and visitors views. We will pass these on. For detailed comments please contact the owners or managers direct.

Your views and knowledge can help us and them to address your concerns, to enhance your visit and to assist owners in balancing the many demands of woodland management..

Please give your general comments on the book on this side and use the reverse for comments on individual woods / entries.

WOODLANDS TO VISIT IN ENGLAND AND WALES 1995 - READERS AND VISITORS COMMENTS

Comments on the Book:

1. Content

2. Accuracy

3. Style

4. More Information on:

5. Less Information on:

6. Other Comments:

Your Name and Address (or Tel No) - (BLOCK CAPITALS):

Your Specific Interest in Woodland / Preferences

The Forestry Trust

Comments on Woods:

A. Names of Woods (as in book - including County)

1.

2.

3.

4.

5.

B. Comments on Entry (Directions, facilities, description)

1.

2.

3.

4.

5.

C. Other Comments

1.

2.

3.

4.

5.

276

Please cut down the dotted line and send your completed form to the Forestry Trust. It would be a great help if you could send this form to the Trust by no later than 31 October or after you have recorded details of 5 woods, whichever is the earlier. This will allow us to liaise with owners and make any amendments for the 1996 book

<u>*For You Own Record:*</u>

Date Sent:

Remarks:

Owners

We are seeking to increase the number of woodlands included in the book substantially for 1996. Any woodland that offers some level of access or educational opportunities will be welcome but we place particular emphasis on those which are managed for timber production and wildlife conservation.

Some degree of access, controlled or otherwise, is implicit in inclusion in the book and the more woodland owners who subscribe to the scheme the more readily the load can be shared by all. If you own or manage a wood, preferably in excess of 10 hectares, that subscribes to these principles and share our belief in the wider understanding and enjoyment of our forests being in the nation's interests please send off this form to the Forestry Trust today. Although there will be minor changes to the format in 1996, *if you are sure you want to put in a new entry or update an existing one* it would be an immense help to us if you could complete the details on the reverse of this page. We will then send you further details or confirm it before you finally commit yourself to going ahead with an entry for 1996.

Advertisers/Sponsors

Please complete the appropriate section on the form if applicable

WOODLANDS TO VISIT IN ENGLAND AND WALES 1995 - NEW ENTRY REQUEST FORM FOR 1996

OWNERS

I would like to offer the availability of

_____ [WOOD(S)]

in the county of

_____for inclusion in the 1996 book.

1 Name of Owner_____(as for entry in book)

2.Size of Wood(s) in hectares_____

3. Level of Access envisaged at this stage (see criteria on

pages 6 to 7)_____

4. Interested in being a Study Wood (where quality timber is a priority object of management, there is a commitment to wildlife and a willingness to run one or more days per year to illustrate the compatibility of these objectives .
(Please initial here_____)

5. Name address and tel no of Contact for the Forestry Trust in dealing with the entry
Name:_____

Position (ie Owner, Agent,Forester)_____

Address_____

_____

PostalTown_____County_____

POSTCODE_____ Tel No_____

ADVERTISERS/SPONSORS

We are seeking advertisers for next year's book together with sponsorship for the book and other Trust projects. The cost of running the scheme is considerable and the book cannot be funded without commercial sponsorship. If you would like details on advertising or sponsorship please complete para 5 and sign here:

If Wood in 1995 book(please tick and only mark changes)

Name of Wood:

County that wood is in:

Level of Access (F, R, P, A) Circle one as appropriate

Size of Wood in Hectares:

Name of Owner (as it should appear in the book):

Ordnance Survey Sheet Number (if known):

6 Figure Grid Reference with National Prefix (if known):

Telephone Number for Visitor enquiries:
OR
Address for Visitor enquiries:

Charges (if any):

Car parking - Number (and charge if any in brackets):

Coaches - Number (and charge if any in brackets):
Please circle those symbols below that are relevant for your wood
(please refer to pages 7-8)

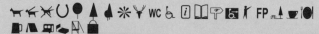

*Directions to wood including from nearest (named) railway station
and (numbered) bus stop:

*Visitor Guidance (Special Instructions):

*Description of Wood (Inviting one please! - max 100 words):

* Please use a continuation sheet where necessary
Willing to take on Study Wood role (see page 6)(please tick)
Awards in last 10 years (see page 7)(C c D d E M -circle as appropriate)
Tick if you provide - Visitor Centre - Mountain Bike Trail(s)

Please cut down the dotted line and send your completed form to the Forestry Trust.

Please make sure that you have put your own name and address clearly on the form.

For You Own Record:

Date Sent:

Remarks:

MEMBERSHIP

Individual Membership
Enjoy and support the work of the Trust by becoming a member. Individual annual membership costs £10 - just complete the form, enclosing your payment and we will send you by return:

A copy of the current Woodlands to Visit book.

Where relevant - details of local Trust pilot projects

Up to 4 Forestry Trust Information Sheets (a member will be able, over time, to build up a library of forestry conservation data and advice)

A Trust publications list

A membership card - explore and enjoy over 700 woods

In early summer we will send you :

The Trust's summer newsletter including a review of the previous year and a summary of the accounts.

Up to a further 4 Forestry Trust Information Sheets

Where relevant - an update on any local Pilot Projects

In the late autumn we will send you:

Our Winter Newslletter with plans for the year ahead

Up to 4 more Forestry Trust Information Sheets

See overleaf for details of Family / Corporate Membership

FORESTRY TRUST MEMBERSHIP FORM

NAME:

ADDRESS:

TELEPHONE NUMBER (optional but useful - for our internal use only)

Please tick here .... if you want a copy of the book (if you already have one and don't need a second copy yourself why not give it as an unusual and rewarding present to a friend)

*Cheque for .... (£10 minimum) enclosed for Individual membership

*Cheque for .... enclosed for family / corporate membership (basic £10 plus £1 for every other member of your family or staff) - Please state number of cards required ....

*Delete as appropriate

Cheques to be made payable to: "The Forestry Trust"

FORESTRY TRUST
MEMBERSHIP (continued)

As a member I would like to help by
(please tick as appropriate)

Entering a wood (separate form attached)

Acting as a forest guide

Offering to be a forest speaker

Co-ordinating new entries

Visiting all (or 5) entries in my county

Fundraising

Developing links with other organizations
(please name)

Developing educational resources

Liaising with schools /teacher training colleges

Providing administrative support for visits to a woodland owner in the book

Offering my services in any useful capacity

Making a donation by:
Covenant (for £25 or more)
Gift Aid (for £250 or more)
Legacy

The Trust will acknowledge all membership offers of help but cannot guarantee that we will be able to take them all up . Nevertheless it would be extremely useful for us to know of those members who are willing to help. We may subsequently be able to take up such kind offers in the future.

How You Can Help The Trust

*1 **Join Now** - For a summary of individual membership benefits see over the page.*

*2. **Take out Family or Corporate Membership** - £10 individual membership plus £1 for every member of your family or staff. You receive the standard pack for individual membership plus a membership card for every additional person for whom you have paid. Contact theTrust for further details*

*3. **Offering Your Services in a Voluntary Capacity**:*
a. As a Woodland Owner - See entry form on previous page
b. As a Forester / Forestry Guide (please state qualifications)
c. As a Forestry Speaker (ICF members preferred)
d. As a coordinator for new entries in the book (forestry qualified preferred)
e. In visiting the existing entries in your county
f. As a Fundraiser, through sponsorship, advertising, contacts or other means
g. In developing links with other organisations
h. In developing our educational resources
i. In liaising with schools or teacher training colleges
j. In offering administrative assistance for visits to a woodland owner in the book
k. In any other capacity

*4. **Make a Donation by:***
Covenant (for £25 or more)
Gift Aid (for £250 or more)
Legacy

Please cut down the dotted line and send your completed form and payment to: The Forestry Trust, The Old Estate Office, Englefield Road, Theale, READING, Berks RG7 5DZ.
Please make sure that you have put your own name and address clearly on the form.
For You Own Record:
Date Sent:
Remarks: